7·3·2005

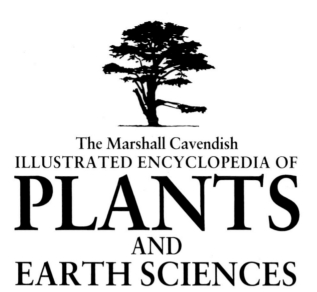

The Marshall Cavendish
ILLUSTRATED ENCYCLOPEDIA OF
PLANTS
AND
EARTH SCIENCES

The Marshall Cavendish
ILLUSTRATED ENCYCLOPEDIA OF
PLANTS
AND
EARTH SCIENCES

VOLUME FIVE

EDITOR-IN-CHIEF
Professor David M. Moore

SPECIALIST SUBJECT EDITORS
Professor V. H. Heywood
Botany
Professor A. Hallam
Earth Sciences
Dr S. R. Chant
Botany

ADVISORY EDITORS
Professor W. T. Stearn
Flowering Plants
Dr I. B. K. Richardson
Flowering Plants
Dr Peter Raven
Plant Ecology
Professor Lincoln Constance
Special Consultant

EDITORIAL DIRECTOR
Dr Graham Bateman

Marshall Cavendish
New York · London · Sydney

CONTENTS

Reference Edition Published 1988

Published by:
Marshall Cavendish Corporation
147 West Merrick Road
Freeport N.Y. 11520

AN EQUINOX BOOK

Planned and produced by:
Equinox (Oxford) Ltd
Littlegate House
St Ebbe's Street
Oxford OX1 1SQ
England

Copyright © Equinox (Oxford) Ltd 1988
Library of Congress Cataloging-in-Publication Data
The Encyclopedia of plants and earth sciences.
  Bibliography: p.
  Includes index.
  1. Botany—Dictionaries. 2. Botany, Economic—Dictionaries.
3. Crops—Dictionaries. 4. Angiosperms-Dictionaries. 5. Earth
sciences—Dictionaries. 6. Ecology—Dictionaries. I. Marshall
Cavendish Corporation.
QK7.E53 1988 580'.3'21 87-23927
  ISBN 0-86307-901-6 (Set)
  ISBN 0-86307-906-7 (Vol 5)

Previous page
Plants belonging to the family Liliaceae (see p.663).

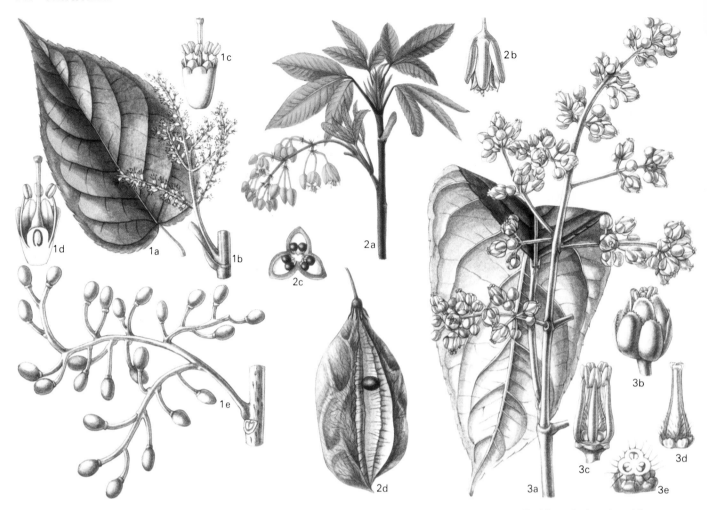

Staphyleaceae. 1 *Tapiscia sinensis* (a) leaflet ($\times\frac{2}{3}$); (b) inflorescence ($\times\frac{2}{3}$); (c) flower showing fused sepals ($\times 4$); (d) vertical section of flower ($\times 6$); (e) indehiscent fruits ($\times\frac{2}{3}$). 2 *Staphylea holocarpa* (a) shoot showing axillary inflorescence and trifoliolate leaves with paired stipules ($\times\frac{2}{3}$); (b) flower with free sepals ($\times 2$); (c) cross section of ovary ($\times 7$); (d) dehiscing fruit ($\times\frac{2}{3}$). 3 *Turpinia insignis* (a) inflorescence and unifoliolate leaf with stalk having a pair of stipules at base and a pair of stipels part of the way up ($\times\frac{2}{3}$); (b) flower ($\times 2$); (c) flower with petals and sepals removed to show stamens with flattened filaments ($\times 3$); (d) gynoecium ($\times 3$); (e) cross section of ovary ($\times 3$).

SAPINDALES

STAPHYLEACEAE
Bladder Nuts

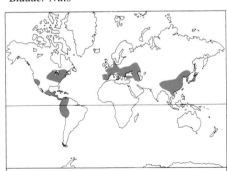

Number of genera: 5
Number of species: about 60
Distribution: N temperate, Cuba, Hispaniola, S America and Asia.
Economic uses: ornamental shrubs, local uses of timber and of fruits in medicine.

The Staphyleaceae is a family of five genera of temperate and tropical trees and shrubs. Some *Staphylea* and *Euscaphis* species are cultivated as ornamental garden plants.

Distribution. *Staphylea* is found throughout the north temperate region. *Tapiscia* is native to China, *Huertea* to Cuba, Hispaniola, Colombia and Peru, *Euscaphis* to east Asia and *Turpinia* to tropical and temperate Asia and America.

Diagnostic features. The leaves are opposite or alternate, trifoliolate or pinnate, with paired stipules. The flowers are regular, bisexual or sometimes unisexual with male and female on the same plant, rarely on separate plants, and are borne in paniculate clusters. There are five imbricate sepals, five imbricate petals and five stamens alternating with the petals, the filaments sometimes being flattened. The ovary is superior and consists of two to four fused carpels (or three to four free in *Euscaphis*), and each locule contains one or a few ovules on axile placentas. The two to four styles are variously free to completely fused together, and the fruits are either berry-like or inflated capsules with an open top. There are few seeds and these have straight embryos, flat cotyledons and a fleshy or horny endosperm. The seeds of *Euscaphis* are arillate and the fruits follicular.

The name *Staphylea* derives from the Greek word *staphyle*, a cluster, relating to the arrangement of the flowers, which may be pink or white in these shrubs.

Classification. The family has no clear and obvious affinities with other members of the Sapindales. Some authorities suggest a relationship with the Cunoniaceae or Celastraceae.

Economic uses. *Staphylea pinnata* is native to Europe and is known as the bladder nut on account of the inflated fruits. It has long been used as a garden ornamental. The Caucasian *S. colchica* has better flowers from a gardener's viewpoint, but poorer fruits than *S. pinnata*, and attempts have been made to combine the better attributes of each plant in hybrids, *S.* × *coulombieri* and *S.* × *elegans* being reputed to be such hybrids. One of the best bladder nuts is the Chinese *S. holocarpa* var *rosea*, a pink-flowered variety of the species introduced from central China.

Euscaphis comprises four species in Japan, China and Vietnam. Known as hung-liang, *Euscaphis japonica* is a common tree or shrub in Japan and central China, where its fruits are used as a drug: in Japan it is called gonzui zoku.

Melianthaceae. 1 *Melianthus pectinatus* (a) shoot with pinnate leaves, small stipules, and inflorescence with flowers and immature fruits (×⅔) ; (b) half flower with irregular sepals and petals and swollen nectar-secreting disk (×1) ; (c) capsule (×⅔). 2 *Bersama tysoniana* (a) leafy shoot with stipules in the axils (×⅔) ; (b) inflorescence (×⅔) : (c) mature flowers with long stamens (×3) ; (d) young androecium with four short stamens fused at the base and ovary crowned by simple style and lobed stigma (×4½) ; (e) cross section of ovary with four locules and ovules on axile placentas (×3) ; (f) fruits (×⅔) ; (g) seed with aril (×1).

Turpinia species number between 30 and 40, of which *Turpinia nepalensis* is a common tree in western China with a useful tough wood. *T. occidentalis* is the cassada wood of the West Indies.   B.M.

MELIANTHACEAE

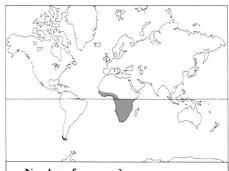

Number of genera: 3
Number of species: 18
Distribution: southern Africa.
Economic uses: limited use of timber and as ornamentals and in medicine.

The Melianthaceae is a small family consisting of three genera and about 18 species of shrubs and small trees of little economic use.

Distribution. The family is native to southern Africa.

Diagnostic features. The leaves are alternate, usually pinnately compound but occasionally simple. The stipules are within the petiole (intrapetiolar). The flowers are irregular, borne in terminal or axillary racemes. They are usually bisexual but occasionally have no stamens or no carpels. The stalks of the flowers twist through 180° at the time of flowering. There are four or five unequal sepals, fused at their bases and frequently swollen at one side. There are four or five petals, unequal in size and distinctly clawed. An annular or crescent-shaped disk, bearing nectar glands, lines the inside of the calyx, within which are inserted four, five or 10 stamens. They alternate with the petals and are often bent forward. The ovary is superior, of four or five fused carpels, and comprises either four or five locules with axile placentation, or one locule with five parietal placentas. There are one or several ovules on each placenta, either erect or pendulous. The ovary is surmounted by a single style which is divided at the tip into four or five stigmatic lobes (sometimes flattened or toothed). The fruit is a papery or woody capsule which dehisces at the apex. The seed contains a straight embryo surrounded by endosperm and in some species it has an external outgrowth (aril).

Classification. Two of the genera (*Melianthus* and *Bersama*) display axile placentation in the ovary while the third, *Greyia*, has parietal placentation. This, and a number of other floral and vegetative features, are considered by some botanists sufficient to place *Greyia* in a separate family (Greyiaceae).

Melianthus (six species) is a genus with pinnate leaves, four stamens and two to four ovules in each locule of the ovary, while *Greyia* (three species) has simple leaves and 10 stamens in the flower. *Bersama* (two polymorphic species) has pinnate leaves, four or five stamens and only one ovule per locule.

The family is closely related to the Sapindaceae, sharing with it such features as leaf form, insertion of stamens within a disk and a superior ovary. However, the Melianthaceae differs in the twisting of the flowers on their stalks before maturation, and in having seeds with copious endosperm.

Economic uses. This family is not economi-

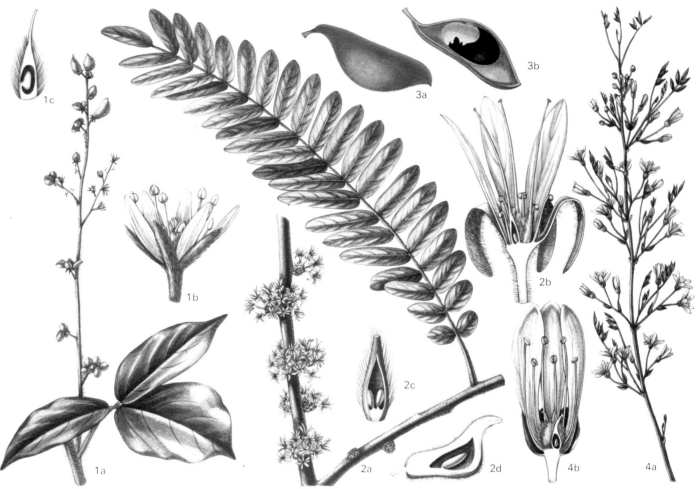

Connaraceae. 1 *Agelaea hirsuta* (a) flowering shoot showing trifoliolate leaf and flowers in terminal panicles (×⅔); (b) flower showing five hairy sepals fused only at the base, five free petals, eight stamens and free styles and stigmas (×6); (c) vertical section of a single carpel (×12). 2 *Cnestis laurentii* (a) flowering shoot (×⅔); (b) half flower (×6); (c) vertical section of single carpel showing two erect ovules (×12); (d) vertical section of fruit—a follicle (×⅔). 3 *Connarus monocarpus* fruit (a) entire (×⅔) and (b) in vertical section showing large seed with an aril (×⅔). 4 *Rourea foenum-graecum* (a) flowering shoot (×⅔); (b) half flower (×6).

cally important, but species of all three genera are grown as ornamentals in warm regions. Species of *Melianthus* emit a strong scent, for example *Melianthus major*, a shrub with large, reddish-brown flowers, and the smaller *M. comosus*, with long racemes of orange, red-spotted flowers. The cultivated species of *Greyia* is *Greyia sutherlandii*, a small tree with light-colored bark and conspicuous scarlet flowers in large racemes. The root, bark and leaves of *M. comosus* are used in South Africa for treating snake bites, while a decoction of the leaves of *M. major* is used for healing wounds. *Bersama abyssinica*, a medium-sized tree, produces a hard, heavy wood used for house construction in West Africa. S.R.C.

CONNARACEAE
Zebra Wood

The Connaraceae is a dicotyledonous family of tropical trees or twining shrubs.

Distribution. The family is pantropical. The most important genera are *Byrsocarpus* (about 20 species in Africa and Madagascar), *Connarus* (about 100 species distributed in Africa, Asia, the Pacific, Australasia, and tropical America), *Rourea* (about 90 species widely distributed in Australia and the Pacific), *Cnestis* (about 40 species in Africa, Madagascar and Malaysia), and *Agelaea* (50 species in tropical Africa, Madagascar, Southeast Asia and Malaysia).

Diagnostic features. The leaves are alternate and without stipules, and are pinnate or trifoliolate, a few species being unifoliolate.

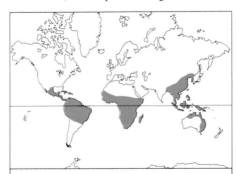

Number of genera: 16
Number of species: about 350
Distribution: pantropical.
Economic uses: timber (zebra wood), some species yield medicines, tannins and fibers are used locally.

The flowers, which are produced in panicles, are generally bisexual and either regular or slightly irregular. The calyx has five sepals, which are either free or fused. The five petals are free or slightly fused. There are generally five or 10 stamens, rarely four or eight, often bent downwards with their filaments joined below. Sometimes a thin, nectar-secreting disk is present. The ovary is superior, with one to five free carpels containing two erect ovules in each locule. The fruit is generally a follicle containing a single seed which may or may not contain endosperm. The seeds often have an outer appendage (aril).

Classification. This family is sometimes regarded as being related to the Dilleniaceae, Crossosomataceae, and Brunelliaceae. It shares with these families its tree or shrub-like habit, pinnate leaves, bisexual flowers, superior, free carpels and arillate seeds. In evolutionary terms it is considered to be rather more advanced than the Leguminosae, possibly on a line leading to the Oxalidaceae. In this work its traditional place among the Sapindales is retained.

Economic uses. The family is economically important for zebra wood, which is obtained

Sapindaceae. 1 *Dodonaea bursarifolia* (a) flowering shoot ($\times \frac{2}{3}$); (b) male flower ($\times 4$); (c) female flower ($\times 4$); (d) fruit ($\times 1\frac{1}{2}$); (e) cross section of fruit ($\times 1\frac{1}{2}$); (f) vertical section of part of fruit ($\times 4$). 2 *Litchi chinensis* fruits entire and in section ($\times \frac{2}{3}$). 3 *Serjania exarata* shoot tip with coiled tendrils, winged fruits and inflorescences ($\times \frac{2}{3}$). 4 *Paullinia thalictrifolia* (a) flowering shoot ($\times \frac{2}{3}$); (b) flower ($\times 4$); (c) flower with two petals removed ($\times 4$); (d) gynoecium ($\times 6$). 5 *Cupaniopsis anacardioides* (a) pinnate leaf ($\times \frac{2}{3}$); (b) inflorescence ($\times \frac{2}{3}$); (c) flower viewed from above ($\times 2$); (d) gynoecium surrounded by disk and calyx ($\times 2$); (e) cross section of ovary ($\times 4$).

from *Connarus guianensis*, a native of Guyana. The seeds of the African *C. africanus* are made into a flour which is effective as an anthelmintic. The leaves of the West African tree *Agelaea villosa* are used to treat dysentery, while those of *A. emetica* (native to Madagascar) yield an essential oil which promotes vomiting. The West African species, *Cnestis corniculata* and *C. ferruginea*, have leaves which are the source of an astringent and a laxative respectively. The bark of *Rourea glabra* (native to Central America) is used for tanning animal skins a dark blue or purple color. The roots of this plant yield a strong fiber used for rope-making. Its seeds and the fruits of the Pacific *R. volubilis* are used for poisoning dogs. S.R.C.

SAPINDACEAE
Akee, Litchi and Rambutan

The Sapindaceae contains about 150 tropical and subtropical genera and 2,000 species. About 300 species are lianas, and the rest are trees and shrubs including the economically important food plants in such genera as *Litchi* and *Blighia* and the ornamentals in *Koelreuteria*, *Xanthoceras* and *Dodonaea*.

Distribution. The family is found throughout the tropics and subtropics.

Diagnostic features. The leaves are normally alternate, simple or compound, and without stipules. The flowers may be regular or irregular and are often unisexual, or func-

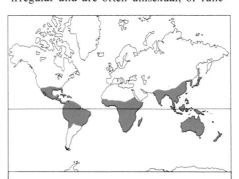

Number of genera: about 150
Number of species: about 2,000
Distribution: tropical and subtropical.
Economic uses: edible fruits (akee, litchi and rambutan), stimulating beverages from *Paullinia* species (guarana) and some cultivated ornamentals.

tionally so, borne in cymose inflorescences. There are usually five free or fused sepals, and five free petals, which may be absent, and a well-marked disk between the petals and stamens. The stamens are in two whorls of five, often with two stamens missing and so appearing as eight. The filaments are free and often hairy. The ovary is superior, of three fused carpels, may be lobed, divided or simple and has one to four locules, each with one or two (rarely many) ovules on a central axis or rarely on parietal placentas. The style is terminal, simple or divided; rarely there are two to four styles. The fruits are various: capsules, nuts, berries, drupes, samaras or schizocarps, often red, containing seeds which are often arillate. They lack endosperm, and the embryos are folded or curved.

The woody lianas in genera such as *Serjania* or *Paullinia* make up an important ecological component of tropical woodland, climbing by tendrils which are modified inflorescence axes, and having anomalous stem anatomy in comparison with other woody plants, brought about by the climbing habit and the consequent internal stem stresses experienced. The tissues of many sapindaceous plants contain resinous or laticiferous compounds secreted by specialized cells.

Classification. The family is related to the Aceraceae, Hippocastanaceae and Melianthaceae. The monotypic Australian genus *Akania* is sometimes placed in the Sapindaceae, although other authorities place it in its own family, the Akaniaceae.

Economic uses. *Blighia sapida*, akee in the West Indies, or akye in Africa, is native to the forests of West Africa, where the aril is eaten, tasting rather like scrambled egg when cooked; it is poisonous if not eaten at the correct stage of ripeness. The plant was introduced to the West Indies and in particular has become naturalized in Jamaica where it is the national fruit. Litchi or lychee, *Litchi chinensis* (*Nephelium litchi*), is a native of southern China, but is widely grown in all tropical regions for its sweet acid aril. Its relative the mamoncillo, *Melicocca bijuga*, is grown in America. *Nephelium lappaceum* is the rambutan, a much-prized fruit eaten in the Old World tropics.

Paullinia cupana, one of 180 American species of liana, is the source of guarana, much drunk in Brazil. *Paullinia* yields yoco, a drink similarly rich in caffeine. *Sapindus saponaria*, from Florida, the West Indies and South America, has berries rich in saponins which form a lather with water and are used as a soap substitute. *Schleichera trijuga* is the source of macassar oil, used in ointments and for illumination.

Of sapindaceous ornamentals perhaps *Koelreuteria* is the most important, making good street trees. Also with bladder fruits is *Cardiospermum halicacabum*, the balloon vine of the tropics and subtropics. The tree *Xanthoceras sorbifolia* is cultivated for its attractive flowers. B.M.

SABIACEAE

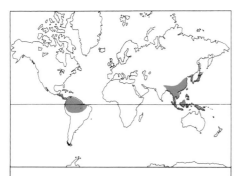

Number of genera: 4
Number of species: about 80
Distribution: tropical and subtropical Asia and America.
Economic uses: a few species are cultivated as ornamentals.

The Sabiaceae is a small tropical and subtropical family of trees or shrubs and a few climbers of limited use as ornamentals.

Distribution. The four genera of the family are *Sabia* (20–30 species from Southeast Asia and Malaysia), *Meliosma* (50–60 species from tropical and subtropical Asia and America), *Phoxanthus* (one species from the Amazon basin) and *Ophiocaryon* (one species from Guyana).

Diagnostic features. The leaves are alternate and are odd-pinnate or simple, without stipules. The flowers are regular, bisexual or unisexual with both sexes on the same plant, and are borne in terminal or axillary cymes or panicles. They have five (rarely three or four) imbricate, unequal sepals which are opposite five (rarely four) imbricate petals, the inner two of which are often smaller. There are five stamens (rarely four or six) which are opposite the petals, but the outer three are often reduced to staminodes. The ovary is superior, of two fused carpels, and usually has a disk at the base. It has two locules (rarely three) and each locule has one ovule (rarely two). The fruit is indehiscent and drupaceous, and the seeds have little or no endosperm.

Classification. *Sabia* has five fertile stamens. The other three genera, which have only two fertile stamens, are sometimes regarded as constituting a separate family, the Meliosmaceae. The position of the sepals, petals and stamens opposite to each other is most unusual and some authorities regard the family as closely related to the Menispermaceae (Ranunculales), although others place it in the Sapindales.

Economic uses. *Sabia latifolia* and *S. schumanniana* are cultivated for their attractive blue fruits. Several species of *Meliosma* are cultivated for ornament, eg *Meliosma beaniana*, western China, which is very free-flowering with drooping panicles of flowers 8in (20cm) long. M.C.D.

JULIANIACEAE

The Julianiaceae is a small family comprising two genera and five species of resinous trees and shrubs not unlike the genus *Rhus* in habit.

Distribution. The family is found in Central America, from Mexico to Peru.

Diagnostic features. The leaves are alternate, pinnate (rarely simple), covered in fine hairs, and are without stipules. The leaflets have serrated edges. The flowers are green, small and unisexual, the separate sexes occurring on different plants; male flowers are numerous in pendulous or erect panicles and consist of a three- to nine-lobed calyx, no petals, and as many stamens as sepals in alternate arrangement; female flowers are in stalked clusters of three or four subtended by a collar of bracts, and lack sepals and petals, having only a superior ovary, with one locule, and a single three-lobed style. A single ovule is inserted at the base of the locule. The fruits are dry and club-shaped, do not open on the tree and are enclosed by the enlarged collar of bracts. The fruit stalk may become broad and flattened in *Amphi-*

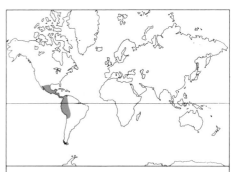

Number of genera: 2
Number of species: 5
Distribution: Central America.
Economic uses: some medicinal uses and produce tannins and a red dye.

pterygium (*Juliania*), or not so in the monotypic *Orthopterygium*.

Classification. On the basis of anatomy, pollen and habit this family is closely related to the Anacardiaceae.

Economic uses. The Mexican *Amphipterygium adstringens*, known variously as "quetchalalatl" or "cuachalala," has a bark used medicinally as an astringent, for malaria and hardening the gums. The bark also contains tannins and a red dye. B.M.

HIPPOCASTANACEAE
Horse Chestnuts and Buckeyes

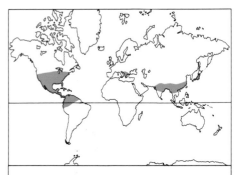

Number of genera: 2
Number of species: 15
Distribution: north temperate (*Aesculus*) and S Mexico and tropical S America (*Billia*).
Economic uses: ornamentals, timber and local medicinal uses.

The Hippocastanaceae is a small family of trees comprising two genera, *Aesculus* (horse chestnuts and buckeyes) with 13 deciduous species and *Billia* with two evergreen species.

Distribution. *Aesculus* is widespread in north temperate regions, while *Billia* is restricted to southern Mexico and tropical South America.

Diagnostic features. Characteristic of the family are the large winter buds covered with resinous scale leaves. The leaves are opposite, palmate and without stipules. The inflorescence is usually a raceme with lateral cymes, but in *Billia* it is paniculate. The

Hippocastanaceae. 1 *Billia hippocastanum* (a) leaf ($\times\frac{2}{3}$); (b) sepal ($\times 2$); (c) flower with sepals removed to show five slightly unequal petals and six stamens ($\times 1\frac{1}{2}$); (d) gynoecium with curved style and simple stigma ($\times 4\frac{1}{2}$); (e) cross section of trilocular ovary with ovules on axile placentas ($\times 10$). 2 *Aesculus hippocastanum* (a) leafless mature tree; (b) digitate leaf and inflorescence ($\times\frac{2}{3}$); (c) half flower with fused sepals and unequal petals ($\times 1$); (d) dehiscing fruit (a capsule) exposing seeds ($\times\frac{1}{2}$); (e) seed with large hilum ($\times\frac{1}{2}$); (f) cross section of ovary ($\times 4$); (g) vertical section of ovary ($\times 4$).

upper flowers, which are functionally male, open first, to be followed by the protogynous bisexual flowers below. The flowers are irregular, comprising five sepals, united at the base (free in *Billia*), and a large whitish, yellowish or red corolla of four or five free petals. There is an irregular disk between the petals and the five to eight stamens. The ovary is superior, consisting of three fused carpels and three locules (rarely two or one by abortion), each locule containing two ovules on axile placentas. The style is elongated, with a simple stigma. The fruit is a leathery capsule, usually three-valved and single-seeded. The seed is large and without endosperm.

Classification. The family is probably related to the Sapindaceae, but is readily distinguished by the palmate leaves, leathery capsule and the relatively large, usually solitary seed.

Economic uses. Species of *Aesculus* have various medicinal uses, and extracts from some have been used by North American Indians to stupefy fish. The wood is light but not very durable, and is used for making boxes and charcoal. The genus is best known for its ornamental trees, notably the horse chestnut (*Aesculus hippocastanum*), which is grown for its winter buds, large leaves and striking inflorescences; its shiny brown seeds are the "conkers" much prized by children.

I.B.K.R.

ACERACEAE
Maples

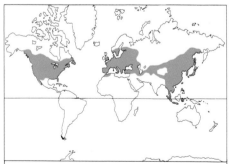

Number of genera: 2
Number of species: 102–152
Distribution: cosmopolitan, centered in China.
Economic uses: ornamentals (maples), timber and maple sugar.

The Aceraceae is a family of predominantly medium to small, deciduous trees of north-ern temperate regions. It includes some large trees and evergreens, and a few subtropical species. There are only two genera, *Acer*, the maples, and *Dipteronia*.

Distribution. The two *Dipteronia* species are found in central and southern China. Maples have an enormous geographical range centered in China, where 100–150 species are found. A few species occur through southern China to Malaysia and Java, and these are evergreen, as are some of the many ranging to and along the Himalayas. There are 19 maples in Japan and two on Formosa. Eight species are native to Asia Minor and the Caucasus Mountains, and there are 10 in southern Europe, one of which, *Acer campestre*, is the only species to occur in Africa and also the only native species in the British Isles. In North America there are four maples native to the western states only, eight native to the eastern and southern states while one, *A. negundo*, is found from Montreal to southern California.

Diagnostic features. The branches grow in opposite pairs. The leaves are opposite and highly variable in shape: simple or com-pound, entire or deeply toothed, unlobed or deeply lobed. Stipules are absent. The

Aceraceae. 1 *Acer platanoides* (a) shoot with opposite, palmately-lobed leaves and fruits comprising pairs of winged samaras (×⅔) ; (b) shoot with terminal inflorescence, young leaves and bud scales (×⅔) ; (c) male flower with four sepals, four petals, eight stamens and central vestige of the ovary (× 3) ; (d) half bisexual flower showing winged ovary with forked style and short stamens on a lobed disk (× 3) ; (e) silhouette of a leafless tree showing the much branched habit.

flowers are regular, with five free sepals and five free petals, the latter often absent. Species are andromonoecious (male and bisexual flowers on same plant), androdioecious (male and bisexual flowers on separate plants) or dioecious (male and female flowers on separate plants). The male and bisexual flowers have 4–10 stamens, normally eight, and in male flowers a vestigial ovary is often present. The ovary is superior, of two fused carpels and two locules each containing two ovules on axile placentas. The paired fruits are samaras, each with a membranous wing. The seeds are solitary and without endosperm.

Classification. *Acer* is distinguished from *Dipteronia* by having obovate wings attached to the seeds; *Dipteronia* seeds are surrounded by a circular membrane. The family is related to the Sapindaceae and Hippocastanaceae.

Economic uses. Many maples are grown for ornamental purposes, often in towns, and are prized for their beautiful foliage and spectacular autumn colors. Many species produce good timber, particularly the sycamore (*Acer pseudoplatanus*), while the sugar maple (*Acer saccharum*) and some other species yield maple sugar.   A.F.M.

BURSERACEAE
Frankincense and Myrrh

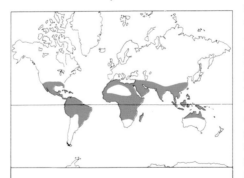

Number of genera: about 17
Number of species: about 500
Distribution: tropical, especially Malaysia, Africa and America.
Economic uses: aromatic resins (including frankincense and myrrh), used for making incense, perfumes, soap and paints.

The Burseraceae is a family of tropical trees and shrubs; important products include frankincense and myrrh.

Distribution. The family is found throughout the tropics, but especially in Malaysia, South

America and Africa. Trees of the Burseraceae are a common constituent of the main story of lowland dipterocarp forests of central and southern Malaya. *Canarium*, *Dacryodes* and *Santiria* are the three main genera, growing particularly in the lowlands. One of the principal members of this family in Africa and Madagascar is *Commiphora*. Various different species abound in hot, dry bushveld, desert, thorn scrub and throughout vast areas of savannah. Other species grow on alluvial slopes and in coastal belts along tidal mangrove swamps and in tropical rain forests. Large trees such as *Dacryodes* and *Canarium* and smaller trees such as *Santiria* are quite common in Africa, but are different from the species found in Malaya. *Boswellia serrata* is a component of deciduous forests and often gregarious on dry hillsides in India. Trees and shrubs of the genera *Bursera* and *Protium* are particularly well represented in South America. *Tetragastris* and *Dacryodes* also grow in various parts of South America and the West Indies.

Diagnostic features. All parts of the plants, especially the bark, contain resin. The leaves are spirally arranged, usually crowded at twig-tips, imparipinnate (pinnate with terminal leaflets) and may or may not have

Burseraceae. 1 *Boswellia popoviana* (a) twig with leaves crowded at tip ($\times \frac{2}{3}$); (b) flower ($\times 4$); (c) cross section of ovary with five locules ($\times 12$). 2 *Commiphora marlothii* (a) terminal cluster of fruits ($\times \frac{2}{3}$); (b) fruit ($\times 1$). 3 *Canarium hirtellum* (a) inflorescence ($\times \frac{2}{3}$); (b) flower ($\times 2$); (c) flower with perianth removed to show stamens and globose stigma ($\times 3$); (d) section of trilocular ovary ($\times 3$). 4 *Boswellia papyrifera* habit. 5 *Protium guianense* (a) inflorescence ($\times \frac{2}{3}$); (b) section of ovary with five locules ($\times 6$); (c) shoot with imparipinnate leaf and fruits ($\times \frac{2}{3}$).

stipules. The flowers are grouped in panicles, also usually crowded at twig-ends. They are small, often unisexual (with each sex on separate plants), and usually greenish or cream, with parts in threes to fives. The sepals are fused, and either imbricate or valvate; the petals are usually free, also either imbricate or valvate. The stamens are equal to or double the number of petals. The ovary is superior and has three to five carpels and two to five locules, with two ovules (rarely one) on axile placentas in each locule. The style is simple. The fruit is usually a drupe, sometimes a capsule. The seeds lack endosperm.

Classification. The family can be divided into three tribes:

PROTIEAE. Drupe with two to five, free or adhering parts but not fused in the stony endocarp; exocarp occasionally splitting by valves. Six genera, including *Protium* and *Tetragastris*.

BURSEREAE. Drupe with an endocarp of fused parts; exocarp always dehiscing by valves. Five genera, including *Boswellia*, *Bursera* and *Commiphora*.

CANARIEAE. Drupe with an endocarp of fused parts. Six genera, including *Canarium* and *Santiria*.

This family is distinguished from the Rutaceae and the Simaroubaceae by the presence of resin ducts in the bark, by the distinct stamens and short single style, and by the usual absence of transparent glandular dots on the leaves.

Economic uses. The wood of *Canarium littorale*, *Dacryodes costata*, *Santiria laevigata* and *S. tomentosa* in Malaya and *Aucoumea* and *Canarium schweinfurthii* in Africa is used for general building construction and carpentry. Frankincense comes from *Boswellia carteri* (Somaliland) and some other species. Myrrh, used in incense and perfumes, is obtained from *Commiphora abyssinica*, *C. molmol* and some other species which are cultivated in Arabia and Ethiopia. Varnish is obtained from several species of *Bursera* in Mexico and probably elsewhere.   H.P.W.

ANACARDIACEAE
Cashew, Mango, Sumacs and Poison Ivy

The Anacardiaceae contains about 600 species of trees, shrubs and lianas including some popular ornamental trees as well as species producing commercially valuable fruit and nuts, such as the cashew, pistachio, Dhobis, hog plum, Jamaican plum, mango.

Distribution. The family is mainly tropical and subtropical, and is equally well represented in South America, Africa and Malaysia. Some are native to temperate North America and Eurasia. (See also p. 878.)

Diagnostic features. Most members of the family have resinous tissues, although the leaves are not gland-dotted. Sometimes the resinous exudate is poisonous, causing severe irritation of the skin, as in poison ivy (*Rhus radicans*). The irritant substances may be distributed throughout the plant body or concentrated in particular organs, eg in the fruit wall of the cashew, *Anacardium occidentale*. The leaves are alternate (rarely opposite) and usually pinnately compound, although simple leaves occur, for example in *Cotinus*, *Anacardium* and *Mangifera*. Stipules are absent. The flowers are regular and bisexual (or sometimes unisexual), typically with five fused sepals, five free petals and five to 10 or more stamens. Between the stamens and ovary is a fleshy disk of tissue, the torus. The ovary is usually superior and comprises one to five carpels, usually united, very rarely free, each containing a single pendulous ovule. There are one to three styles, often widely separated. The fruit is usually a drupe; the solitary seed may have very thin

Anacardiaceae. 1 *Pistacia lentiscus* (a) shoot with imparipinnate leaves and male inflorescences ($\times\frac{2}{3}$); (b) male flower with short, lobed calyx and stamens with very short filaments ($\times$10); (c) female flower with three spreading stigmas ($\times$14); (d) vertical section of fruit ($\times$4). 2 *Anacardium occidentale* (a) shoot with inflorescence and fruits, the latter with swollen, a pear-shaped stalk and receptacle with the kidney-shaped fruit below ($\times\frac{2}{3}$); (b) simple leaves ($\times\frac{2}{3}$); (c) male flower with a single stamen protruding ($\times$3); (d) bisexual flower with petals removed showing all stamens except one to have short filaments ($\times$4); (e) vertical section of fruit ($\times$1). 3 *Rhus trichocarpa* habit.

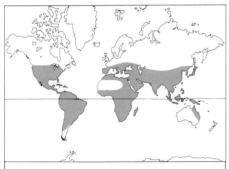

Number of genera: about 77
Number of species: about 600
Distribution: mainly tropical and subtropical with a few temperate representatives.
Economic uses: sources of tannins (*Cotinus, Pistacia, Schinopsis* and *Rhus*), fruits (eg cashew, pistachio, mango), and grown as ornamentals (eg sumac, smoke tree).

endosperm, or none, and fleshy cotyledons.
Classification. The family, which comprises about 77 genera, has been classified into four tribes largely on the basis of differences in the number and degree of fusion of the carpels.

ANACARDIEAE. Flowers with five free carpels, and compound leaves; or flowers with a solitary carpel and simple leaves. Old World tropics (eight genera, including *Mangifera*) and South America (*Anacardium*).

SPONDIEAE. Flowers with four or five united carpels each containing one ovule which develops into a seed. Pantropical (21 genera, including *Spondias*).

SEMECARPEAE. Flowers with an inferior ovary of three united carpels. Only one ovule develops. Old World tropics (six genera, including *Semecarpus*).

RHOIDEAE. Flowers with a superior ovary of three united carpels. Only one ovule develops. Pantropical, temperate Eurasia, South Africa and North America (42 genera, including *Cotinus, Pistacia, Rhus, Schinopsis* and *Schinus*).

The Anacardiaceae is closely related to several other families in the order Sapindales, notably the Sapindaceae, Aceraceae, Hippocastanaceae, Burseraceae and Juliianiaceae. The latter two share with the Anacardiaceae the possession of specialized resin ducts.

Economic uses. Several of the more important uses of the Anacardiaceae are related to

their resinous properties. Species of *Cotinus, Pistacia, Schinopsis* and *Rhus* are major sources of tannins for the leather industry. The resin of *Rhus verniciflua*, native to China, is the basis of lacquer. Mastic and pistachio turpentine are produced from species of *Pistacia*.

The family yields some important fruits and nuts, eg cashew nuts and cashew apples (*Anacardium occidentale*), pistachio nuts (*Pistacia vera*), Dhobi's nut (*Semecarpus anacardium*), the mango (*Mangifera indica*) and the Otaheite apple, hog plum and Jamaica plum (fruits of *Spondias* species). Some species produce useful timber: examples are *Schinopsis quebracho-colorado* (quebracho) and the cashew tree. The Anacardiaceae also includes some commonly grown ornamental trees, such as the sumacs (*Rhus* species), the smoke or wig tree (*Cotinus coggygria*) and the pepper tree or American mastic tree (*Schinus molle*). A mildly alcoholic drink is made from the latter species in its native Peru and the ground seeds may be used as a condiment and/or an adulterant for pepper, and the tree also produces a gum resin of the mastic type. The smoke tree yields a yellow dye.   F.K.K.

Simaroubaceae. 1 *Quassia amara* (a) shoot with trifoliolate leaves and inflorescence (×⅔); (b) flower with petals removed to show numerous stamens (×1½); (c) calyx and gynoecium with disk at base (×1½); (d) fruits (×⅔); (e) cross section of fruit (×⅔). 2 *Harrisonia abyssinica* (a) flowering shoot with pinnate leaf (×⅔); (b) flower bud (×3); (c) flower (×3); (d) calyx and gynoecium crowned by five styles (×3⅓); (e) stamen with hairy scale at the base (×6); (f) fruiting shoot (×⅔); (g) fruit (×2). 3 *Ailanthus excelsa* (a) part of pinnate leaf (×⅔); (b) fruits—twisted samaras (×⅔); (c) half section of fruit showing single seed (×⅔).

SIMAROUBACEAE
Quassia and Tree of Heaven

The Simaroubaceae is a medium-sized family of trees and shrubs which include the medicinal genus *Quassia* and the ornamental genus *Ailanthus*.

Distribution. The family is found throughout the tropics and subtropics.

Diagnostic features. The leaves are alternate, pinnate, rarely simple, and usually without stipules. The often numerous small flowers are regular, bisexual or unisexual, and are borne in cymose spikes or dense panicles. There are three to seven free or united sepals and petals, the petals rarely being absent altogether. A ring or cup-like disk occurs between the petals and the stamens which are free and as many as or double the number of petals. The ovary is superior, of two to five carpels which are fused or free below and united above by the style or stigma. There are two to five styles, and each of the one to five locules contains a single ovule (rarely two) inserted on an axile placenta. The fruit is a samara, schizocarp, or capsule, the seeds with or without endosperm, having thick cotyledons and a straight or curved embryo.

Classification. The family is closely related to

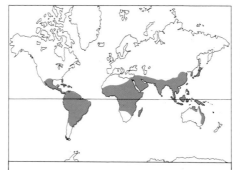

Number of genera: about 20
Number of species: about 120
Distribution: tropical and subtropical.
Economic uses: quassia wood and other medicinal species, ornamental trees, and timber.

the Rutaceae, but differs conspicuously in lacking pellucid glands on the leaves.

Economic uses. *Ailanthus* (10 species) is the most important decorative genus in the family, with *Ailanthus altissima*, the tree of heaven, being widely grown. The male trees smell offensively in flower, so that females are best grown in urban environments.

Quassia amara, one of 40 species from the tropics, has been widely cultivated both as an attractive shrub or small tree with red flowers, and for its bitter wood which has medicinal value in the form of the glucoside, quassiin. The properties of quassia wood are like those of the genus *Picrasma*, the Old World genus of six species, and as a consequence *Picrasma* has been used as a quassia substitute.

The genus *Picramnia*, comprising about 50 species in tropical America, and often encountered in montane woodland, also has medicinal value. *Picramnia antidesma*, from the West Indies and Central America, has bitter leaves and bark with a flavor some compare to liquorice. It is still employed in rural medicine, and was once exported, in bark form, to Europe as a treatment for erysipelas and venereal disease.

Kirkia comprises eight southern African species of tree, *Kirkia acuminata*, the white syringa, being the most attractive and commonest. It is a graceful, 60ft (18m) tall tree with corky bark, pinnate leaves to 18in (45cm) long, wood which is well colored and figured when worked into furniture, flooring or ornaments, and swollen roots which store

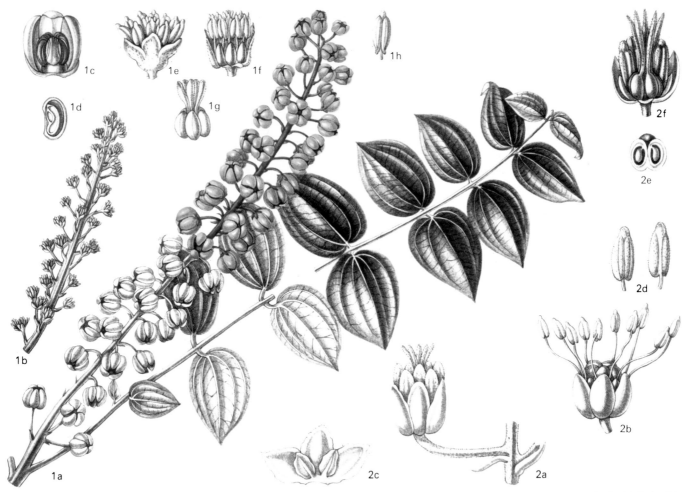

Coriariaceae. 1 *Coriaria terminalis* (a) leafy shoot with fruits (pseudodrupes) surrounded by fleshy petals ($\times\frac{2}{3}$); (b) inflorescence ($\times\frac{2}{3}$); (c) fruit with two petals removed ($\times$2); (d) vertical section of achene ($\times$3); (e) flower showing large anthers ($\times$2); (f) flower with two sepals removed to show small petals ($\times$2); (g) gynoecium with ovary surrounded by five petals ($\times$3); (h) stamen ($\times$3). 2 *C. ruscifolia* (a) young protogynous flower with stigmas fully emerged ($\times$6); (b) fertilized flower with mature stamens ($\times$6); (c) part of perianth showing three sepals and two small petals ($\times$6); (d) anthers ($\times$12); (e) vertical section of ovary ($\times$8); (f) young flower with some of petals and sepals removed to show free carpels ($\times$6).

liquid which is readily tapped in times of drought.

The "berries" of certain species of the genus *Brucea* are used in the treatment of dysentery.   B.M.

CORIARIACEAE
Coriarias

The Coriariaceae is a small family of warm temperate shrubs comprising a single genus, *Coriaria*.

Distribution. The family is found in warm temperate areas in central and western South America, the Mediterranean region, the Himalayas, and into eastern Asia, New Guinea and New Zealand. It is notably absent from Africa and Australia. *Coriaria* is a good example of a genus with a discontinuous geographical distribution pattern. The Northern Hemisphere coriarias belong to one section of the genus, the Southern to another.

Diagnostic features. The family are shrubs, sometimes spreading, with opposite or whorled angular branches which are often frond-like in appearance. The leaves are opposite, ovate to lanceolate, entire, with three or more veins arising from the base,

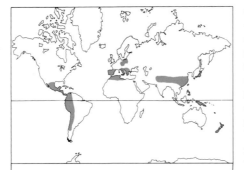

Number of genera: 1
Number of species: 8
Distribution: warm temperate zones.
Economic uses: *Coriaria myrtifolia* yields fly poison, tannin and ink, and some species are cultivated as ornamentals.

and without stipules. The flowers are regular small, green, bisexual or unisexual (with both sexes on the same plant), often borne on the previous year's wood, axillary (or terminal when on current growth) and either solitary or racemose. There are five persistent sepals, five shorter, keeled, fleshy petals, 10 stamens with large anthers, either all free or five fused to the petal keels. The ovary is superior, comprising five to 10 free carpels and five to 10 locules, each with a single pendulous, anatropous ovule. The styles are elongated and conspicuous. The often purplish petals become succulent after fertilization, and being intruded between the carpels enclose them, forming a pseudodrupe before the compressed seeds are released. The seed has a thin endosperm when mature. The infructescences are often attractive, although several species are poisonous and all should be regarded as such in the context of their value as garden ornamentals.

Classification. The family is difficult to place satisfactorily in any taxonomic group. In the system adopted in this work it is placed in the Sapindales.

Economic uses. Redoul, *Coriaria myrtifolia*, is native to the Mediterranean region, and the fruits when crushed in water make a good fly poison. The leaves are rich in tannins and used for making ink and curing leather. It is a deciduous shrub up to 6ft (2m) high, with small greenish flowers in 1in (3cm) long racemes from the joints of the previous year's wood.

A popular ornamental species is the

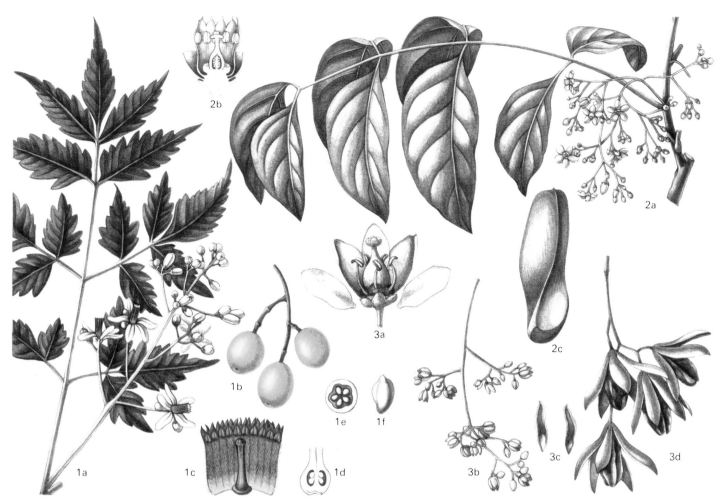

Meliaceae. 1 *Melia azedarach* (a) bipinnate leaf and axillary inflorescence ($\times\frac{2}{3}$); (b) fruits ($\times\frac{2}{3}$); (c) staminal tube opened out to show anthers attached and gynoecium with basal disk ($\times 2$); (d) vertical section of ovary with ovules on axile placentas ($\times 6$); (e) cross section of fruit ($\times\frac{2}{3}$); (f) seed ($\times 4$). 2 *Swietenia mahagoni* (a) shoot with pinnate leaf and axillary inflorescence ($\times\frac{2}{3}$); (b) half flower showing staminal tube ($\times 8$); (c) winged seed ($\times\frac{2}{3}$). 3 *Cedrela australis* (a) flower opened out showing free stamens arising from the disk and superior ovary crowned by discoid stigma ($\times 3\frac{1}{2}$); (b) part of inflorescence ($\times\frac{2}{3}$); (c) winged seeds ($\times 1$); (d) fruits surrounded by persistent sepals ($\times\frac{2}{3}$).

rhizomatous and spreading *C. terminalis* from the Sino–Himalayas, which has good autumnal leaf-tints, and black or yellow fruiting clusters about 9in (22cm) long, each fruit being about 0.4in (1cm) in diameter. It grows to about 4ft (1.3m). Another is *C. japonica* from Japan, this being only about 2ft (60cm) high, also with good autumnal leaf-color and coral-red to black fruits.

Several authorities state that the succulent fruits of several species other than *C. myrtifolia* are edible and taste rather like bilberries, but as the seeds and other plant parts are reputed to be poisonous, caution is recommended. Convulsions like those produced by strychnine characterize *Coriaria* poisoning.   B.M.

MELIACEAE
Mahoganies

The Meliaceae is a family of mostly trees and shrubs, economically important chiefly because of its high-quality timbers, including the true mahoganies. It also includes a number of fruit trees.

Distribution. The family is restricted to the tropics and subtropics and comprises about 50 genera and some 550 species, which are

Number of genera: about 50
Number of species: about 550
Distribution: tropical and subtropical.
Economic uses: important timber, including mahogany, some edible fruits, and some ornamentals.

particularly common as understory trees in rain forests.

Diagnostic features. The family consists of trees or shrubs, sometimes unbranched "tuft trees," rarely herbaceous plants with woody stocks. The leaves are alternate, usually pinnate, sometimes simple and rarely bipinnate, and are without stipules. The flowers are often in cymose panicles and may be borne on the trunk or branches or in the axils of undeveloped leaves, or may be terminal or, rarely, borne on the leaves (*Chisocheton*). They are regular, and are usually bisexual, but often unisexual (the sexes borne on separate plants), although they may appear bisexual. There are three to five united or free sepals, three to five (rarely up to 14) usually free petals and five (rarely three) to ten (rarely up to 23) stamens, which may be free but are usually united into a staminal tube. The style may be absent and the stigma is often disciform or capitate. The ovary is superior with two to six (rarely one or up to 20) locules with one, two or more pendulous ovules in each locule. The fruit is a capsule, berry or drupe, or, rarely, a nut. The seeds are often winged while others have a fleshy aril or fleshy testa (sarcotesta); they are with or without endosperm and have a straight or curved embryo.

Classification. The family is divided into five subfamilies, of which three are small and restricted to Madagascar, while the other two, Melioideae and Swietenioideae, are pantropical.

The MELIOIDEAE have unwinged seeds

and usually have a fleshy sarcotesta or aril. They include *Turraea* (about 65 species, Old World), *Melia* (five species, Old World), *Azadirachta* (two species, Indomalaysia and the Pacific), *Guarea* (35 species, Africa and America), *Chisocheton* (52 species, Indomalaysia), *Dysoxylum* (60 species, Indomalaysia and Pacific) and *Xylocarpus* (two or three species in the mangrove and coastal forests of the Old World).

The SWIETENIOIDEAE have winged seeds and include the commercial mahoganies, *Swietenia* (seven or eight species, America), *Entandrophragma* (11 species, Africa), *Khaya* (eight species, Africa), *Cedrela* (nine species, America), *Toona* (15 species, Asia and Australasia) and *Lovoa* (two species, Africa).

The Meliaceae is undoubtedly allied to the pinnate-leaved tree families in the Sapindales such as the Anacardiaceae, Burseraceae, Sapindaceae, Simaroubaceae and Rutaceae, from all of which Meliaceae may be distinguished by the androecium.

Economic uses. The true mahoganies are Swietenioideae, particularly *Swietenia* in the Americas and *Khaya* in Africa. All are highly prized for their excellent color, working properties and finish. Important meliaceous timbers besides these include sapele *Entandrophragma cylindricum*, utile (*E. utile*), omu (*E. candollei*) and species of *Melia, Carapa, Azadirachta, Guarea, Cedrela, Toona, Soymida, Chukrasia, Dysoxylum, Lovoa, Aglaia* and *Owenia*.

Oils for soap-making have been extracted from the seeds of *Trichilia emetica* in Uganda, and oil from the Malayan *Chisocheton macrophyllus* has been used as an illuminant. Insecticides have been derived from *Melia* and *Azadirachta* species. The flowers of *Aglaia odorata* are used in the East in flavoring tea. The fruit of some *Aglaia* and *Lansium* species is important locally, and the most important commercial one, langsat from *Lansium domesticum*, is popular in Southeast Asia, as is the santol, *Sandoricum koetjape*. Many genera are very ornamental and are increasingly seen in cultivation, particularly *Aglaia, Chisocheton, Dysoxylum, Melia* and *Turraea*. D.J.M.

CNEORACEAE
Spurge Olive
The Cneoraceae is a family containing a single genus, *Cneorum*, which has two species, *Cneorum tricoccum* (the spurge olive) and *C. pulverulentum*. The latter has been placed in a separate genus *Neochamaelea* by some botanists.

Distribution. *Cneorum tricoccum* is native to the western Mediterranean region, *C. pulverulentum* to the Canary Islands.

Diagnostic features. *Cneorum* are evergreen shrubs with alternate gray-green, narrow, leathery leaves without stipules. The yellow flowers are solitary (*C. pulverulentum*) or in small corymbs (*C. tricoccum*) in the axils of

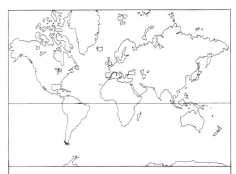

Number of genera: 1
Number of species: 2
Distribution: western Mediterranean and Canary Islands.
Economic uses: local medicinal use as a purgative and rubefacient.

terminal leaves. They are regular, bisexual and usually have three (sometimes four) free sepals, petals and stamens, a single style and an elongate receptacle or disk. The ovary is inferior, of three or four fused carpels, and lobed, with two pendulous ovules in each locule. The hard, red-brown fruit is composed of three (sometimes four) globose segments each with two seeds which contain endosperm.

Classification. The Cneoraceae is considered to be closely allied to the Zygophyllaceae but differs in having only one whorl of stamens, no ligules and no stipules, and in having oil glands in the leaves. The Cneoraceae shares this latter feature with other families in the Sapindales such as the Rutaceae.

Economic uses. The leaves and fruits of *C. tricoccum* are used locally as a purgative and a skin rubefacient. M.C.D.

RUTACEAE
The Citrus Fruit Family

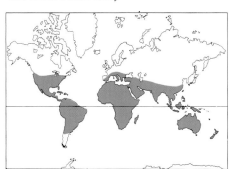

Number of genera: 150
Number of species: about 900
Distribution: tropical and warm temperate regions particularly S Africa and Australia.
Economic uses: citrus fruits (lemon, orange, grapefruit etc) and oils in perfumery and medicine (*Ruta, Galipea, Toddalia*).

The Rutaceae is a large family of shrubs and trees, and occasionally herbs, which are of great economic importance yielding the citrus fruits of commerce (lemons, oranges, mandarins, tangerines, limes, grapefruit) as well as some attractive ornamental species such as *Choisya* and *Skimmia*.

Distribution. The Rutaceae has a more or less cosmopolitan distribution, but are largely centered in the tropics and temperate regions of the Southern Hemisphere, especially Australia and South Africa. Commercially, citrus fruits are grown in the tropical and warm temperate "citrus belt" which spans the whole globe, notably in the Mediterranean region, southern United States of America, Mexico, South Africa and Australia.

Diagnostic features. The family owes its name to the rue (*Ruta graveolens*), a small, hardy, evergreen, aromatic shrub which for centuries has been grown in herb gardens as a medicinal plant. Like most other members of the family, the crushed leaves of rue produce a strong foetid aroma from oil glands which can be seen as small, translucent black dots on the leaves. This is the most distinctive feature of the Rutaceae.

Ruta is somewhat typical for the family and can be characterized as a genus of 60 hardy shrubs, subshrubs and perennials, with strong-smelling, alternate, trifoliolate or compound, pinnate leaves without stipules and terminal inflorescences (corymbs or panicles) that are subtended by leafy bracts. The flowers are insect-pollinated, greenish-yellow in color and composed of a four- or five-lobed persistent calyx, four or five overlapping, toothed or ciliate (having fine hairs or projections) petals, a thick basal disk of eight to ten glands or pits from which nectar is secreted and eight to ten stamens. The ovary is superior, deeply lobed, with five or four fused carpels forming four or five locules each with numerous ovules. The fruit is a berry and the seeds have endosperm. Of course, there are many deviations from this pattern and some of the more obvious ones are: the tree growth habit in various prominent genera such as *Citrus, Poncirus*, and *Phellodendron*; simple leaves in *Diosma, Boronia* and *Skimmia*; leaves reduced to thorns in various species of the orange subfamily (Aurantioideae); leaves not dotted with glands in *Leptothyrsa* and *Phellodendron*; stamens more numerous than 10 in *Peltostigma, Citrus* and *Asterolasia*; and the

Rutaceae. 1 *Ruta graveolens* (a) shoot with bipinnate leaves and cymose inflorescences ($\times\frac{2}{3}$); (b) flower with four sepals, four petals, eight stamens and a superior, lobed ovary with a basal disk and crowned by a single style ($\times 2\frac{2}{3}$); (c) vertical section of ovary ($\times 6$); (d) cross section of ovary showing four locules and ovules on axile placentas ($\times 4$). 2 *Citrus aurantium* (sweet orange) (a) half flower with numerous stamens and prominent disk at the base of the ovary ($\times 2$); (b) fruit—a pulpy berry ($\times\frac{2}{3}$). 3 *Ptelea trifoliata* winged fruit—an unusual feature for the family ($\times 1\frac{1}{3}$). 4 *Citrus limon* (lemon) flowering shoot ($\times\frac{2}{3}$). 5 *Crowea saligna* flowering shoot ($\times\frac{2}{3}$).

flowers epiphyllous, ie emerging from the leaves, in some species of *Erythrochiton*. The flowers are irregular in *Cusparia* and unisexual in *Toddalia*. The ovary is semi-inferior in *Platyspermatica* and many species have two ovules in each locule. The fruits are very variable between different subfamilies and tribes, being schizocarps, drupes or berries. The seeds may lack endosperm.

Classification. The Rutaceae can be divided into four subfamilies as follows:

RUTOIDEAE. Ovaries with two to five deep lobes, the carpels quite separate and connected only by the styles and stigmas. The fruit is a berry. Tribe RUTEAE: herbs and shrubs of the Northern Hemisphere (*Ruta*, *Dictamnus* and *Thamnosma*). Tribe ZANTHOXYLEAE: South American and Australian trees and shrubs (*Melicope*, *Pelea*, *Choisya*, *Euodia*, *Fagara* and *Zanthoxylum*). Tribe BORONIEAE: perennial herbs and shrubs from Australia (*Eriostemon*, *Phebalium*, *Asterolasia*, *Correa*, *Boronia* and *Dipholaena*). Tribe DIOSMEAE: mostly perennial herbs or shrubs and rarely trees of South Africa (*Diosma*, *Calodendrum*, *Barosma*, *Agathosma* and *Macrostylis*). Tribe CUSPARIEAE: shrubs and trees of South America (*Flindersia*, *Esenbeckia*, *Galipea*, *Cusparia* and *Ravenia*).

TODDALOIDEAE. Ovaries entire (not lobed) or slightly two- to five-lobed with two to five incompletely or completely united carpels. The fruit consists of two to four drupelets or is a thick-skinned drupe. They are predominantly Old World tropical and temperate trees and shrubs (*Phellodendron*, *Ptelea*, *Amyris*, *Vepris*, *Toddalia*, *Skimmia*).

RHABDODENDROIDEAE. Ovaries two- to five-lobed and the carpels united but distinguished by the possession of unique bowl-shaped receptacles. Comprising a single tree genus, *Rhabdodendron*.

AURANTIOIDEAE. Ovaries entire, and the fruit a large, pulpy berry (*Aegle*, *Citrus*, *Atalantia*, *Glycosmis*, *Murraya*, *Clausena* and *Micromelum*).

The Rutaceae belongs to an order of plants known as the Sapindales, a group of 16 families characterized, with few exceptions, as woody plants with mostly compound leaves. The principal character separating the Rutaceae from the other families is the presence of oil glands in the leaves.

Economic uses. The Rutaceae is important for a large number of crop and garden plants. It includes the citrus fruits of the subfamily Aurantioideae. The commonly cultivated fruits belong to three genera, *Citrus*, *Fortunella* and *Poncirus*. *Citrus* is undoubtedly the most important genus in the whole family and of the 60 known species most are cultivated. Botanically, the citrus fruit is a berry with a tough leathery skin containing aromatic oil glands and a flesh composed of enlarged cells filled with juice. The most widely cultivated species include the lemon (*Citrus limon*), the citron (*C.*

medica), the sour or Seville orange (*C. aurantium*), the edible or sweet orange (*C. sinensis*), the mandarins, satsumas and tangerines (*C. reticulata*), the limes (*C. aurantifolia*) and the grapefruit (*C. paradisi*). Lesser-known fruits include the kumquats belonging to the genus *Fortunella* and the inedible trifoliolate orange, *Poncirus trifoliata*.

Many species are cultivated for their essential oils (fragrant aromatic compounds). The bergamot, a dwarf variety of the Seville orange, produces the valuable "bergamot oil" (for use in perfumes) from its fruit and "oil of neroli" (for use in Eau de Cologne) from its blossom. The Mexican *Choisya ternata* is a very beautiful shrub frequently grown in hothouses and sheltered gardens. Popular park plants include: shrub species of *Skimmia*, notably *Skimmia japonica* and *S. reevesiana* and their hybrid, *S. × foremannii*; the highly scented hop tree of North America (*Ptelea trifoliata*); and the "cork" trees *Phellodendron japonicum*, *P. amurense* and *P. sachalinense*. Desirable house plants include the heavily scented shrubs of the genus *Diosma* (which means divine scent), various species of *Agathosma* and *Barosma*, and the scented indoor heather-like shrubs *Coleonema album* and *C. pulchrum*.

The burning bush (*Dictamnus albus*) is covered with oil glands that exude a strong, spice-scented secretion. Its oil production is so high that on really hot days the plants can easily be ignited without damaging the bush. The extremely poisonous rue plant (*R. graveolens*) was an ancient herbal remedy for faintness, cramp, hysteria and diseases of the womb, as well as its bizarre use for treating croup in poultry.

Other valuable medicinal oils have been obtained from the bark glands of species of the genera *Galipea* and *Toddalia*. Only one species of the Rutaceae has any value as timber, yielding valuable hardwoods, namely the West Indian silkwood (*Zanthoxylum flavum*). Jaborandi (the source of the alkaloid pilocarpine) is obtained from the dried leaves of the South American shrubs, *Pilocarpus jaborandi* and *P. microphyllus*.

C.J.H.

ZYGOPHYLLACEAE
Lignum Vitae

The Zygophyllaceae is a largely tropical and subtropical family of shrubs, some herbs and a few trees, many of which are adapted to dry or salty habitats. It includes some valuable timber trees such as lignum vitae (*Guaiacum* species).

Distribution. The family is found widely in the tropics and subtropics, often in drier areas, forming a conspicuous element of scrub vegetation, with some temperate representatives.

Diagnostic features. The branches are sometimes jointed at the nodes, The leaves are fleshy or leathery, usually opposite, rarely

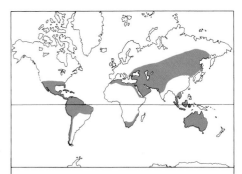

Number of genera: about 25
Number of species: about 240
Distribution: mainly tropical and subtropical, mostly in dry areas.
Economic uses: timber (lignum vitae), medicinal resins, some edible fruits and dyes.

alternate, with stipules which are sometimes spiny or become spiny as they develop.

Apart from one genus (*Neoluederitzia*), the flowers are bisexual, usually regular and borne solitary, paired or in cymes. There are four or five free, imbricate sepals, and four or five free petals also generally imbricate, rarely absent. The stamens are in one, two or three whorls of five, the outer series lying opposite the petals. The filaments are separate and often have a scale at the base. A disk is usually present. The ovary is superior, usually of five fused carpels (rarely two to 12) often with wings. There are usually five locules with one to numerous pendulous ovules on axile placentas. The lobed or flattened stigmas are sessile or borne on a short style. The fruit is generally a capsule, sometimes splitting into five portions, rarely berry-like or drupe-like. The seeds have a straight or slightly curved embryo usually surrounded by endosperm.

Classification. The family is divided into five or six subfamilies largely on the basis of fruit structure. The most important genera are *Guaiacum*, *Bulnesia*, *Nitraria*, *Peganum*, *Balanites*, *Neoschroetera*, *Zygophyllum* and *Tribulus*. The family clearly belongs in the complex of orders Sapindales-Geraniales-Polygalales, but any closer relationships are difficult to determine.

Economic uses. Several species of *Guaiacum*, especially *Guaiacum officinale* and *G. sanctum* (from tropical America and the West Indies) are the source of lignum vitae, a heavy, durable wood which resists splitting. The fruits of some *Balanites* and *Nitraria* species are edible. The tropical American trees, *Bulnesia arborea* (Maracaibo lignum vitae) and *B. sarmienti* (Paraguay lignum vitae), provide useful timber as well as an essential oil used in perfumes. *Neoschroetera tridentata*, the creosote plant from Mexico and adjacent areas, is used medicinally, and its flower buds are used as a caper substitute, as are the buds of *Zygophyllum fabago*. The seeds of the Mediterranean *Peganum harmala* produce the dye, turkey red.　　S.R.C.

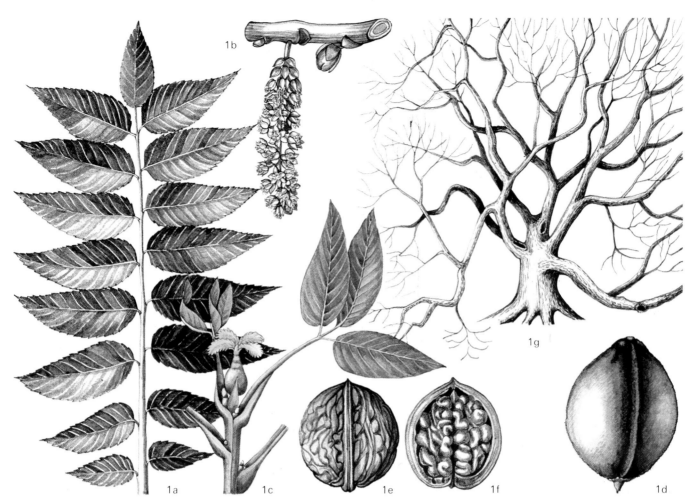

Juglandaceae. 1 *Juglans regia* (a) imparipinnate leaf (×⅔) ; (b) male, catkin-like inflorescence borne on old wood (×⅔) ; (c) tip of shoot with female flower with plumose stigmas (×⅔) ; (d) fruit (×⅔) ; (e) fruit with fleshy husk removed to show hard, sculptured endocarp (inner fruit wall) (×⅔) ; (f) fruit with endocarp removed to show seed with contorted cotyledons (×⅔) ; (g) habit of old tree.

JUGLANDALES

JUGLANDACEAE
Walnuts, Hickories and Pecan Nuts
The Juglandaceae is a small family of deciduous trees, whose best-known members are the walnuts (*Juglans*) and hickories (*Carya*).
Distribution. The family is basically north temperate and subtropical, with extensions southwards to India, Indochina and down the Andes in South America.
Diagnostic features. In winter, the shoots bear brown, hairy buds. The leaves are alternate (rarely opposite), pinnate and without stipules. The flowers are bracteate and unisexual, male and female being borne on the same plant, the males usually in catkin-like, pendulous inflorescences forming on the previous year's twigs, the females in smaller erect spikes forming on the new twigs. The perianth is typically four-lobed, but is often reduced or absent by abortion. The male flowers have three to 40 free stamens in two or more series, with short filaments and bilocular anthers opening lengthwise. Pollination is by wind. The ovary of the female flowers is inferior and consists of two fused carpels forming a single locule containing one erect, orthotropous ovule.

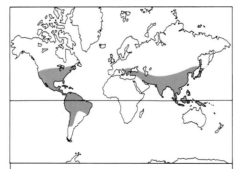

Number of genera: 7
Number of species: about 50
Distribution: mainly N temperate and subtropical.
Economic uses: nuts and oil (walnut, hickory and pecan), timber and ornamentals.

The style is short, with two stigmas. The fruit is a drupe or nut; the characteristic "boats" from a walnut shell do not correspond to the two carpels, but the suture is along their midribs. The seeds have no endosperm.
Classification. The family has been divided into two subfamilies, the JUGLANDOIDEAE with two genera, *Juglans* and *Carya* and the OREOMUNNEOIDEAE with six genera, *Pterocarya*, *Engelhardtia*, *Oreomunnea*, *Platycarya* and *Alfaroa*. The subfamilies are characterized by their fruits, being drupes and winged nuts, respectively. The two best-known genera, *Juglans* and *Carya* are distinguished by the former having an indehiscent, sculptured "nut" and the latter a dehiscent, smooth "nut" inside the fleshy part of the drupe.

The relationships of the family are obscure, although there may be a connection with the Anacardiaceae. The family Rhoipteleaceae represented by a single Chinese tree species *Rhoiptelea chiliantha*, is often regarded a primitive type of the order Juglandales leading to the more advanced Juglandaceae. It differs from the Juglandaceae in having bisexual and female flowers, a superior ovary, stipulate leaves and fruit a samara.
Economic uses. The family is best known for its edible nuts, the walnuts (*Juglans regia* and other species), pecan nuts (*Carya pecan*, *C. illinoensis*) and hickory nuts (*C. ovata*). The oil from the nuts is also used in foods and in the manufacture of cosmetics and soap and as a drying agent in paints.

Both *Juglans* and *Carya* produce valuable timber and are much prized for their fine grain and their toughness.

Species of walnut, hickory and *Pterocarya* (wing nut) are grown for their ornamental value, particularly in autumn.   I.B.K.R.

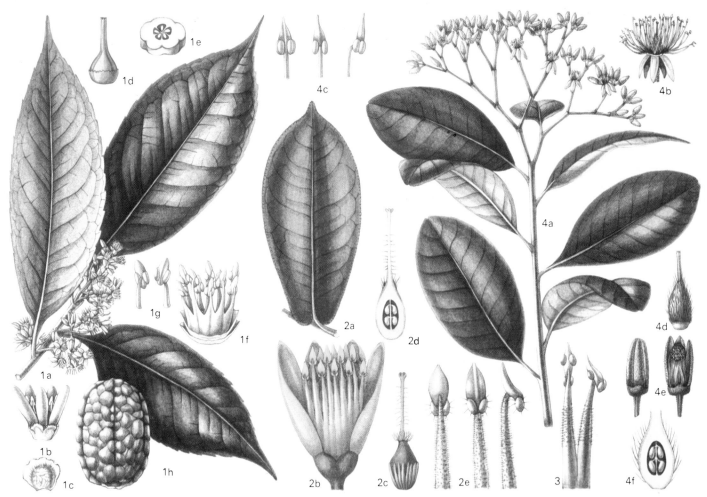

Houmiriaceae. 1 *Sacoglottis amazonica* (a) part of shoot with leaves and axillary inflorescences ($\times\frac{2}{3}$); (b) flower ($\times 2$); (c) sepal ($\times 4\frac{1}{2}$); (d) gynoecium ($\times 4$); (e) cross section of ovary ($\times 8$); (f) androecium ($\times 4$); (g) views of anthers ($\times 7$); (h) fruit—a drupe ($\times\frac{2}{3}$). 2 *Houmiria balsamifera* (a) leaf ($\times\frac{2}{3}$); (b) flower with one petal removed ($\times 6$); (c) gynoecium with toothed, ring-like disk ($\times 6$); (d) vertical section of gynoecium ($\times 6$); (e) stamens ($\times 14$). 3 *Duckesia verrucosa* stamens each with four anther lobes ($\times 14$). 4 *Vantanea parviflora* (a) leafy shoot ($\times\frac{2}{3}$); (b) flower ($\times 2$); (c) stamens ($\times 14$); (d) gynoecium ($\times 7$); (e) flower bud and bud with one petal removed ($\times 1\frac{1}{2}$); (f) vertical section of gynoecium ($\times 10$).

GERANIALES

HOUMIRIACEAE
Bastard Bullet Tree

The Houmiriaceae is a family of mainly tropical American trees and shrubs.

Distribution. The family is native to Central and tropical South America, with only two species (of *Sacoglottis*) also occurring in West Africa.

Diagnostic features. The leaves are alternate, simple, entire or crenate, without stipules. In some members of the family, such as *Sacoglottis*, the petiole is swollen at the base where it joins the stem. The flowers are regular and bisexual, borne in axillary or terminal cymes. There are five sepals, free or slightly connate in the lower part, sometimes covered with fine hairs. There are five free petals, persistent or caducous shortly after opening. There are 10, 20, 30 or more stamens in one, two or several whorls, with filaments more or less connate in the lower part. The anthers are versatile (attached near the middle and moving freely), with two or four locules opening by lengthwise slits. The flower possesses a ring-like disk, often toothed or

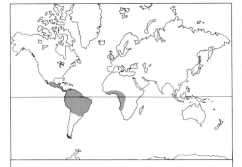

Number of genera: 8
Number of species: about 50
Distribution: Central and tropical S America with two species also in W Africa.
Economic uses: wood and fruit used locally.

made up of separate glands between the stamens and surrounding the base of the ovary. The ovary is superior, consisting of five fused carpels and bearing a simple undivided style with a capitate stigma; it has five locules, each with one or two anatropous ovules, pendulous from the apex. The fruit is drupaceous, with a rather thin fleshy pericarp and a hard woody endocarp often with resin-filled cavities. It has five locules but usually only one or two seeds. The seeds contain fleshy, oily, copious endosperm surrounding a straight embryo with short cotyledons.

Classification. The family includes *Houmiria* (*Humiria*) (three or four species), *Endopleura*, *Duckesia* and *Hylocarpa* (each with one species), *Vantanea* (14 species), *Schistostemon* (seven species) and *Humiriastrum* (12 species). Distinguishing characters include the number of stamens and the nature of the anthers and ovary. *Vantanea* flowers have numerous stamens with four locules in the anthers, while *Houmiria* and *Sacoglottis* flowers have 10 or 20 stamens with two locules in the anthers. The ovary of flowers of *Houmiria* contains two ovules per locules, that of flowers of *Sacoglottis* only one ovule per locule.

The family is related to the Linaceae.

Economic uses. The only member of this family of economic importance is *Houmiria floribunda* (bastard bullet tree); the durable red-brown hardwood is used locally for construction purposes. The fruit of *Sacoglottis gabonensis* is used locally to make a fermented beverage.   S.R.C.

Linaceae. 1 *Linum grandiflorum* (a) leafy shoot with cymose inflorescence (×⅔) ; (b) petal (× 2) ; (c) flower with petals removed to show five blue stamens and five pink staminodes (× 3) ; (d) vertical section of ovary showing axile, pendulous ovules (× 4). 2 *Hugonia castaneifolia* (a) leafy shoot showing hook-like modifications at the base of the inflorescence and flower buds (× 1) ; (b) flower (× 3) ; (c) stamens in two whorls of five surrounding the gynoecium which has three styles (× 4) ; (d) vertical section of fruit (× 1½). 3 *Reinwardtia sinensis* (a) leafy shoot and inflorescence (×⅔) ; (b) fruit—a capsule (×⅔) ; (c) cross section of ovary (× 3) ; (d) whorl of stamens and small staminodes (× 3) ; (e) calyx and four styles (× 3).

LINACEAE

Flax and Linseed

The Linaceae is a small but widespread family of herbs and some shrubs, of which flax (*Linum usitatissimum*) is the most economically important member.

Distribution. The family is chiefly distributed in temperate zones, with some tropical representatives.

Diagnostic features. The leaves are usually alternate, small, entire and with or without stipules. The inflorescence is cymose, bearing regular bisexual flowers. In the tropical genus *Hugonia* the lower parts of the inflorescence are modified as hooks for climbing. The calyx is composed of five (occasionally four) sepals which are either free or united at their base. It is usually persistent through to the stage of seed liberation. The petals are equal in number to the sepals, usually free but sometimes joined at the base, and wither away and fall early. The stamens usually equal the number of petals and are alternate with them. Their filaments are usually short and fused at their bases to form a glandular ring. There may also be five staminodes alternating with the stamens. The ovary is superior and consists

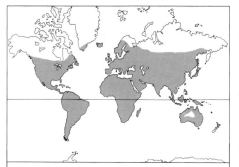

Number of genera: 13
Number of species: about 300
Distribution: chiefly temperate, with some tropical representatives.
Economic uses: fibers, linseed oil and cattle feed from flax, some fruits and locally used timber, and garden and greenhouse ornamentals.

of two to five fused carpels. It may, however, have four to ten locules owing to the development of additional (false) septa. The placentation is axile with one or two pendulous ovules in each locule. The two to five styles are separate. The fruit is usually a capsule but in some species drupaceous. The

seed contains a straight embryo and endosperm ranges from none to copious. The seed of flax (*Linum*) has a mucilaginous coat which swells upon wetting.

Classification. The genera can be distinguished on the basis of habit and floral characteristics such as presence or absence of staminodes, number of locules in the ovary, number of styles and type of seed. The most important genera are *Linum* (230 species, mainly Mediterranean), *Hugonia* (40 species, Africa and the Far East), *Reinwardtia* (two species of shrubs, northern India and China), *Anisadenia* (two species, China), *Roucheria* (eight species, tropical South America) and the monotypic genus *Radiola* (Europe and North Africa). The genus *Ctenolophon* is considered by some authorities to constitute a separate family (Ctenolophonaceae).

This family is characterized by the usually early-falling petals and the fusion of the short stamen filaments. It is placed in the same order as the Geraniaceae with which it shares such features as regular flowers, two whorls of stamens or staminodes, and a gynoecium of two to five fused carpels with axile placentation. The genus *Anisadenia* is considered to show features which link the

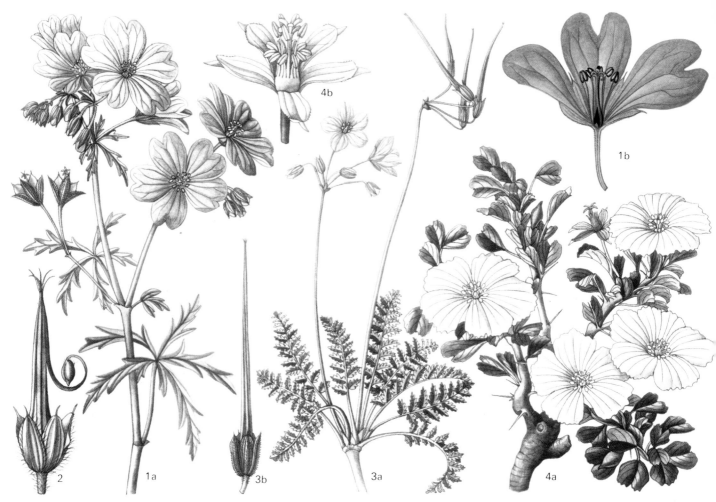

Geraniaceae. 1 *Geranium malviflorum* (a) shoot with compound leaves and inflorescences ($\times \frac{2}{3}$): (b) vertical section of flower showing bilobed petals ($\times 1\frac{1}{3}$). 2 *G. sanguineum* fruit with persistent calyx and with one awn separating from the central axis to disperse a seed ($\times 1\frac{1}{3}$). 3 *Erodium romanum* (a) tip of leafy shoot with inflorescence and fruits ($\times \frac{2}{3}$); (b) fruit before dehiscence ($\times 1\frac{1}{3}$). 4 *Sarcocaulon patersonii* (a) fleshy stem with thorns (remains of leaf stalks) and solitary flowers ($\times 1$); (b) flower with petals removed showing five pointed sepals and fifteen stamens of two lengths and with fused filament bases ($\times 3$).

Linaceae with the more advanced Plumbaginaceae.

Economic uses. *Linum* is the most important genus as it includes the flax and linseed plant, *Linum usitatissimum*, an annual herb cultivated for both its stem fibers and its seeds. The fibers are durable and have great tensile strength. They are used in the manufacture of linens, fine writing paper and cigarette paper. Linseed oil is prepared by extraction from the pressed seed and is chiefly used in the manufacture of paints, varnishes and printing ink; the residual oilcake makes valuable cattle food. Europe is the chief center of fiber production, Argentina the world's largest producer of linseed oil.

The African species of *Hugonia* (*Hugonia obtusifolia* and *H. platysepala*) provide edible fruits while the Malaysian tree *Ctenolophon parvifolium* provides a hard durable timber used in house construction. A number of other *Linum* species are grown as ornamentals, either as rockery plants (eg *L. arboreum*) or as border plants (*L. flavum*), while *Reinwardtia trigyna*, with bright yellow flowers, is an attractive winter-flowering shrub grown in greenhouses in temperate zones. S.R.C.

GERANIACEAE
Geraniums and Pelargoniums

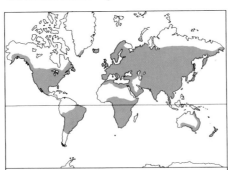

Number of genera: 11
Number of species: about 750
Distribution: mainly temperate and subtropical.

Economic uses: geranium oil from *Pelargonium* species, and garden and greenhouse ornamental, including *Pelargonium* (geranium), *Geranium* (cranesbill) and *Erodium* (storksbill).

The Geraniaceae is a family of mostly temperate and subtropical annual or perennial herbs and a few small shrubs. It includes the garden geraniums (*Pelargonium* species)

which should not be confused with the genus *Geranium* (cranesbill) in the same family.

Distribution. The family is widely distributed in temperate and subtropical regions of both Northern and Southern Hemispheres. Some species of *Geranium* are found within the Arctic while others occur in Antarctica.

Diagnostic features. The stems often have jointed nodes and these, and the leaves, are frequently covered with glandular hairs. The leaves are opposite or alternate, simple or compound, often with stipules. The flowers are regular (rarely slightly irregular), bisexual and borne either solitary or in cymose inflorescences. There are usually five sepals and five, often large and brightly colored petals surrounding one, two or three whorls each of five stamens (and/or staminodes), which usually have the filaments fused at the base. If there are two whorls, the outermost lies opposite the petals. Nectaries are often present at the base of the stamens. The ovary is superior and comprises usually five carpels fused around a central axis (carpophore); there are one or two ovules on axile placentas in each of the five locules. Each of the five styles terminates in a separate stigma. The fruit is a schizocarp (rarely a capsule as in

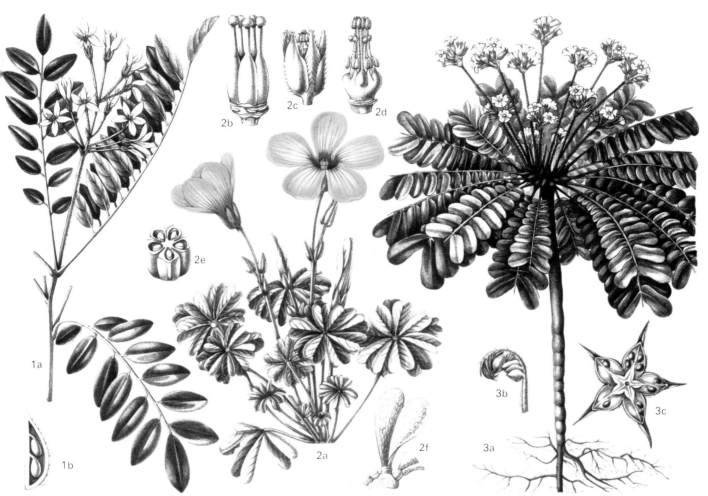

Oxalidaceae. 1 *Eichleria blanchetiana* (a) flowering shoot showing imparipinnate leaves and flowers in a cymose inflorescence ($\times\frac{2}{3}$); (b) vertical section of part of ovary ($\times14$). 2 *Oxalis adenophylla* (a) habit showing palmate leaves ($\times\frac{2}{3}$); (b) gynoecium comprising five united carpels each with a capitate stigma ($\times4\frac{1}{2}$); (c) flower with petals removed ($\times2$); (d) androecium and gynoecium showing trimorphic heterostyly (ie stamens in two rows each at different levels to the stigmas) ($\times3$); (e) section of base of fruit ($\times2$); (f) leaflet and short petiolule ($\times2$). 3 *Biophytum sensitivum* (a) habit showing pinnate leaves with the terminal leaflet reduced to a bristle ($\times\frac{2}{3}$); (b) leaf unfolding ($\times\frac{2}{3}$); (c) dehiscing fruit ($\times3$).

Viviania), and the carpels with their long persistent styles (awns) split off elastically at the base of the central axis. The seeds contain a curved embryo and little or no endosperm.

Classification. The 11 genera can be disposed into five subfamilies:

GERANIOIDEAE, characterized by the presence of a beaked ovary, contains nearly half of the genera: *Geranium, Erodium, Pelargonium, Monsonia* and *Sarcocaulon*. Three other subfamilies (BIEBERSTEINIOIDEAE, VIVIANIOIDEAE and DIRACHMOIDEAE) lack a beaked ovary and each contain a single genus: *Biebersteinia* (ovary contains only one seed), *Viviania* (fruit a capsule) and *Dirachma* (eight carpels present), respectively. *Vivianaia* (30 South American species) is sometimes separated off as a separate family, the Vivianiaceae. The other subfamily, WENDTIOIDEAE (sometimes with a beaked ovary), contains the other three genera, *Balbisia, Wendtia* and *Rhynchotheca* and is separated by some authorities as the family Ledocarpaceae.

The family is closely related to the Tropaeolaceae, Oxalidaceae, Linaceae and possibly the Balsaminaceae.

Economic uses. The so-called geraniums grown so extensively in gardens and greenhouses in fact belong to the South African genus *Pelargonium*. Most of the horticultural pelargoniums are hybrids, as in the case of zonal pelargoniums, which are the result of crosses between *Pelargonium zonale* and *P. inquinans*, or the large-flowered regal pelargoniums, which are the result of crosses between *P. cucullatum, P. fulgidum* and *P. grandiflorum*. Other species of *Pelargonium*, notably *P. graveolens, P. odoratissimum, P. capitatum* and *P. radula*, are cultivated for geranium oil, which can be distilled from the leaves and shoots, and finds wide uses in the perfume and oil industries. A number of species of *Geranium* (cranesbill) and *Erodium* (storksbill) are cultivated as border and as rockery plants.   S.R.C.

OXALIDACEAE
Wood Sorrel and Bermuda Buttercup

The Oxalidaceae is a family of mainly tropical and subtropical annual and perennial herbs including a number of ornamentals.

Distribution. Most of the family is native to tropical and subtropical Asia and Africa, and tropical America. Some are temperate.

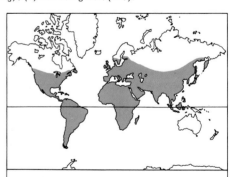

Number of genera: 3
Number of species: about 900
Distribution: centered in the tropics and subtropics, but widespread in temperate regions.
Economic uses: tubers and leaves of some *Oxalis* species eaten and some rock garden ornamentals.

Diagnostic features. The leaves are alternate and without stipules, sometimes simple but often pinnately or palmately compound. Many species of *Oxalis* possess leaflets which fold downward at night and in cold weather; in some species of *Biophytum* the leaflets bend when touched. In a few species of

Oxalis, such as *Oxalis bupleurifolia*, the ordinary leaves are replaced by phyllodes (leaf-like petioles).

The flowers are regular, bisexual, and borne either solitary or in cymose inflorescences. They have five, free, persistent sepals and five petals which may be free or fused just at the base. There are 10 stamens arranged in two whorls and connate at the base, the outer whorl of five lying opposite the petals. Sometimes the outer stamens are sterile. The anthers are two-celled and dehisce lengthwise. The ovary is superior, consisting of five free (as in *Biophytum*) or fused (as in *Oxalis*) carpels with five free styles and capitate stigmas. There are five locules, each with one or two rows of ovules on axile placentas. Many species of *Oxalis* display trimorphic heterostyly, ie flowers with long styles and medium and short stamens, medium styles and long and short stamens, and short styles and long and medium stamens. Fertile crosses are only possible between different flower-types. The Eurasian species *Oxalis acetosella* (wood sorrel) has flowers which in cold conditions exhibit cleistogamy (pollination and fertilization before flower-opening).

The fruit is a capsule. The seeds have a straight embryo surrounded by fleshy endosperm. The seeds of some species of *Biophytum* and *Oxalis* may have a fleshy aril at the base. The turgid inner cell layers of the aril turn inside out rapidly, separate from the testa, and the seed is explosively flung out.

Classification. The three genera are *Oxalis* (about 800 species), with leaves with one to 20 or more leaflets; *Biophytum* (70 species), whose leaves possess a bristle representing the end leaflet; and *Eichleria* (two species), whose leaves possess a terminal leaflet. Classification within *Oxalis* is based on features such as the number, shape and size of the leaflets and the form of inflorescence and color of flowers.

The family is related to the Geraniaceae and Linaceae but is distinguished for example from the Geraniaceae by the five distinct styles and by the possession of arillate seeds. The tree genera *Averrhoa* and *Connaropsis* were at one time included in the Oxalidaceae but are now sometimes separated as the family Averrhoaceae.

Economic uses. The Oxalidaceae is of minor economic use. *Oxalis crenata*, a small Peruvian perennial herb, has tubers which are boiled and eaten as a vegetable and the leaves used in salads. The leaves of *O. acetosella* are sometimes used in salads instead of sorrel and the bulbous stems of *O. pes-caprae* (*O. cernua*, Bermuda buttercup) are sometimes used as a vegetable in southern France and North Africa. The tubers of the Mexican species *O. deppei* are also used as food and are cultivated in France and Belgium.

A number of *Oxalis* species are cultivated as rock garden plants and some are troublesome weeds.   S.R.C.

ERYTHROXYLACEAE
Coca/Cocaine

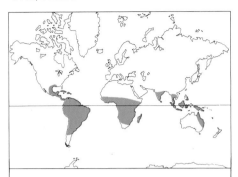

Number of genera: 4
Number of species: about 260
Distribution: tropical and subtropical centered in S America.
Economic uses: cocaine, widely used in medicine, and local uses of wood, bark dye and essential oils.

This tropical and subtropical family of trees and shrubs includes the important cocaine-producing coca plant.

Distribution. The family is centered in the Andes and Amazonian basin of South America and also occurs in Africa, Madagascar, Southeast Asia and tropical Australia.

Diagnostic features. The plants have simple, alternate (rarely opposite), ovoid leaves and stipules within the petioles (intrapetiolar). The terminal or axillary flowers are very small, occurring in fascicles. They are usually regular and bisexual, rarely unisexual (and then the sexes are on separate plants). The calyx is bell-shaped with five imbricate lobes and the corolla consists of five free, imbricate, deciduous petals. The ten stamens are in two series joined at their bases. The ovary is superior and consists of three or four fused carpels containing three or four locules, only one or two of which are fertile, each containing one or two pendulous, anatropous ovules. There are three fused or free styles. The fruit is an ovoid drupe borne beyond the persistent calyx. The seeds have endosperm and a straight embryo.

Classification. The family comprises four genera, readily distinguished by leaf and floral characteristics. *Aneulophus* (two species, parts of tropical Africa) has opposite leaves. *Erythroxylum* (about 250 species, tropical South America, Africa and Madagascar) has alternate leaves and filaments fused in a tube. *Nectaropetalum* (six species, tropical and southern Africa) has alternate leaves, filaments free and sessile flowers in fascicles in the leaf axils. *Pinacopodium* (two species, parts of tropical Africa) has alternate leaves, filaments free and stalked flowers in axillary or terminal fascicles.

The Erythroxylaceae is a well-defined group closely allied to and often included in the family Linaceae.

Economic uses. The leaves of *Erythroxylum*

coca and *E. novagranatense* (coca) yield the important alkaloid cocaine, a narcotic widely used in modern medicine. They are chewed as a stimulant by South American Indians and are cultivated in South America, Sri Lanka and Java for the cocaine, used as a local anaesthetic and in some medicines. Other species are of local importance for their wood, bark dye, wood tar, essential oil or medicinal uses.

C.J.H.

LIMNANTHACEAE
Poached Egg Flower

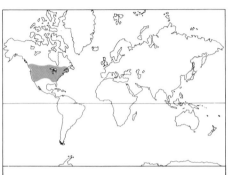

Number of genera: 2
Number of species: 11
Distribution: N America, chiefly California.
Economic uses: limited as cultivated ornamentals.

The Limnanthaceae is a small North American family of two genera of delicate, sometimes attractive, annual herbs.

Distribution. Most of the 11 species are Californian, and all are North American, growing in moist habitats.

Diagnostic features. These fragile, sappy, annual herbs have alternate, pinnatifid leaves without stipules. The solitary flowers are regular, usually white, bisexual and borne in leaf axils. There are three or five valvate sepals and an equal number of contorted petals. There are six or ten stamens. The ovary is superior, of three or five carpels, which are almost free but have a common gynobasic style. Each carpel locule contains one ascending ovule, and at maturity the fruit separates into three or five tuberculate nutlets; the seeds lack endosperm and have a straight embryo.

Classification. In *Limnanthes* the flower parts are in fives. In the monotypic *Floerkea* they are in threes and the petals are shorter than the sepals. Although generally similar to the Polemoniaceae and Hydrophyllaceae, the family is more closely related to the Geraniaceae.

Economic uses. Of the 10 species of *Limnanthes* (Greek: marsh flower) the best-known is *Limnanthes douglasii* (poached egg flower). Its striking flowers have yellow petals with white tips. Borne in profusion, they are very attractive to bees. It is grown in gardens and in glasshouses.   B.M.

Balsaminaceae. 1 *Hydrocera triflora* (a) irregular flower (×1); (b) section of fruit—a berry (×1). 2 *Impatiens walleriana* leafy shoot and flowers (×⅔). 3 *I. balsamina* (a) fruit (×1⅓); (b) leafy shoot and axillary flowers (×⅔). 4 *I. glandulifera* (a) irregular flower with posterior spurred sepal and small anterior sepals (×1); (b) stamens fused around the ovary (×3); (c) anterior sepal (×3); (d) lateral petal (×1); (e) anterior petal (×1); (f) fruit—a capsule (×1½).

BALSAMINACEAE

Balsams

The Balsaminaceae is a family of annual and perennial herbs with watery, translucent stems. The major genus is *Impatiens*, several species of which are cultivated.

Distribution. The family is represented throughout temperate and tropical Eurasia, Africa, Madagascar, and Central and North America.

Diagnostic features. The leaves are alternate or opposite, toothed, and usually without stipules. The flowers are bisexual and very irregular. There are usually three free sepals, the posterior one petaloid and usually spurred, and in addition sometimes two small or aborted anterior sepals. There are five unequal petals, the four lower ones connate in lateral pairs. There are five stamens with short, flat filaments and introrse anthers which are more or less united to form a cap over the ovary. The ovary is superior, consisting of five fused carpels, with five locules containing numerous ovules on axile placentas. There are one to five, more or less sessile stigmas. The fruit is a capsule or rarely a berry, and the seed has no endosperm and a straight embryo.

Classification. The genus *Impatiens* has

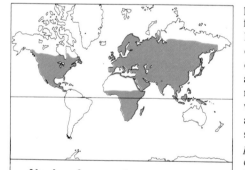

Number of genera: 4
Number of species: 500–600
Distribution: temperate and tropical regions.
Economic uses: valued greenhouse and pot plants of the genus *Impatiens*.

leaves that are oval to lanceolate, toothed and petiolate, and alternate or opposite. The flowers appear to have only four sepals but the anterior one, which is notched at the apex, probably originated as two. The posterior one, which may appear anteriorly as the flower hangs on the pedicel, is the largest and forms a spurred sac. The brightly colored corolla of pink, red, purple, white or yellow has five petals, the laterals united in

pairs. The fruit is an explosive capsule, with a fleshy pericarp, the outer cells of which are highly turgid and create an intense pressure on the whole fruit. The explosive method of dehiscence is termed septifragal dehiscence and is initiated by touch, when the fruit is ripe, and valves roll inwards from the base with a violent explosion which is clearly audible to the human ear, and the black seeds are scattered in all directions. *Impatiens* exhibits dimorphism, bearing small cleistogamic flowers which are fertilized in bud and never open, and large showy ones which rarely produce seeds that ripen.

Impatiens (with 500–600 species) is distinguished from the genus *Hydrocera* by two characters: the lateral petals are connate in pairs and the fruit is a capsule in *Impatiens*, while in *Hydrocera* the lateral petals are free and the fruit is a berry. *Hydrocera* is represented by one species from Indomalaysia, *Hydrocera trifolia* (*H. angustifolia*), an erect marsh plant, about 3ft (1m) tall with an angled stem and alternate, narrow leaves. The flowers are borne one to three together. The outer petals are large and concave, and the sepals are colored. The fruit is a red berry. Two further genera of the Balsaminaceae, of somewhat doubtful tax-

Tropaeolaceae. 1 *Tropaeolum majus* (a) prostrate stem bearing peltate leaves, solitary, spurred flowers and fruit—a schizocarp comprising three mericarps (×1); (b) vertical section of mericarp containing a single seed (×2). 2 *Magallana porifolia* (a) stem with deeply palmate leaves, flowers and fruits (×⅔); (b) irregular flower with two of the petals differing from other three and eight stamens (×2); (c) base of flower opened out to show free stamens (×3); (d) gynoecium (×10); (e) winged fruits (×10).

onomic status, are *Semeiocardium*, represented by one species in Indomalaysia, and *Impatientella* with one species in Madagascar.

The presence of a spur in the flowers of the Balsaminaceae has led people to associate the family with the Geraniaceae and Tropaeolaceae, but the spur is strictly an outgrowth of the calyx, whereas in the other families there is evidence that receptacle tissue is involved in spur formation. Therefore the spurs are of different origins and it is doubtful whether the supposed relationship is as close as often stated.

Economic uses. The only economic value of the Balsaminaceae lies in the cultivation of *Impatiens* species as greenhouse or pot plants or garden ornamentals. The plants known commercially as "busy lizzies" are hybrids between *Impatiens holstii* and *I. sultanii*, and have white, pink, red or orange flowers and green, red or bronze foliage.   S.A.H.

TROPAEOLACEAE
Nasturtiums and Canary Creeper
This small family of climbing succulent herbs includes the cultivated *Tropaeolum majus* (garden nasturtium – not to be confused with the genus *Nasturtium*, family Cruciferae).

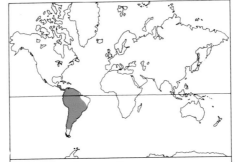

Number of genera: 2
Number of species: about 90
Distribution: mountainous C and S America.
Economic uses: ornamentals (garden nasturtium), and pickled seeds of *Tropaeolum majus* are a caper substitute.

Distribution. The family is native mainly to the mountains from Mexico to central Chile and Argentina.

Diagnostic features. The plants are usually succulent herbs with an acrid mustard oil present in the sap, as in the family Cruciferae. Sometimes root tubers are produced. The stems are prostrate, though frequently climbing by means of sensitive petioles,

which twine around any support in a similar manner to those of *Clematis*. The leaves are alternate, peltate, sometimes deeply lobed, and without stipules. The showy flowers are bisexual, irregular and spurred, and usually borne solitary in the axils of leaves. The perianth consists of a calyx with five distinct sepals, one modified to form a long nectar-spur, and a corolla with five distinct, usually clawed petals, the upper two smaller than the lower three. There are eight stamens. The ovary is superior, formed of three fused carpels, with three locules each containing one axile, pendulous ovule; the single apical style has three stigmas. The fruit is a three-seeded schizocarp, each mericarp separating to become an indehiscent "seed," lacking endosperm. The embryo is straight and has thick fleshy cotyledons.

Classification. There are only two genera; *Tropaeolum*, with about 90 species, and *Magallana*, with only one. *Magallana* is native to Patagonia and is named after the Portuguese navigator Fernando Magellan (1480–1521). It differs from *Tropaeolum* in having winged fruits.

The family was at one time placed in the Geraniaceae but is now kept separate, as it differs in having distinct stamens and no

Malpighiaceae. 1 *Malpighia coccigera* (a) flowering shoot (×⅔); (b) flower with petals removed (×2⅔); (c) sepal dorsal view (×5⅓); (d) gynoecium (×5). 2 *M. heterantha* (a) cross section of ovary (×6); (b) fruit (×2). 3 *Acridocarpus natalitius* (a) inflorescence (×⅔); (b) flower with petals removed (×2); (c) gynoecium (×2⅔); (d) vertical section of ovary (×3); (e) cross section of ovary (×2⅔); (f) winged fruit (×⅔). 4 *Sphedamnocarpus pruriens* (a) leafy shoot and terminal inflorescence (×⅔); (b) flower with filament bases united in a ring (×2); (c) gynoecium (×3).

beak on the fruit. Other relationships have been suggested with the Limnanthaceae and Sapindaceae.

Economic uses. About eight species are cultivated for ornament; most commonly met with are *Tropaeolum majus*, the garden nasturtium, and *T. peregrinum* (*T. canariense*), canary creeper or canary-bird flower. The unripe seeds of *T. majus* are occasionally pickled and used like capers. The leaves or tubers of some species (eg *T. tuberosum*) are eaten locally.   S.L.J.

POLYGALALES

MALPIGHIACEAE

The Malpighiaceae is a family containing numerous tropical climbers as well as shrubs and trees. The fruits as well as the flowers of many species are highly attractive.

Distribution. Members of this family are found in the tropics, especially in South America.

Diagnostic features. The leaves are simple, usually opposite, glandular below or on the stalk, and with or without stipules. The flowers are borne in racemes, and are regular or irregular, bisexual (rarely male, female

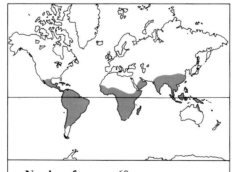

Number of genera: 60
Number of species: 800
Distribution: tropics, especially S America.
Economic uses: some ornamentals, a few edible fruits, cordage and occasional local uses.

and bisexual all on the same plant). There are five imbricate sepals each of which often has paired glands at the base, five imbricate, usually clawed petals, and 10 (rarely fewer) stamens with filaments often fused at the base. The ovary is superior, formed of three fused carpels, with only one pendulous ovule on an axile placenta in each of the three locules, and is set obliquely to the central axis

of the flower. The styles are usually distinct. The mature schizocarpic fruit-parts are often winged when they fall apart, or the fruit may be a fleshy or woody drupe. The seeds have no endosperm. The family is often recognizable by a special type of single-celled branched hair.

Classification. There are two groups within the family: PYRAMIDOTORAE (torus pyramidal and fruits winged, chief genera *Tetrapteris*, *Banisteriopsis*, *Heteropterys*, *Acridocarpus*, *Stigmaphyllon*); PLANITORAE (torus flat or concave and fruits not winged, chief genera *Malpighia*, *Bunchosia*, *Byrsonima*).

The genus *Stigmaphyllon* comprises some 65 tropical American species. They are woody vines, the leaves having two glands at the top of the leaf stalk. The showy yellow flowers are borne in umbel-like corymbs. There are six anther-bearing stamens and four infertile ones situated opposite each of the four sepals, each of which has two glands. The five hairless petals are unequal in size. The stigmas are leaf-like. The fruits are samaras. *Tristellateia* comprises about 20 Old World species ranging from Africa through Madagascar, southeast Asia and into Australasia. *Banisteria* has been split up by some botanists into the genera *Banisteri-*

opsis and *Heteropterys*, both with about 100 species.

The African genus *Acridocarpus* comprises about 50 species, and extends into Madagascar, Arabia and New Caledonia. In the shrubby genus *Camarea*, some eight species from Brazil tending to grow in dry savanna regions, a tough bulbous rootstock has evolved which affords the plant some protection from periodic drought or fire hazards.

The Malpighiaceae has been associated with the Trigoniaceae and Tremandraceae within the order Polygalales and with the Houmiriaceae (Geraniales) and Zygophyllaceae (Sapindales) outside this order. It is usually considered a primitive family within the Polygalales.

Economic uses. A number of species make fine ornamentals, particularly in warm temperate and tropical gardens, for example *Stigmaphyllon ciliatum, Tristellateia australasiae, Hiptage benghalensis, Acridocarpus alternifolius, A. smeathmannii* and *A. natalitius, Heteropterys beecheyana, Banisteria laevifolia,* and *Malpighia glabra.* Cordage is made from some species of *Banisteria.* The leaves and shoots of *Banisteria caapi* yield a hallucinatory drug. The leaves of *Hiptage benghalensis* are used in India to treat skin diseases. The fruits of some species of *Malpighia* are edible, being eaten raw or in jellies.   B.M.

TRIGONIACEAE

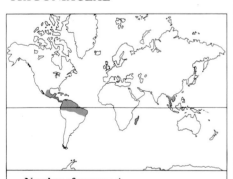

Number of genera: 4
Number of species: about 35
Distribution: tropical S America, Malaysia and Madagascar.
Economic uses: wood used locally for furniture.

The Trigoniaceae is a small family of shrubs and trees of no real economic importance.

Distribution. The family is native to tropical South America, Malaysia and Madagascar.

Diagnostic features. The leaves are opposite or alternate, simple, and generally with small stipules. In some species the bases of the stipules on opposite leaves are fused.

The flowers are irregular, bisexual and borne in racemose inflorescences. There are five overlapping sepals which are either free or united at the base, and five or three unequal petals, the posterior (dorsal) one being the largest. There is a variable number

of stamens and staminodes (3–12) with the filaments fused at the base. There is often a disk gland opposite the posterior petal. The ovary is superior and comprises three fused carpels, with three locules (rarely one), each with two to numerous ovules on axile placentas. It is surmounted by a single style. The fruit is a capsule, sometimes winged, rarely a samara, containing seeds which are usually hairy and have a straight embryo and no endosperm.

Classification. Criteria used to separate the four genera include the leaf arrangement, the presence or absence of wings on the fruit, the number of ovules per fruit and the number of stamens per flower. The genera are *Euphronia* (three species, tropical America), *Trigonia* (30 species, tropical America), *Trigoniastrum* (one species, Malaysia) and *Humbertiodendron* (one species, Madagascar). Examples of the generic differences can be seen in *Euphronia* which has three to five stamens and two ovules per locule, and *Trigonia* which has up to 12 stamens and an ovary with numerous ovules. *Euphronia* has opposite leaves, while *Trigonia* has alternate leaves.

The family is related to the Polygalaceae and the Vochysiaceae and possibly to the Sapindaceae.

Economic uses. *Trigoniastrum* provides wood used locally for furniture.   S.R.C.

TREMANDRACEAE

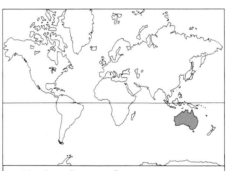

Number of genera: 3
Number of species: 43
Distribution: Australia.
Economic uses: ornamentals.

The Tremandraceae is a family of small shrubs, bearing flowers which sometimes combine moderate size with extravagant color.

Distribution. The family is confined to Australia.

Diagnostic features. With occasionally winged stems and reduced foliage, these shrublets often have glandular or rarely starshaped hairs. The leaves are alternate, sometimes opposite or whorled, simple, entire or toothed, without stipules and often narrow. The flowers are regular, bisexual, frequently red or purple, solitary and axillary, with three to five free sepals and petals. There are twice as many stamens as petals, the anthers having two or four locules and

opening by a single apical pore. The receptacle is sometimes swollen and glandular, lobed between the stamens and petals. The ovary is superior and comprises two fused carpels forming two locules, each with one to three apical, pendulous ovules. The style is slender with a small stigma. The fruit is a compressed capsule opening by slits which follow the locule partitions or are at right angles to them. The seeds have an outgrowth at one end, a straight embryo and copious endosperm, and are sometimes hairy.

Classification. The three genera are *Tremandra* (two species), *Tetratheca* (39 species) and *Platytheca* (two species). The family is related to the Pittosporaceae by some botanists, and to the Polygalaceae by others. The habit of growth of many species resembles that of certain species in the Rutaceae or Ericaceae.

Economic uses. One or two species of *Tetratheca* are occasionally cultivated in Australian gardens, but the family has no other economic use.   B.M.

VOCHYSIACEAE

The Vochysiaceae is a small family of trees, shrubs, and climbers.

Distribution. This family is native to tropical Central and South America and West Africa.

Diagnostic features. The leaves are simple and either opposite, in whorls or alternate; stipules are either small or lacking. The flowers are bisexual, slightly irregular, and usually arranged in compound racemes. There are five imbricate sepals, connate at the base, the outer one often the largest and swollen or spurred at the base. The petals vary in number from one to five and are unequal in size. There is only one fertile stamen and two to four staminodes. The anthers have two locules and open longitudinally. The ovary is superior or sometimes attached to the calyx and inferior. It consists of either three fused carpels and three locules or one carpel and one locule; one to numerous axile ovules occur in each locule. There is a single style terminating in a simple stigma. The fruit is a capsule or samara-like, containing one or more seeds which are often winged and sometimes covered with soft hairs. The embryo is straight and the seed is usually without endosperm.

Classification. One of the six genera (*Erismadelphus* with three species) is native to tropical West Africa, while the others (*Erisma* with 20 species, *Callisthene* with 10 species, *Qualea* with 60 species, *Salvertia* with one species, and *Vochysia* with 105 species) are all native to tropical Central and South America. Two genera (*Erisma* and *Erismadelphus*) have an inferior ovary and a unilocular fruit, with the sepals adherent to it and persisting as wings. *Erisma* has an ovary containing two ovules, surmounted by a slender thread-like style, while the corolla is reduced to a single petal. *Erismadelphus* has

Vochysiaceae. 1 *Vochysia divergens* (a) leafy shoot and inflorescence ($\times\frac{2}{3}$); (b) winged fruit ($\times 1\frac{1}{3}$). 2 *V. guatemalensis* (a) vertical section of flower ($\times 1\frac{1}{3}$); (b) stamen ($\times 2$); (c) staminode ($\times 4$); (d) cross section of ovary ($\times 2$); (e) vertical section of ovary ($\times 2$). 3 *V. obscura* winged seed ($\times 1$). 4 *Salvertia convallariodora* part of inflorescence ($\times\frac{2}{3}$). 5 *S. convallariodora* flower showing single fertile stamen ($\times\frac{2}{3}$). 6 *Erismadelphus exsul* var *platiphyllus* (a) flower ($\times 4$); (b) vertical section of flower base ($\times 6$); (c) winged fruit ($\times\frac{2}{3}$).

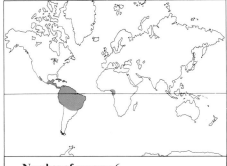

Number of genera: 6
Number of species: about 200
Distribution: tropical C and S America, and W Africa.
Economic uses: timber and a fat from the seeds used for making soap and candles.

a single ovule in the ovary, which is surmounted by a very short, stubby style, while the corolla consists of five subequal petals. All other genera have flowers with a superior three-locular ovary which develops into a three-chambered capsule with winged seeds. *Salvertia* has flowers with five subequal petals, and a club-shaped style with a lateral stigma, while *Vochysia* has flowers

with one to three or more petals and a style with a terminal stigma. Both *Qualea* and *Callisthene* have flowers with only one petal and an ovary containing numerous ovules. These two genera can be distinguished on the basis of a number of characters including the nature of the axis of the capsule.

The family is related to the Trigoniaceae and Polygalaceae, sharing with them the similarity of the tree, shrub or climbing habit, leaf arrangement, floral structure, one- to three-locular ovary and hairy, non-endospermic seeds.

Economic uses. Some members of this family are economically valuable, eg *Vochysia tetraphylla* whose timber is used in furniture-making. The timber of *Vochysia hondurensis* is used in Brazil for boat construction and for fence posts. The seeds of *Erisma calcaratum* are the source of jaboty butter which is used for making candles and soap.

S.R.C.

POLYGALACEAE

The Polygalaceae is a family of herbs, shrubs, small trees, climbers and even saprophytes. The family is remarkable for the superficial resemblance of the flowers to

the well-known papilionaceous flower of the Leguminosae. Over 500 out of about 1,000 species belong to the genus *Polygala*.

Distribution. The family is almost cosmopolitan, being absent only from New Zealand and many of the southern Pacific Islands, and the extreme northern parts of the Northern Hemisphere.

Diagnostic features. The leaves are usually alternate, always simple, and usually without stipules. The flowers are bisexual, irregular, each subtended by a bract and two bracteoles, and are arranged in spikes or racemes or are solitary. The calyx of five (rarely four to seven) sepals is variously modified, most commonly either with the two lowermost united or with the two inner (lateral) enlarged and often petaloid. The corolla is usually reduced to three petals, with the lowest (median) petal often saucer-shaped and sometimes with a fringed crest. The usually eight stamens are generally joined to the very base of the corolla, with their united filaments forming a split sheath; the anthers are basifixed, usually dehiscing by an apical pore; the pollen grains have a distinctive pattern on their outer wall. A ring-shaped disk is sometimes present inside

Polygalaceae. 1 *Xanthophyllum scortechinii* (a) leafy shoot and irregular flowers ($\times\frac{2}{3}$); (b) flower with petals removed showing free stamens ($\times1\frac{1}{2}$); (c) petal ($\times1\frac{1}{2}$); (d) gynoecium ($\times2$); (e) cross section of ovary ($\times2$); (f) globose fruit ($\times\frac{2}{3}$). 2. *Polygala apopetala* (a) inflorescence ($\times\frac{2}{3}$); (b) flower with lateral sepals removed ($\times2$); (c) androecium with filaments united in a split sheath ($\times3$); (d) stamens ($\times4$); (e) gynoecium ($\times3$); (f) vertical section of ovary ($\times8$). 3 *Carpolobia lutea* (a) leaves and fruit—a drupe ($\times\frac{2}{3}$); (b) fruit entire and in cross section ($\times\frac{2}{3}$). 4 *Bredemeyera colletioides* flowering shoot ($\times\frac{2}{3}$). 5 *Securidaca longipedunculata* winged fruits—samaras ($\times\frac{2}{3}$).

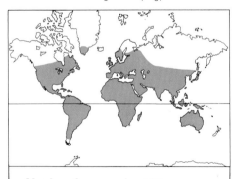

Number of genera: about 17
Number of species: about 1,000
Distribution: almost cosmopolitan.
Economic uses: limited local uses.

the base of the staminal whorl. The ovary is superior, usually of two united carpels with a single pendulous ovule on an axile placenta in each of the two locules, although there are various exceptions to this general structure. The style is simple. The fruit is usually a loculicidal capsule, but several smaller genera have exceptions to this; the seeds, sometimes hairy, generally have an aril, and contain a straight embryo and fleshy endosperm (sometimes absent).

Classification. The family has been divided into three tribes: the POLYGALEAE (about 12 genera), the MOUTABEAE (four genera) and the XANTHOPHYLLEAE (one genus). *Xanthophyllum*, with about 40 species from the Indomalaysian region, has been treated by some authorities as a distinct family, the Xanthophyllaceae, on account of the almost free stamens and close superficial resemblance to the Caesalpinioideae of the Leguminosae. The other tribes and genera are based primarily on fruit differences: while *Polygala* and the tufted-seeded *Bredemeyera* have capsular fruit, *Securidaca* has a samara, *Monnina* and *Carpolobia* have a drupe and *Atroximia* a nut, one of the carpels being rudimentary in the latter cases.

The nearest family to the Polygalaceae is the Krameriaceae, with compound leaves and five petals. The Leguminosae are not related; similarities are due to parallel evolution; their ovary with its single carpel and the stipulate leaves readily distinguish them.

Economic uses. The family is of little importance. Local medicines are extracted from several species; the best-known is snake-root in eastern North America from *Polygala*

senega, the constituent glucoside seregin being used by the Indians to cure snake bites. A few species of *Polygala* produce dyes; *P. butyracea* from tropical Africa yields a fiber.

I.B.K.R.

KRAMERIACEAE

The Krameriaceae is a monogeneric family of shrubs and perennial herbs.

Distribution. The family is native to the United States of America, the West Indies and Central and South America.

Diagnostic features. The stems are often covered with short, soft or silky hairs, as are the leaves, which are alternate, entire, simple or trifoliolate and without stipules.

The flowers are bisexual and irregular, borne either in the axils of leaves or in terminal racemes. The pedicels bear two opposite leaf-like bracteoles. There are four or five free, imbricate, unequal sepals and five petals, of which the three upper are large with long claws, while the two lower are much smaller and sometimes broad and thick. The three larger petals may be partially fused below. There are three or four stamens, inserted either on the receptacle or on the claws of the three upper petals. The

Krameriaceae. 1 *Krameria triandra* shoot with alternate leaves, flowers and fruits (×⅔). 2 *K. tomentosa* (a) half flower (×2) ; (b) cross section of ovary (×4) ; (c) bristly, barbed indehiscent fruit (×2⅔). 3 *K. cistoidea* (a) flowering shoot (×⅔) ; (b) leaf (×3) ; (c) flower with two opposite subtending bracts, five large sepals, five unequal petals, four stamens and a simple style (×2) ; (d) flower side view showing petals of two sizes (×2) ; (e) small anterior petal (×4) ; (f) large posterior petal (×4) ; (g) stamen (×4) ; (h) anther showing porose dehiscence (×12) ; (i) cross section of anther (×12) ; (j) gynoecium (×6). 4 *K. argentea* fruit (×1⅓).

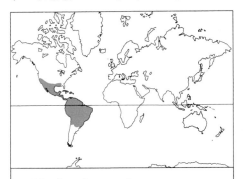

Number of genera: 1
Number of species: 25
Distribution: USA, W Indies, C and S America.
Economic uses: roots yield medicinal extracts, tannins and dyes.

anthers have two locules, opening by terminal pores. The ovary is superior, comprising one free carpel with one locule which contains two pendulous, anatropous ovules. The cylindrical style bears a disk-shaped stigma. The fruit is globose and indehiscent, bearing numerous often barbed bristles, and containing a single non-endospermic seed which has a straight embryo.

Classification. There is only one genus in this family: *Krameria*. In earlier taxonomic systems it was placed in either the Polygalaceae or in the Leguminosae (subfamily Caesalpinioideae). These relationships were argued partly on the basis of anatomical features and partly on vegetative and floral characters. For example, *Krameria* shares with members of the Polygalaceae the herb and shrub habit, bisexual, irregular flowers and seed with a straight embryo. On the other hand, apart from the absence of stipules, *Krameria* shows many similarities to the Caesalpinioideae, such as irregular flowers with five petals, porose dehiscence of the anthers, and a unilocular superior ovary. However, the distinctive features of *Krameria* such as the form of the petals and the number of stamens probably justify its classification as a separate family.

Economic uses. Economically, *Krameria triandra*, a low-growing shrub native to Bolivia and Peru, is important as the source of a medicinal extract made from its dried roots. This extract has astringent properties and was used at one time as a tooth preservative. The root contains a tannin which is used locally for tanning. The root of the tropical American *K. tomentosa* is also used for tanning, while a dye obtained from the roots of *K. parvifolia* (western United States of America and Mexico) is used to color fabrics.

S.R.C.

UMBELLALES

ARALIACEAE
Ivies and Ginseng

The Araliaceae is a medium-sized family of tropical and temperate herbs, shrubs and trees. Its best-known members are ivy and ginseng.

Distribution. Species are distributed throughout the world in both temperate and tropical regions, although the family is mainly tropical, the chief centers being Indomalaysia and tropical America.

Diagnostic features. The leaves are usually alternate and often large and compound; they have small stipules and are frequently covered with stellate hairs. In those species with a climbing habit, aerial roots are modified for clinging to the supporting structures. The flowers are regular, small,

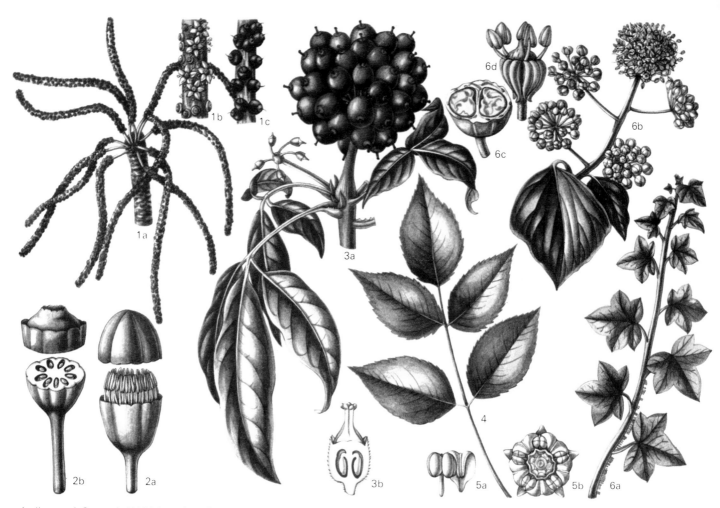

Araliaceae. 1 *Cussonia kirkii* (a) portion of stem crowned by fruiting head (×⅛) : (b) part of inflorescence (×⅔) ; (c) fruit (×⅔). 2 *Tetraplasandra hawaiensis* (a) flower with cap-like corolla which falls off (× 2) ; (b) cross section of fruit (× 2). 3 *Acanthopanax henryi* (a) shoot with stipulate trifoliolate leaves, and young and mature fruits (×⅔) ; (b) vertical section of ovary (× 3). 4 *Aralia scopulorum* pinnate leaf (×⅔). 5 *Mackinlaya macrosciadea* (a) petal and stamen (× 12) ; (b) flower from above (× 12). 6 *Hedera helix* (a) climbing shoot with juvenile leaves and adventitious roots (×⅔) ; (b) shoot with adult leaves and flowers in umbels (×⅔) ; (c) cross section of fruit (× 2) ; (d) flower (× 3).

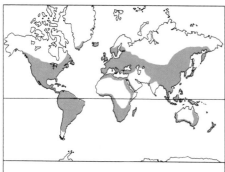

Number of genera: about 55
Number of species: about 700
Distribution: cosmopolitan.
Economic uses: ginseng and some medicinal products, rice paper, ivies (*Hedera*) and other species grown as ornamentals.

often greenish or whitish, and aggregated into clusters (compound umbels). They are bisexual or unisexual (then having sexes on separate plants but occasionally male, female and bisexual on the same plant). They have a very small calyx of four or five teeth, fused to the ovary. There are generally five, but occasionally three petals which may be free or partially fused. The stamens are free, equal in number to the petals, and alternate with them. They are attached to a disk which lies on top of the ovary. The latter is inferior and surmounted by five (occasionally fewer or 10) free or fused styles, the bases of which are confluent with the disk. The ovary, of five fused carpels, has five locules, each with a single pendulous ovule. The fruit is a drupe containing five seeds, each with copious endosperm and a small embryo.

Classification. Various vegetative and floral characters can be used to separate the most important genera. For example *Kalopanax*, *Fatsia*, *Hedera* and *Tetrapanax* all have simple (but often deeply lobed) leaves, while *Aralia*, *Polyscias*, *Dizygotheca*, *Acanthopanax*, and *Panax* all have compound leaves. In the latter group *Aralia* and *Polyscias* have pinnate leaves, while in the other three genera the leaves are all palmate. *Dizygotheca* has flowers with 10 styles, while *Panax* and *Acanthopanax* have flowers with five styles or fewer.

The family shows relationships with the Umbelliferae and the Cornaceae. Features such as the umbellate inflorescence, small simple flowers with one ovule in each locule in the inferior ovary are common to most members of these three families, although the Cornaceae is now regarded as belonging to a separate order.

Economic uses. Economically the family is important for the ginseng (*Panax quinquefolia*) from the roots of which can be obtained an extract with stimulant and supposed aphrodisiac properties. The Chinese also obtain a tonic medicinal product from the roots of *P. repens*. The thin "rice paper" is obtained from the pith of *Tetrapanax papyrifera*. Medicinal extracts have also been obtained from a number of species of *Aralia*, eg *A. cordata* and *A. racemosa*.

There is a number of attractive ornamentals. Many ivies are grown as house plants, in particular the ornamental cultivars of *Hedera helix*. The Canary Island ivy *H. canariensis*, grows to a height of 15ft (5m) in sunny situations. *Fatsia japonica* is also an attractive house and outdoor plant with its glossy green leaves. The bigeneric hybrid of *Fatsia* and *Hedera* (*Fatshedera*) is often grown as a ground-cover plant. Shrubby *Polyscias* and *Acanthopanax* species are used as garden ornamentals. Several ivies are grown outdoors as ground cover.   S.R.C.

UMBELLIFERAE

The Carrot Family

The Umbelliferae or Apiaceae is one of the best-known families of flowering plants, because of its characteristic inflorescences and fruits and the distinctive chemistry reflected in the odor, flavor and even toxicity of many of its members. Several umbellifers were known to the ancient Chinese and Mexican Indian civilizations, as well as to the Mycenaeans Greeks and Romans of the Mediterranean basin. The family was recognized under the name of *Narthekodes* by Theophrastus and the Greek word *Narthex* was replaced by *Ferula* in Latin, the name applied to the dried stalks of umbellifers such as fennel (*Foeniculum*) or *Ferula*. In Greek art Dionysus is often shown bearing a *Ferula* or ferule in his hand. Herbs or condiments such as anise, cumin, coriander, dill and fennel were known to Theophrastus and characterized by their naked seeds and herbaceous stems. The Umbelliferae seems to be the first flowering plant family to be recognized as such by botanists about the end of the 16th century, although only the temperate Old World species were then known. It was also the first group of plants to be the subject of a systematic study published by Robert Morison in 1672.

Distribution. The Umbelliferae contains about 300 genera and 2,500 to 3,000 species. The family is found in most parts of the world, although commonest in temperate upland areas and relatively rare in tropical latitudes. The three subfamilies into which it is divided (see below) have characteristic distributions: the largest, the Apioideae, is bipolar but mainly developed in the Northern Hemisphere in the Old World; the Saniculoideae is also bipolar but better represented in the Southern Hemisphere than the Apioideae; the third subfamily, the Hydrocotyloideae, is predominantly a Southern Hemisphere group. About two-thirds of the species of Umbelliferae are native to the Old World but the distribution of the subfamilies in the Old and New Worlds is different, 80% of the Apioideae being found in the Old World, and 60% of the Hydrocotyloideae in the New World, almost 90% of these occurring in South America, where they form a significant component of the flora of temperate southern zones. The subfamily Saniculoideae is almost evenly split between the Old and New worlds. This pattern reflects the long history of evolution and differentiation of this almost cosmopolitan family. Many curious distributions are found in the Umbelliferae: the Canary Island endemic *Drusa glandulosa* is apparently most closely allied to Chilean species of *Bowlesia* and *Homalocarpus*, although no explanation for such a large geographical disjunction has been offered; and the recently discovered *Naufraga balearica* from Majorca finds its closest affinities with South American genera.

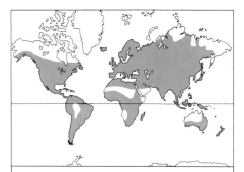

Number of genera: about 300
Number of species: 2,500–3,000
Distribution: near-cosmopolitan, largely temperate uplands.
Economic uses: important foods, herbs, spices or flavoring plants (eg carrot, parsnip, celery, parsley, fennel, dill, anise, angelica); source of gum resins, medicines and perfumes; a few ornamentals.

Diagnostic features. Most of the Umbelliferae are herbaceous, annuals, biennials or perennials, with hollow internodes; sometimes they are creepers (*Hydrocotyle*), stoloniferous (*Schizeilema*), rosette plants (*Gingidia*) or cushion plants (*Azorella*). Several of the herbaceous species develop some degree of woodiness but genuinely woody tree-like or shrubby species also occur, examples being *Eryngium bupleuroides*, *E. sarcophyllum* and *E. inaccessum* of the Juan Fernández Islands which develop a woody trunk, *Myrrhidendron* species from mountain summits above 10,000ft (about 3,000m) in Central and South America, and several shrubby species of *Bupleurum* (eg *Bupleurum fruticosum*). Several species are spiny, such as the thistle-like *Eryngium* species and the New Zealand species of *Aciphylla* with rigid leaf- and bract-segments tipped by needle-sharp spines.

The leaves are alternate, without stipules, and the leaves usually dissected (ternate or variously pinnate). Entire leaves are found in *Hydrocotyle* and *Bupleurum*, the latter often with parallel venation and frequently resembling monocotyledons.

The main type of inflorescence found in the Umbelliferae is a simple or compound umbel, although sometimes much modified and reduced to a single flower as in some species of *Hydrocotyle* and *Azorella*. In *Eryngium* the flowers are stalkless and crowded into a dense head surrounded by spiny bracts. Dichasia are found in *Petagnia*. The characteristic umbel is a flat-topped inflorescence in which the individual flower stalks (pedicels) arise from the same point on the rays (peduncles) and are of different lengths so as to raise all the flowers to the same height. A compound umbel is one in which the ultimate umbels (termed umbellets or umbellules) are themselves arranged in umbels. Bracts are frequently present at the base of the rays of a compound umbel forming an involucre, and bracteoles are present at the base of the umbellets where they form an involucel. The bracts and bracteoles vary in number and size.

The flowers of an umbel and of the component umbellules open in sequence from the outer whorls to the center. Most umbels are protandrous (with the stamens maturing before the pistil), although a few genera are protogynous (with the pistil maturing before the stamens), such as *Hydrocotyle* and *Sanicula*. Sexual differentiation in the umbels is quite marked in some cases and varies from genus to genus according to the degree of protandry, ranging from a few male (staminate) flowers per umbel to umbels which are composed of nothing but male (staminate) flowers. Moreover, the percentage of perfect (bisexual) flowers in the latter cases is higher in the primary umbels and progressively lower in the successive umbels until the last umbels produced are almost entirely composed of male flowers. The degree of organization of the umbel is highly developed in some cases and comparable to that found in the capitula of the Compositae. In some umbels whole flowers which are functionally unisexual take on the role of stamens or pistils (eg *Astrantia*, *Petagnia*, *Sanicula*) or the umbels themselves take on the role of stamens or pistils in more complex inflorescences.

The marginal flowers in the umbel are sometimes irregular as in *Daucus carota* (carrot), *Turgenia latifolia* and *Artedia squamata*, thus serving as an attraction to insect pollinators. The visual impact is also enhanced by an increase in the number and size of the umbellules and a closer spacing of the individual flowers. The bracts forming the involucre may also become enlarged, colored and showy as in various *Eryngium* and *Bupleurum* species. One of the most remarkable examples is the Mexican species *Mathiasella bupleuroides*, which has a showy involucre and involucels which are reminiscent of a malvaceous corolla, surrounding umbellules of staminate flowers with petals and naked pistillate flowers.

Most Umbelliferae are "promiscuous" plants in that they are pollinated by a wide array of insects, mostly flies, mosquitoes or gnats, or some of the unspecialized bees, butterflies and moths. Self-fertility is the normal situation and self-sterile plants are very rare. Pollination is often by geitonogamy, that is the pistils may be pollinated by the anthers of adjacent flowers in the same umbel. A curious feature of the family is the almost complete lack of hybridization – hardly any attested records of interspecific hybrids are known. This leads to serious problems in breeding programs.

The flower of the umbellifers is basically uniform, almost monotonously so, consisting of five petals, five free stamens, a greatly reduced calyx, an inferior ovary with two carpels and two locules, and a stylopodium

supporting two styles. There is a single pendulous, anatropous ovule in each locule. Variations on this basic theme are limited: irregular corollas, the outer petals being sometimes larger and radiate, and unisexuality. A feature showing considerable variation that has been largely overlooked until recently is the stylopodium, the swollen, often colorful nectar-secreting base of the styles which is characteristic of the family. This organ varies widely in shape, size, color and nectar secretion.

The fruit shows a quite remarkable range of variation. Basically it is a dry schizocarp which splits down a septum (commisure) into two one-seeded mericarps which normally remain for some time suspended from a common forked stalk, the carpophore, finally separating at maturity. The outer surface of the mericarp normally has five primary ridges, one dorsal, two lateral and two commisural, and between them four secondary vallecular ridges, all of which run longitudinally from the base to the stylar end of the fruit. In the furrows between the primary ridges, in the ridges themselves or all over the fruit, oil cavities or resin canals (vittae) are often found. Crystals of calcium oxalate may be present in the pericarp. The fruit surface may bear spines, hooks, hairs or tubercles of various kinds; in some fruits the lateral ridges are extended into wings. All these features are related to their dispersal strategy: variations in shape, size, color, wings and spines are numerous; some fruits are remarkable constructions and scarcely bear any resemblance to the basic umbelliferous type, such as those of *Petagnia*, *Scandix* and *Thecocarpus*. The seed has oily endosperm and a small embryo.

Classification. The Umbelliferae is usually divided into three subfamilies and several tribes following the system proposed (1897–98) by Drude. Other classifications

Umbelliferae. 1 *Eryngium biscuspidatum* shoot with spiny leaves and bracts, and flowers in a dense head ($\times\frac{2}{3}$). 2 *Centella asiatica* creeping leafy stem bearing axillary flowers ($\times\frac{2}{3}$). 3 *Sanicula europaea* leafy shoot and inflorescences (compound umbels) ($\times\frac{2}{3}$). 4 *Heracleum sphondylium* (a) leaf shoot bearing large inflorescences—note the outer flowers are irregular and have deeply cut petals ($\times\frac{2}{3}$); (b) regular flower from center of inflorescence ($\times6$). 5 *Eryngium maritimum* barbed fruit—a schizocarp ($\times6$). 6 *Petroselinum crispum* (a) schizocarp—comprising two mericarps ($\times8$); (b) cross section of a single mericarp with a central seed and canals (vittae) in the fruit wall ($\times12$). 7 *Psammogeton canescens* schizocarp ($\times8$). 8 *Daucus carota* schizocarp with spines on the ridges ($\times6$). 9 *Artedia squamata* winged schizocarp ($\times3$). 10 *Hydrocotyle vulgaris* (a) schizocarp ($\times10$); (b) cross section of schizocarp showing flattened appearance, and a narrow wall (commisure) between the two single seeded mericarps each with prominent ridges ($\times10$). 11 *Sanicula europaea* schizocarp ($\times6$). 12 *Peucedanum ostruthium* (a) winged schizocarp ($\times4$); (b) cross section of schizocarp ($\times4$).

have been produced by later authors, notably that of the Russian Kozo-Poljansky in 1915 which relied heavily on the anatomical features of the fruit, but they have not gained much acceptance. The three subfamilies are clearly natural but their division into tribes, especially in the subfamily Apioideae, is not entirely satisfactory and is evidently artificial in places. An outline of Drude's system, indicating the main genera, is as follows.

SUBFAMILY HYDROCOTYLOIDEAE
Fruit with a woody endocarp, without a free carpophore; no secretory canals (vittae) or only in the primary ribs; stipules present.
HYDROCOTYLEAE. Mainly Southern Hemisphere. Fruits with a narrow commisure, flattened laterally. *Hydrocotyle*.
MULINEAE. Southern Hemisphere. Fruits with a flattened or rounded back. *Azorella*.

SUBFAMILY SANICULOIDEAE
Fruit with a soft parenchymatous endocarp; base of style surrounded by a ring-like disk; secretory canals various.
SANICULEAE. Ovary with two locules; fruit two-seeded, with broad commissure; vittae distinct. *Eryngium, Astrantia, Sanicula*.
LAGOECIEAE. Ovary with one locule; fruit one-seeded; vittae indistinct. *Lagoecia, Petagnia* (both Mediterranean).

SUBFAMILY APIOIDEAE
Fruit with a soft endocarp, sometimes hardened by woody subepidermal layers; style on apex of disk; stipules absent.
ECHINOPHOREAE. Fruit enclosed by hardened stalks of male flowers. *Echinophora*.
SCANDICEAE. Parenchyma around carpophore with crystal layer. *Scandix, Chaerophyllum, Anthriscus, Myrrhis*.
CORIANDREAE. Parenchyma without crystal layer; fruits usually ovoid-spherical, nut-like, with woody subepidermal layer. *Coriandrum*.
SMYRNIEAE. Mericarps rounded outward. *Smyrnium, Conium, Cachrys, Scaligeria*.
APIEAE (Ammieae). Primary ridges of mericarps all similar; seeds semicircular in sections. *Bupleurum, Pimpinella, Apium, Seseli, Oenanthe, Ligusticum, Foeniculum*.
PEUCEDANEAE. Lateral ridges much broader, forming wings; seeds narrow in section. *Angelica, Ferula, Heracleum, Pastinaca*.
LASERPITEAE. Vallecular ridges on mericarps very distinct, often extended into wings. *Laserpitium, Thapsia*.
DAUCEAE (Caucalideae). Mericarps with spines on ridges. *Daucus, Torilis, Caucalis*.

The Umbelliferae has frequently been associated with the mainly tropical family Araliaceae in the order Umbellales or sometimes united with it into a single family. No clear dividing line can be drawn between the Umbelliferae and Araliaceae and nearly every vegetative or floral feature that characterizes the Umbelliferae can be found in the Araliaceae; there are also similarities in chemistry and pollen characters between them. They probably both arose from a common ancestral stock and have evolved

separately and to some degree in parallel. The Cornaceae in the broad sense is regarded by some authorities as related to the Umbellales and included within it or treated as a separate but parallel order. The whole complex has been held to have arisen from the Hamamelidales, Rosales, Myrtales or Rhamnales and recent studies suggest a relationship between the Cornales and the Rosales on the one hand, and the Umbelliferae with the Sapindales on the other.

Economic uses. One of the remarkable features of umbellifers is the wide range of uses made of different species, ranging from food and fodder to spices, poisons and perfumery. However, only the carrot (*Daucus carota*) is a near staple food and also used as animal feed. Carrots and parsnips (*Pastinaca sativa*) are the only umbellifers of international repute as root crops, but other members of the family have been so used, whether cultivated or not, such as the tubers of the great earthnut (*Bunium bulbocastanum*) and the pignut (*Conopodium majus*). Species of *Lomatium*, the largest genus of umbellifers in the United States of America, have been true staple foods for several groups of Indians in the northwest of the country and in western Canada. Stems, petioles and leaves may be used for food as in angelica (*Angelica* and *Archangelica* species), celery (*Apium graveolens*) and lovage (*Levisticum officinale*).

Herbs used for flavoring include chervil (*Anthriscus cerefolium*), fennel (*Foeniculum vulgare*, also used as a salad vegetable) and parsley (*Petroselinum crispum*). Spices derived from fruits or seeds (which contain essential oils) are numerous in the Umbelliferae, examples being dill (*Anethum graveolens*), coriander (*Coriandrum sativum*), cumin (*Cuminum cyminum*), caraway (*Carum carvi*) and anise (*Pimpinella anisum*). Several of these are used for flavoring alcoholic beverages, especially anise.

Many umbellifers have medicinal uses, for gastrointestinal complaints, cardiovascular ailments and as stimulants, sedatives, antispasmodics, etc. They are also a source of gum resins and resins, such as asafetida, derived from *Ferula asafoetida* and other species, the exudate being collected from cuts made at the base of the stem or at the top of the root; another is galbanum, an oleo-gum resin obtained from *Ferula galbaniflua*. There are many poisonous species, the most celebrated being hemlock (*Conium maculatum*), which was responsible for the death of Socrates but is also used as a medicine.

Only a few umbellifers are grown in gardens for ornament. Examples are *Eryngium giganteum* and various cultivars, *Astrantia* (masterwort), *Bupleurum fruticosum*, *Ferula communis* and *F. tingitana*, a variegated form of *Aegopodium podagraria*, and *Heracleum* species (cow parsley), especially the spectacular *Heracleum mantegazzianum* (giant hogweed).   V.H.H.

ASTERIDAE

GENTIANALES

LOGANIACEAE
Buddleias and Strychnine

The Loganiaceae is a diverse family of trees, shrubs and climbers. They are important to Man, being a source of timber, of well-known ornamentals and of some lethal poisons, notably strychnine.

Distribution. Members of the family are found in the tropics, subtropics and temperate zones of the world. They grow in dry lowland habitats, rarely above 10,000ft (3,000m). Though widespread they are seldom abundant, never forming dense stands but usually found singly or in small groups of minor ecological importance.

Diagnostic features. The leaves are opposite, entire, pinnately-nerved, often with reduced stipules. The wood sometimes has phloem tubes scattered throughout the xylem (intraxylary phloem). The flowers are regular, bisexual and are borne in terminal cymes or rarely solitary; the four or five lobes of the calyx are always imbricate; the corolla is tubular, four- or five-lobed (occasionally up to 16-lobed) and usually imbricate to varying degrees but sometimes valvate. The corolla-lobe characters are useful in the classification of the family. There are four or five stamens (rarely 16), attached in a ring to the petals. The ovary is superior, formed of two fused carpels, and in some genera is sunk in a disk. There are two to five locules, each with one to numerous axile ovules. The style is two-lobed. The fruit is a capsule or berry. The seeds have fleshy endosperm and a straight embryo, and are often winged.

Classification. The family can be classified conveniently into seven tribes: POTALIEAE (sometimes separated as a family, the Potaliaceae), BUDDLEIEAE (sometimes separated as the Buddleiaceae), ANTONIEAE (sometimes separated as the Antoniaceae), GELSEMIEAE, STRYCHNEAE (sometimes separated as the Strychnaceae), LOGANIEAE and SPIGELIEAE (sometimes separated as the Spigeliaceae). Some authors have used anatomical characters as a basis for the division of the family into two subfamilies, the LOGANIOIDEAE (intraxylary phloem present, superficial cork development, hairs simple) and the BUDDLEIOIDEAE, comprising the single tribe Bud-

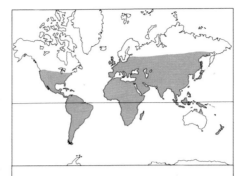

Number of genera: about 30
Number of species: about 600
Distribution: tropics, subtropics and temperate regions.
Economic uses: strychnine and curare from *Strychnos* species and several ornamentals, including buddleias.

Loganiaceae. 1 *Fagraea lanceolata* (a) flowering shoot ($\times \frac{2}{3}$); (b) five-lobed corolla opened and showing epipetalous stamens ($\times \frac{1}{2}$); (c) calyx tube and style with a capitate stigma ($\times \frac{1}{2}$); (d) fruit—a berry ($\times \frac{2}{3}$). 2 *Buddleia crispa* (a) leafy shoot and terminal inflorescence ($\times \frac{2}{3}$); (b) flower ($\times 2\frac{2}{3}$); (c) half flower ($\times 3$); (d) stamen ($\times 8$); (e) gynoecium ($\times 5$). 3 *Strychnos tieute* leafy shoot with axillary inflorescences and coiled spines ($\times \frac{2}{3}$). 4 *Spigelia marilandica* (a) cross section of ovary ($\times 4$); (b) fruit ($\times 2$). 5 *Logania campanulata* flower ($\times 1\frac{1}{3}$).

dleieae (intraxylary phloem absent, cork developing from the pericycle, hairs stellate or glandular).

Chemistry and anatomy have provided some clues to the relationships of the Loganiaceae with other families. It is a very mixed family, probably containing several distinct groups which are no more related to each other than to parts of other families. The Buddleioideae seems to be related to the Scrophulariaceae whereas the Loganioideae resembles more closely the Apocynaceae and Rubiaceae.

Economic uses. Many members of the Loganiaceae are extremely poisonous, causing death by convulsions. Poisonous properties are largely due to indo-derivative alkaloids such as those found in *Strychnos*, *Gelsemium* and *Mostuea*. Glycosides in the form of pseudo-indicans are also present, as loganin in *Strychnos*, and the related substance aucubin in *Buddleia*.

Two large genera have more pleasant associations, for they are well-known ornamentals, *Buddleia* and *Fagraea*. The garden and cool greenhouse buddleias are of tropical or subtropical origin, mostly from China. They are shrubs or trees with clusters of fragrant flowers in shades of lilac, orange or white. *Buddleia davidii* is widely cultivated, its flowers being particularly attractive to butterflies. *Fagraea* is an Asiatic genus with some large trees which yield good timber, eg *Fagraea fragrans*, *F. elliptica* and *F. crenulata*. *F. fragrans* is often planted as an ornamental tree in tropical climates on account of its large showy flowers. Some of the shrubby species have exceptionally large flowers up to 12in (30cm) across (eg *F. auriculata*), which are probably pollinated by bats. S.W.J.

GENTIANACEAE
Gentians

The Gentianaceae is a family of annual and perennial herbs (and a few shrubs), including the gentians and other plants with medicinal "bitter principles."

Distribution. The family is cosmopolitan. Many species are arctic and mountain rosette herbs, many are found in salty or marshy areas, and some live on decayed vegetation, for example *Voyria* in tropical America and West Africa.

Diagnostic features. The plants are usually rhizomatous, and have opposite leaves (alternate in *Swertia*), no stipules, and regular, bisexual flowers borne in cymose

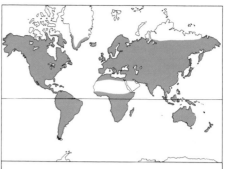

Number of genera: about 80
Number of species: about 900
Distribution: cosmopolitan.
Economic uses: many cultivated ornamentals, and several species yield bitter principles used medicinally and in flavorings.

inflorescences. There are four or five (rarely more) united sepals and usually four or five united petals forming a bell- or salver-shaped corolla. The stamens are attached to the corolla and are equal in number to and alternate with the lobes. Occasionally the lobes have long thread-like projections (as in the East African *Urogentias*). The ovary is superior and has two united carpels with a

Gentianaceae. 1 *Chironia purpurascens* (a) flowering shoot ($\times\frac{2}{3}$); (b) corolla opened out showing epipetalous stamens with coiled anthers ($\times 1$); (c) cross section of ovary with two parietal placentas ($\times 3$). 2 *Voyria primuloides* (a) habit ($\times\frac{2}{3}$); (b) flower from above ($\times\frac{2}{3}$); (c) half flower with epipetalous stamens and globose stigma ($\times 3$). 3 *Gentiana depressa* (a) habit ($\times\frac{2}{3}$); (b) ovary with part of wall cut away ($\times 3$); (c) corolla opened out ($\times 1$). 4 *Sabatia campestris* (a) flowering shoot ($\times\frac{2}{3}$); (b) section of ovary ($\times 2$); (c) corolla opened out ($\times 1$).

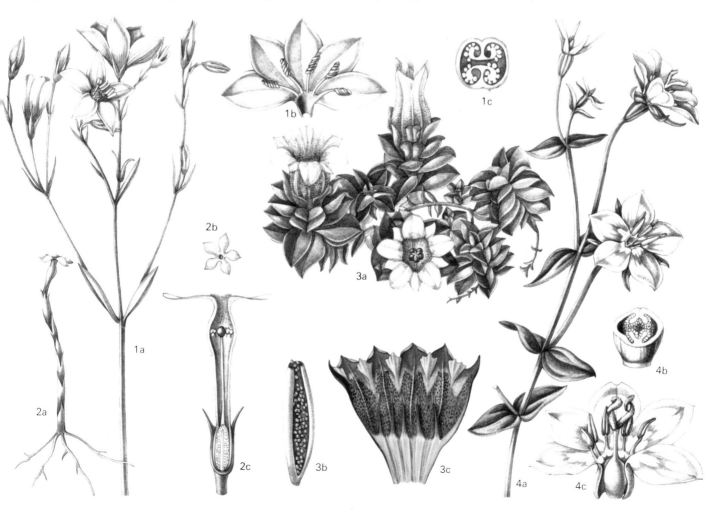

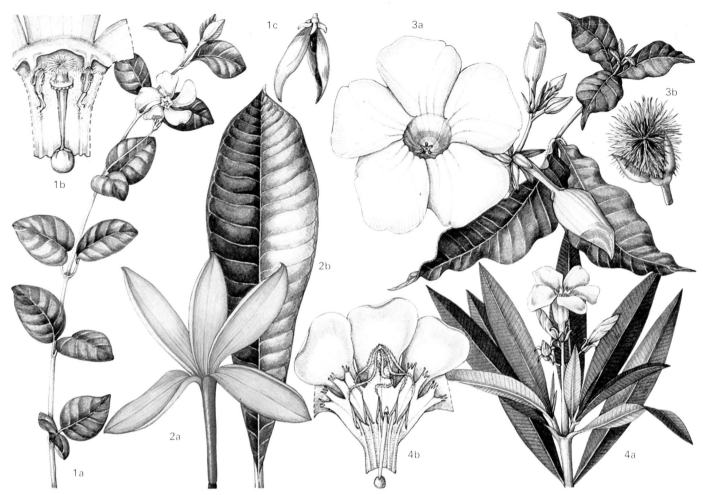

Apocynaceae. 1 *Vinca minor* (periwinkle) (a) shoot with opposite leaves and solitary flower (×⅔) ; (b) part of dissected flower showing epipetalous stamens and thickened, hairy stigma (×3) ; (c) paired fruits (×1). 2 *Plumeria rubra* (a) flower (×1) ; (b) leaf (×1). 3 *Allamanda cathartica* var *grandiflora* (a) flowering shoot (×1) ; (b) dehiscing fruit (×1). 4 *Nerium oleander* (a) flowering shoot (×⅔) ; (b) dissected flower with two petals removed, showing the sagittate (arrow-shaped) anthers prolonged into spines which are united at their tips (×1½).

glandular disk at the base; there is usually one locule with two parietal placentas, sometimes two locules each with an axile placenta; the ovules are anatropous and usually numerous. The style is simple, and the stigma simple or two-lobed. The fruit is usually a dehiscent capsule, rarely a berry, with small endospermous seeds. The vascular bundles are bicollateral, ie they have phloem strands lying inside the stele as well as outside. Mycorrhiza are very common.

Classification. The generic limits in this family are still a matter of debate, but at present the large genera recognized include *Gentiana* (about 400 species, cosmopolitan, except Africa), *Gentianella* (125 species, north and south temperate zones except South Africa), *Sebaea* (100 species, Old World tropics to New Zealand) and *Swertia* (100 species, chiefly north temperate). *Menyanthes*, *Nymphoides* and *Villarsia*, once included in this family, are now referred to Menyanthaceae.

Some authorities regard the Gentianaceae as being allied to the Menyanthaceae. Others see it as being allied to the Loganiaceae, and perhaps Asclepiadaceae and Apocynaceae or even Melastomataceae.

Economic uses. Many species of *Gentiana* and *Sabatia* (rose pinks) are cultivated for ornament. The bitter principles of the rhizomes are of medicinal value as in gentian root (*Gentiana*), chiretta (*Swertia*) and, more locally, *Centaurium*. In France a popular aperitif drink, Suze, is made from gentian. In southern Africa, *Chironia baccifera* is fried in butter and applied to sores; it is also a purgative and is said to clear the complexion. Portland powder, formerly a popular remedy for gout, was made up from equal parts gentian, centaury (*Centaurium*), *Teucrium germander*, *Aristolochia clematitis* and *Ajuga chamaepitys*. A yellow dye has been extracted from the seeds of the European *Blackstonia perfoliata*. D.J.M.

APOCYNACEAE
Periwinkles and Oleanders

The Apocynaceae is a large, tropical family of tall rain forest trees, many smaller trees, shrubs and lianas, all usually of rather isolated occurrence, and also a few temperate perennial herbs.

Distribution. The family is pantropical, with a few temperate representatives such as *Vinca*. The tropical rain forests and swamps of India and Malaya have small to very tall, evergreen, often buttressed trees such as

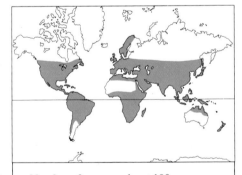

Number of genera: about 180
Number of species: about 1,500
Distribution: throughout tropics, particularly in rain forest regions.
Economic uses: drugs, alkaloids, latex (rubbers) and ornamentals such as oleanders and periwinkles.

Alstonia and *Dyera*. *Cerbera* and *Ochrosia* are smaller, evergreen trees growing along coasts from Madagascar to northern Australia. Smaller, deciduous trees, such as *Carissa, Wrightia* and *Holarrhena* occur sporadically in the deciduous forests of Africa and India. Evergreen trees and shrubs are more common, eg *Rauvolfia* and *Tabernaemontana* (tropical America, India,

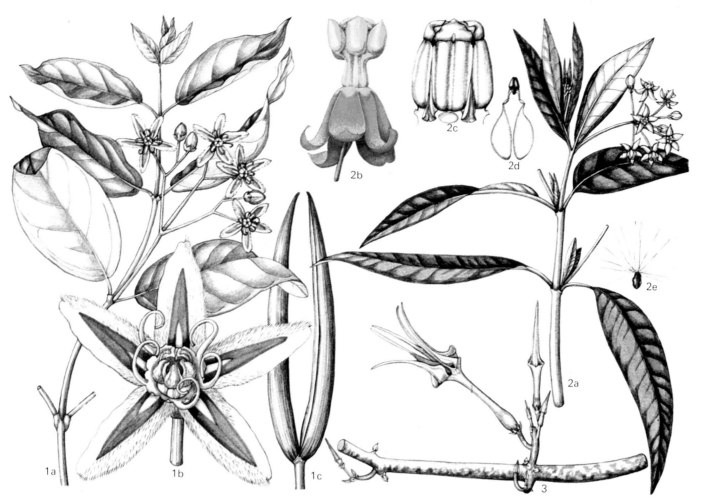

Asclepiadaceae. 1 *Periploca graeca* (a) shoot with opposite leaves and axillary inflorescence ($\times\frac{2}{3}$); (b) flower with coiled corona filaments ($\times 3$); (c) fruit comprising two follicles ($\times\frac{2}{3}$). 2 *Asclepias curassavia* (a) leafy shoot and umbellate inflorescence ($\times\frac{2}{3}$); (b) flower with down-curved petals and anthers united around the style—a gynostegium ($\times 3$); (c) gynostegium ($\times 10$); (d) pair of pollinia united by thread-like caudicles ($\times 14$); (e) seed with terminal cluster of hairs ($\times 10$). 3 *Ceropegia stapeliiformis* shoot with flowers in which the corolla tube widens at the base ($\times\frac{2}{3}$).

Burma and Malaya) and *Acokanthera* (Kaffir plum). The widely cultivated frangipani (*Plumeria*) originates from Central America. Forests of South America, Africa and Madagascar have many lianas, such as *Landolphia*. The oleanders (*Nerium*) are native to waterside habitats in the Mediterranean region.

Diagnostic features. The leaves are simple, opposite or in whorls and rarely have stipules. The sap of all parts of the plant is a milky latex. The inflorescence is a cyme. The flowers are bisexual, regular and are often large, showy and fragrant. There are usually five sepals fused into a tube and five petals also united below into a tube and with free lobes. There are five stamens with the anthers joined to each other. The ovary is superior or half-inferior, formed of two united or free carpels. There are one or two locules, each with two to numerous pendulous, anatropous ovules. The fruits are paired, either fleshy and not splitting or dry and splitting. The seeds may or may not have endosperm and the embryo is straight.

Classification. The Apocynaceae is divided into two subfamilies: the PLUMERIOIDEAE (stamens free from the stylar head, anthers full of pollen, seeds usually hairless) and the APOCYNOIDEAE (stamens firmly joined to stylar head, anthers empty at base, seeds hairy). The family is most closely related to the Asclepiadaceae.

Economic uses. Cardiac glycosides are obtained from *Cerbera, Thevetia, Apocynum, Nerium, Strophanthus* and *Acokanthera*. *Strophanthus* seeds yield ouabain and cymarin. *Rauvolfia* produces the alkaloids reserpine and rescinnamine. Latex (rubber) is of commercial importance from some species of *Landolphia, Carpodinus, Hancornia, Funtumia* and *Mascarenhasia*. Ornamentals include *Amsonia, Nerium* (oleanders), *Vinca* (periwinkles), *Carissa* (Natal plum), *Allamanda, Plumeria* (frangipani), *Thevetia* (yellow oleander) and *Mandevilla*.

H.P.W.

ASCLEPIADACEAE

Milkweeds and Wax Plant

The Asclepiadaceae is a fairly large family best known for ornamentals of the genera *Asclepias* (milkweeds and butterfly flowers) and *Hoya* (wax plant).

Distribution. This family is principally tropical and subtropical with many representatives in South America. There are several large genera in southern Africa but temperate

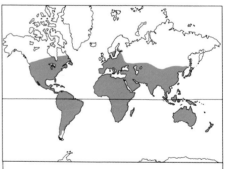

Number of genera: about 250
Number of species: 1,800 to 2,000
Distribution: mainly tropical and subtropical centers in S America and southern Africa.
Economic uses: Many ornamentals (eg milkweeds and butterfly flowers), low quality "down" from seeds, and local medicinal uses.

regions generally have very few.

Diagnostic features. The Asclepiadaceae is a family of perennial herbs, shrubs, woody climbers or trees, sometimes succulent and usually with milky sap. The leaves are usually opposite or whorled, rarely alternate, simple and generally entire; in some

Oleaceae. 1 *Forsythia viridissima* (a) shoot with flowers borne on previous year's side shoots ($\times\frac{2}{3}$); (b) vertical section of ovary ($\times 4$); (c) part of corolla opened out to show epipetalous stamens ($\times 1$). 2 *Fraxinus platypoda* (a) winged fruit—samaras ($\times\frac{2}{3}$); (b) vertical section of samara base ($\times 2$); (c) vertical section of seed ($\times 2$). 3 *Phyllyrea vilmoriniana* fleshy fruits ($\times\frac{2}{3}$). 4 *Syringa vulgaris* (a) leaves and inflorescence ($\times\frac{2}{3}$); (b) half flower ($\times 1\frac{1}{2}$); (c) cross section of ovary ($\times 6$); (d) corolla opened out to show epipetalous stamens ($\times\frac{2}{3}$); (e) dehisced fruits—bilocular capsules ($\times\frac{2}{3}$).

succulent taxa they are caducous or vestigial. Minute stipules are normally present. The inflorescence is most often a cyme or may be racemose or umbelliform. The flowers are regular and bisexual. The calyx, comprising five partly fused sepals, is deeply divided with the odd sepal in a posterior position. The corolla is formed of five fused petals with the lobes contorted or valvate; both or either the corolla and stamens may bear secondary appendages of various types which form a double or single corona. The filaments are short or may be completely absent and the anthers are usually fused to the gynoecium to form a gynostegium. The anthers have two locules and the pollen of each half-anther is usually united into a waxy pollinium; each pollinium bears a translator or arm for pollen transfer and the two pollinia are united by means of a corpusculum or gland. In the subfamily Periplocoideae the pollen is granular, free and united in tetrads and is transferred by means of the spoon-shaped translator which ends in a sticky disk. The translators and pollinia adhere to the heads and legs of insect visitors by means of the sticky base or the corpusculum and the retiring visitor thus carries away the whole

pollen mass and on visiting another flower may deposit pollen on the stigma surface.

The ovary is semi-inferior and consists of two almost separate carpels, each with a style but a common, five-lobed, large stigma. Each carpel contains numerous ovules in several rows on a single placenta. The fruit consists of a pair of follicles (often only one develops fully). The seeds are usually flattened, ovate to oblong and bear a coma of long, silky hairs; endosperm is present and the embryo is straight.

Classification. There are two subfamilies:
PERIPLOCOIDEAE: pollen granular and in tetrads.
CYANCHOIDEAE: pollen massed in pollinia; four tribes: ASCLEPIADEAE, SECAMONEAE, TYLOPHOREAE (which contains succulent members such as *Ceropegia* and *Stapelia*) and GONOLOBEAE.

The Asclepiadaceae is closely related to the Apocynaceae from which it differs by the very specialized androecium and pollen-transfer-system and the presence of a gynostegium.

Economic uses. Several genera are grown as ornamentals in warmer areas, eg the milkweeds and butterfly flowers of the genus *As-*

clepias, wax plant (*Hoyacarnosa*), *Stephanotis floribunda* and many succulents such as *Stapelia*, *Huernia*, *Caralluma* and *Ceropegia*.

In some regions, such as the southern United States of America, the coma hairs are used as a low-quality "down" and several species are traditionally considered by the local Indian populations to have medicinal properties (such as emetics and purgatives).

D.B.

OLEACEAE
Olives, Ashes and Lilacs

The Oleaceae is a medium-sized family of trees and shrubs, widely distributed in temperate and tropical regions and containing several genera of economic or horticultural value, eg *Olea* (olive), *Fraxinus* (ash), *Jasminum* (jasmine) and *Syringa* (lilac).

Distribution. The family is almost cosmopolitan in range with the 29 genera and 600 species showing diverse distribution patterns but with concentrations in Southeast Asia and Australasia. Genera of restricted distribution include *Abeliophyllum* (Korea), *Amarolea* (eastern North America), *Haenianthus* (West Indies), *Hesperelaea* (northwest Mexico, Guadalupe Islands),

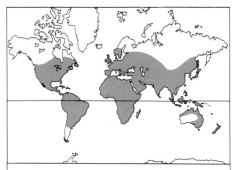

Number of genera: 29
Number of species: about 600
Distribution: almost cosmopolitan, centered in SE Asia and Australasia.
Economic uses: olives and olive oil, timber from *Fraxinus* species, and lilac, forsythia, jasmine and other cultivated ornamentals.

Noronhia (Madagascar, Mauritius, Comoro islands), *Notelaea* (eastern Australia), *Picconia* (Canary Islands, Madeira, Azores) and *Tessarandra* (Brazil). Others of wide distribution include *Fraxinus* (Eurasia and North America), *Jasminum* (Eurasia, Africa, Australia, Oceania and tropical America) and *Ligustrum* (Europe to northern Iran, Asia, Indomalaysia and New Hebrides).

Diagnostic features. All are deciduous or evergreen shrubs, the latter sometimes woody climbers or scramblers. The indumentum characteristically consists of scale-like peltate hairs, in addition to normal hairs, often giving a grayish or silvery appearance to the twigs and leaves. The leaves are usually opposite, without stipules, simple, trifoliolate or pinnate, often entire or lobed. The inflorescence is basically a dichasial cyme but usually modified so as to give the appearance of a raceme, panicle or fascicle. The flowers are bisexual, rarely unisexual (the male and female then being borne on separate plants, either alone or with bisexual flowers). The petals are sometimes absent, usually four but ranging from two to six or twelve, free or united, often with a long or short tube. There are usually four sepals. The stamens are two or four, attached to the petals, alternating with the carpels, with short filaments. The ovary is superior, of two fused carpels, containing two locules usually with two (sometimes one, or four or numerous) anatropous ovules per locule, attached to the apex, side or base of the partition. The style is simple with an entire, bilobed or bifid stigma. The fruits are various – capsule, berry, nut, drupe or samara, dry or fleshy, dehiscent or indehiscent, with one to four seeds.

Classification. The most recent classification divides the family into two subfamilies, and seven tribes, as follows:

SUBFAMILY OLEOIDEAE

Ovules two in each locule (rarely more), pendulous. Petals usually in fours, occasionally fives or sixes, sometimes absent.

FRAXINEAE. Fruit dry, indehiscent (samara). Leaves deciduous, imparipinnate, rarely trifoliolate or unifoliolate. Only genus *Fraxinus*.

OLEEAE. Fruit either fleshy (drupe or berry) or a bilocular capsule. Leaves evergreen or deciduous, simple, rarely lobed or pinnatisect. *Syringa, Ligustrum, Olea, Tetrapilus, Linociera, Haenianthus, Tessarandra, Noronhia, Notelaea, Gymnelaea, Amarolea, Osmanthus, Siphonosmanthus, Phillyrea, Picconia, Hesperelaea.*

SUBFAMILY JASMINOIDEAE

Ovules one, four or numerous in each locule, or if two then ascending. Petals four to twelve, never absent.

JASMINEAE. Low shrubs with simple or one- to three-pinnatisect leaves, or erect or scrambling shrubs or woody climbers with imparipinnate trifoliolate or unifoliolate leaves. Corolla large with well-developed tube and four to twelve lobes. Fruit a capsule or berry. *Menodora, Jasminum.*

FONTANESIEAE. Shrubs with deciduous, simple leaves. Corolla with free petals or united at the base in pairs. Fruit indehiscent, compressed, with a surrounding wing. Only genus *Fontanesia*.

FORSYTHIEAE. Shrubs with deciduous simple trilobed or trifoliolate leaves. Corolla gamopetalous, four-lobed. Fruit a leathery or hard capsule or indehiscent compressed with a surrounding wing. *Abeliophyllum, Forsythia.*

SCHREBEREAE. Shrubs or trees with evergreen imparipinnate or simple leaves. Corolla gamopetalous with four lobes. Fruit a woody capsule. *Comoranthus, Schrebera, Noldeanthus.*

MYXOPYREAE. Scrambling climbers. Leaves simple. Corolla fused, with a short tube and four lobes. Fruit fleshy. Only genus *Myxopyrum*.

The relationships of this family are uncertain. It shows affinity with the other families of the Gentianales in which it is placed here but differs, for example, in its placentation and structure of the androecium. It has also been placed along with the Loganiaceae in an order Loganiales or in an order on its own, the Ligustrales. It shows clear signs of derivation from some of the polypetalous families.

Economic uses. The main species of economic importance in the family is the olive (*Olea europaea*). Several genera provide valuable trees or shrubs grown in parks or gardens. *Fraxinus* includes the European ash (*Fraxinus excelsior*) which yields a valuable timber, the American or white ash (*F. americana*) which is also commercially important, and the flowering or manna ash (*F. ornus*) which is cultivated in Sicily for its sweet exudate (manna). *Forsythia* comprises several species of popular early-flowering shrubs, the yellow flowers appearing before the leaves, especially *Forsythia suspensa* and *F. viridissima* (both natives of China) and hybrids between them (*F. × intermedia*).

Jasminum, a tropical and subtropical genus of some 200–300 species, contains several popular widely cultivated species, including the common jasmine, *Jasminum officinale* and winter jasmine, *J. nudiflorum*; some species are cultivated for perfume such as *J. sambac* (Arabian jasmine). *Ligustrum* contains several ornamental trees or shrubs, sometimes used for hedging, including the common privet, *Ligustrum vulgare* (Europe and Mediterranean). *Osmanthus* and *Siphonosmanthus* species are also cultivated for ornament, and the fragrant flowers and leaves of *Osmanthus fragrans* are used to perfume tea in China. *Syringa vulgaris* is the common lilac which is one of the most popular of cultivated shrubs. Other species are grown as garden ornamentals. V.H.H.

POLEMONIALES

NOLANACEAE

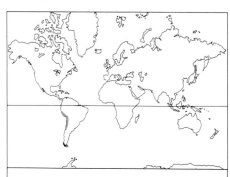

Number of genera: 2
Number of species: 83
Distribution: Chile and Peru.
Economic uses: some ornamentals.

The Nolanaceae is a small distinctive family of herbs or low shrubs many species of which are seashore plants with fleshy leaves.

Distribution. The family is confined to temperate and subtropical Chile and Peru.

Diagnostic features. The leaves are alternate (opposite when in the region of the flowers), simple, often fleshy and glandular-hairy, and are without stipules. The flowers are bisexual, solitary, axillary and regular. There are five connate and persistent sepals. In bud the corolla is pleated like a fan; the five-lobed, blue to pink or white flowers unfold to the shape of a bell or a funnel. The five stamens are unequal, alternating with the corolla lobes; the anthers have two locules, with longitudinal dehiscence. The disk is well developed. The style is single, and the stigma two-to five-lobed. The ovary is superior and has five usually free carpels, which are often divided longitudinally or transversely to give 10–30 segments; placentation is axile. The fruits are one- to seven-seeded nutlets which correspond in number to the divisions of the carpels. The seeds have endosperm and a curved or spiral embryo.

Classification. The six species of *Alona* are

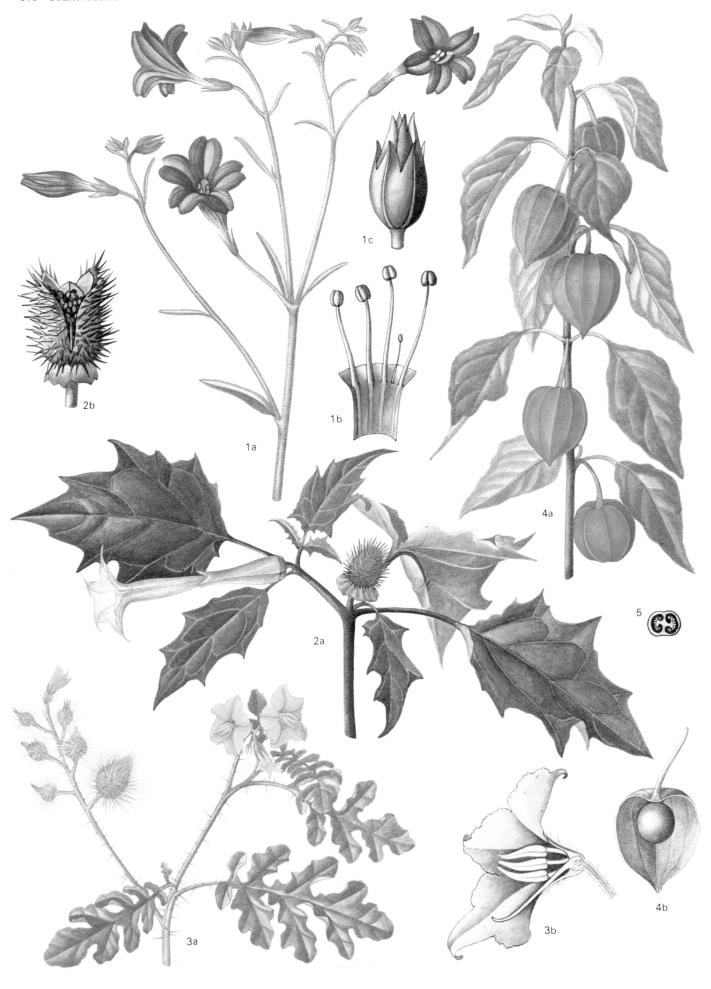

low shrubs with the nutlets of the fruit broadly fused to each other. The 77 species of *Nolana* are either herbs or low shrubs, with the nutlets only slightly fused or not fused at all and often further divided longitudinally and transversely.

The family has resemblances to the Convolvulaceae and the Boraginaceae, but is usually considered closest to the Solanaceae.

Economic uses. A few species of *Nolana*, but principally the Chilean *Nolana paradoxa*, are grown as garden annuals.   D.M.M.

SOLANACEAE
The Potato Family

The Solanaceae, a cosmopolitan family of herbs and a few shrubs and trees, is one of the most important serving mankind. It contains not only many essential vegetables and fruits such as potatoes, tomatoes, aubergines, paprika, chillies, green and red peppers and Cape gooseberries, but also garden ornamentals such as the petunia. Many species are poisonous (eg deadly nightshade).

Distribution. The family is widely distributed throughout tropical and temperate regions. Solanaceous species occur on every continent, but are particularly concentrated in Australia and in Central and South America, where approximately 40 genera are endemic. Its great concentration in South America has led to the hypothesis that the family may have originated in that subcontinent.

Diagnostic features. Most Solanaceae are erect or climbing, annual or perennial herbs; some are shrubs (eg *Lycium*, *Cestrum*), and a few are small trees (eg some *Cyphomandra* species and *Dunalia*). The leaves vary greatly in size and shape, and are entire or variously dissected; they are always without stipules and usually alternate. The inflorescence is typically an axillary cyme or combination of cymes, though in some cases it is reduced to a solitary flower (eg *Datura*, *Nierembergia*, *Mandragora*). The flowers are bisexual, usually regular and composed of five (rarely three to ten) sepals and five (rarely up to ten) petals. The sepals are partly fused, usually persistent and often enlarged around the fruit (eg *Physalis*, *Nicandra*). The petals are variously fused, making the corolla round and flat (eg *Solanum*, *Lycopersicon*), bell-shaped (eg *Nicandra*, *Withania*, *Mandragora*) or tubular (eg *Cestrum*, *Nicotiana*); rarely the corolla is two-lipped as in *Schiz-*

Solanaceae. 1 *Salpiglossis atropurpurea* (a) flowering shoot ($\times\frac{2}{3}$); (b) part of flower showing two pairs of unequal stamens and a single infertile reduced stamen ($\times 1\frac{1}{3}$); (c) fruit ($\times 2$). 2 *Datura stramonium* var *tatula* (a) flowering shoot ($\times\frac{2}{3}$); (b) fruit—a capsule ($\times\frac{2}{3}$). 3 *Solanum rostratum* (a) flowering shoot ($\times\frac{2}{3}$); (b) flower with two petals and two stamens removed ($\times 2$). 4 *Physalis alkekengi* (a) shoot showing fruits enclosed in a persistent orange-red calyx ($\times\frac{2}{3}$); (b) calyx removed to show the fruit ($\times\frac{2}{3}$). 5 *Nicotiana tabacum* cross section of ovary showing two locules and axile placentas ($\times 6$).

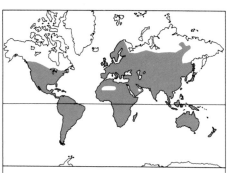

Number of genera: about 90
Number of species: 2,000–3,000
Distribution: cosmopolitan with centers in Australia, Central and S America.
Economic uses: food plants (potato, aubergine, tomato, peppers), ornamentals, alkaloids used in medicine and tobacco.

anthus. There are five (rarely four to eight) stamens attached to the corolla tube and alternating with the petal lobes. The anthers are usually touching but not fused, equal, though occasionally unequal (eg *Salpiglossis*), bilocular, and dehisce inwards or by terminal pores. The ovary is superior, of two fused carpels with a single style, and usually contains two locules, sometimes more, generally with numerous axile ovules. The fruit, containing many seeds, is either an indehiscent berry (eg *Solanum*, *Atropa*, *Capsicum*, *Saracha*, *Nicandra*), or less commonly a capsule (eg *Datura*, *Hyoscyamus*, *Scopolia*, *Salpiglossis*). The seeds contain copious endosperm.

Classification. More than 90 genera, containing between 2,000 and 3,000 species, have been variously included in the Solanaceae. The family can be divided into five tribes, the first three having curved embryos, the last two having straight or only slightly curved embryos.

NICANDREAE. Ovary with three to five locules, the walls dividing the placentas irregularly. Only genus *Nicandra* (one species).

SOLANEAE. Ovary with two locules. Includes *Lycium* (80–90 species), *Atropa* (four species), *Hyoscyamus* (20 species), *Physalis* (100 species), *Capsicum* (50 species), *Solanum* (about 1,700 species), *Lycopersicon* (seven species), *Mandragora* (six species).

DATUREAE. Ovary with four locules, the walls dividing the placentas equally. Only genera *Datura* (10 species), *Solandra* (10 species).

CESTREAE. Five fertile stamens. Includes *Cestrum* (150 species), *Nicotiana* (21 species), *Petunia* (40 species).

SALPIGLOSSIDEAE. Two or four fertile stamens. Includes *Salpiglossis* (18 species), *Schizanthus* (15 species).

The family is closely related to the Scrophulariaceae, from which it is most easily distinguished by the presence of phloem on both the inner and outer sides of the xylem in the vascular bundles, and by the

development of oblique ovaries. The flowers may also be used as a distinguishing feature, those of the Scrophulariaceae being typically irregular, while those of the Solanaceae are usually regular. *Schizanthus* with its highly irregular flowers forms a borderline genus. Although sometimes placed in the Scrophulariaceae, its anatomical features comply with those associated with the Solanaceae. The family also has affinities with the Nolanaceae, Convolvulaceae, Boraginaceae and Gesneriaceae.

Economic uses. Various species of *Browallia*, *Brunfelsia*, *Datura*, *Nicotiana*, *Nierembergia*, *Petunia*, *Salpiglossis*, *Schizanthus*, *Solanum* and *Solandra* are cultivated for their showy flowers. Some *Capsicum* and *Solanum* species are widely grown for their colorful fruits, while certain *Cestrum*, *Lycium*, *Solanum* and *Streptosolen* species are popular shrubs. *Physalis* provides the Chinese lantern plant, *Physalis alkekengi*, which is extensively used in dried floral arrangements.

Among the most familiar solanaceous food plants are the potato (*Solanum tuberosum*), aubergine (*S. melongena*), tomato (*Lycopersicon esculentum*) and the peppers (various *Capsicum* species which include paprika, chillies, one kind of pimenta, cayenne pepper, green peppers, red peppers and sweet peppers). Others, popular in tropical America but relatively little known outside this area, include the husk tomato (*Physalis pubescens*), the tomatillo (*P. ixocarpa*), the Cape gooseberry (*P. peruviana*), the tree tomato (*Cyphomandra betacea*), the pepino (*Solanum muricatum*), the cocona (*S. topiro*), the lulita (*S. hirsutissimum*) and the naranjilla or lulo (*S. quitoense*).

Tobacco (*Nicotiana tabacum*), grown extensively for use for smoking, chewing and snuff manufacture, is one of the most popular and yet harmful plants in the world. Many *Nicotiana* species contain the highly toxic alkaloid nicotine, which is used to advantage as a powerful insecticide.

Plants that are both poisonous and of medicinal use are found in most solanaceous genera. Lesser-known examples include *Cestrum*, *Nicandra* and *Physalis*. The notoriously poisonous members, however, are belladonna or the deadly nightshade (*Atropa belladonna*), jimson weed or stramonium (*Datura stramonium*), the mandrake (*Mandragora officinarum*) and black henbane (*Hyoscyamus niger*). These plants have all been used medicinally since earliest times. They contain alkaloids of the tropane group. Steroid alkaloids are characteristic of many *Solanum* and some *Capsicum* and *Lycopersicon* species.   J.M.E.

CONVOLVULACEAE
Bindweeds, Morning Glory and Sweet Potato

The Convolvulaceae is a family of herbaceous and woody, often climbing plants, containing a few members that are important food sources, weeds or ornamentals.

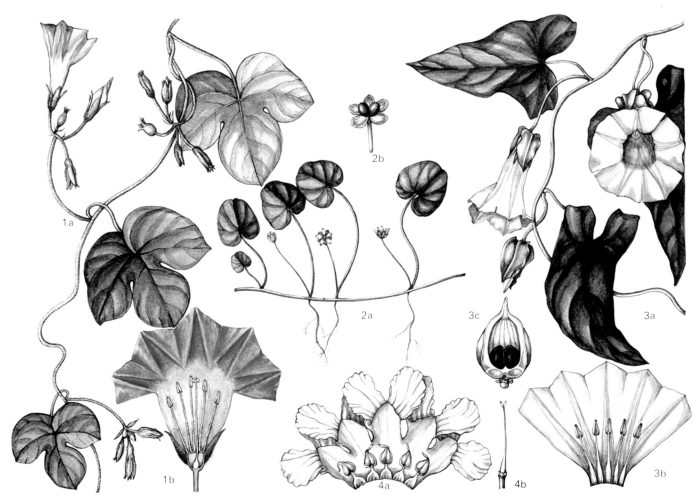

Convolvulaceae. 1 *Ipomoea purpurea* (a) twining stem with axillary flowers (×⅔) ; (b) flower with corolla opened out showing stamens inserted at its base with a superior ovary surmounted by a thin style and lobed stigma (×1). 2 *Dichondra repens* (a) habit (×⅔); (b) fruit comprising two mericarps (×2). 3 *Calystegia sepium* (a) twining stem with solitary axillary flowers (×⅔) ; (b) corolla opened out to show epipetalous stamens (×1) ; (c) fruit with part of wall removed (×1). 4 *Erycibe paniculata* (a) corolla opened out showing each lobe with two divisions at the apex and stamen filaments with broad bases (×⅔) ; (b) gynoecium (×3).

Distribution. The family is represented throughout temperate and tropical regions of the world, in a wide range of habitats.

Many representatives have long trailing and twining stems (eg *Ipomoea* and *Calystegia*), and are especially characteristic of rich bushy vegetation, or open, drier places (including sand dunes). In dry, Mediterranean or semidesert climates woody shrubs are more common, many of these possessing trailing or climbing young branches. The woody species are particularly characteristic of tropical or subtropical areas, and in scrub or open woodland large shrubs or even trees over 33ft (10m) high occur. A few species have exploited such habitats as salt marshes, mountain tops and freshwater. *Cuscuta* (dodder) is more or less parasitic on host plants.

Diagnostic features. The leaves are alternate, simple, rarely with stipules. The flowers are bisexual, regular, often with an involucre of bracts. They comprise five free sepals (sometimes united), five fused petals and five stamens fused to the base of the corolla tube. The ovary is superior, of two (rarely three to five) fused carpels forming two locules each with two (rarely one or four) axile ovules.

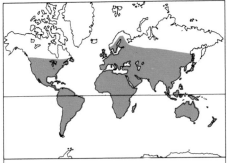

Number of genera: about 50
Number of species: about 1,800
Distribution: cosmopolitan.
Economic uses: ornamentals, eg *Ipomoea* (morning glory), food plants (sweet potatoes and yams of the genus *Ipomoea*), and many minor uses.

The style may be simple or forked and the stigmas simple, lobed or capitate. The fruit is a capsule, often dehiscent. The seeds are sometimes hairy, with little endosperm and a curved embryo often with folded cotyledons.

Classification. The characters of the ovary, style(s) and stigma(s) are considered important in delimiting three to about ten tribes according to opinion. The most distinct of these, the DICHONDREAE (two genera *Dichondra* and *Falkia*), the HUMBERTIEAE (one genus, *Humbertia*), and the CUSCUTEAE (one genus, *Cuscuta*) are sometimes separated as distinct families, the Dichondraceae, Humbertiaceae and Cuscutaceae, respectively.

The Convolvulaceae is most closely related to the Solanaceae, Boraginaceae and Polemoniaceae.

Economic uses. The most important crop plant is *Ipomoea batatas* (sweet potato), hundreds of varieties of which, some known (incorrectly) as yams, are cultivated throughout tropical regions, Japan being a major producer. Many species of this family also have local uses as foods (particularly at times of famine) and as medicines. The roots of *Convolvulus scammonia* (scammony) and of *Ipomoea purga* (jalap) yield a drug used medicinally as a cathartic. A number of species, particularly of the genera *Ipomoea* and *Convolvulus* (some of the bindweeds), are grown as garden ornamentals, notably the morning glory (*Ipomoea purpurea*).   C.A.S.

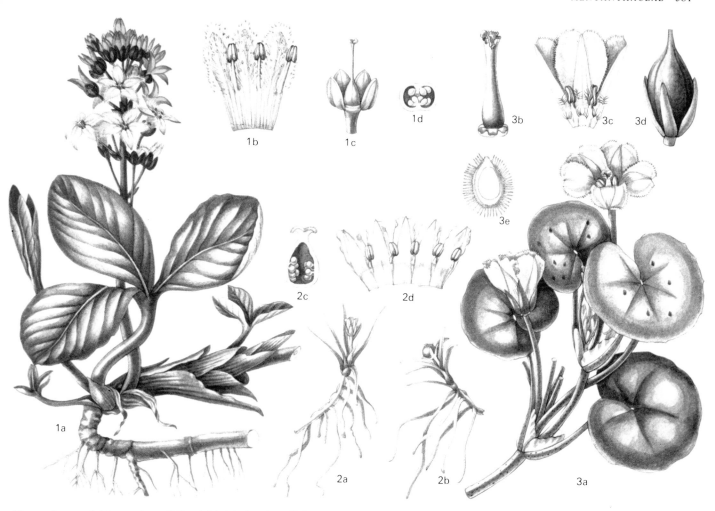

Menyanthaceae. 1 *Menyanthes trifoliata* (a) habit showing trifoliolate leaves and hairy flowers in an erect raceme (×⅔) ; (b) part of hairy corolla showing epipetalous stamens (×2) ; (c) gynoecium and calyx with one sepal removed (×2) ; (d) cross section of unilocular ovary with ovules on two parietal placentas (×4). 2 *Liparophyllum gunnii*, entire plant (a) with flower and (b) with fruit (×⅔) ; (c) vertical section of gynoecium (×4) ; (d) corolla opened out to show epipetalous stamens (×3). 3 *Nymphoides peltata* (a) shoot with peltate leaves and solitary flowers (×⅔) ; (b) gynoecium (×2) ; (c) part of corolla with basal crests of hairs and epipetalous stamens (×1) ; (d) fruit—a capsule (×1) ; (e) seed (×3).

MENYANTHACEAE
Bogbean

The Menyanthaceae is a small family of aquatic or wetland herbs which includes some graceful ornamentals.

Distribution. The genus *Nymphoides* is almost cosmopolitan. *Menyanthes* and *Nephrophyllidium* are found in the Northern Hemisphere, while *Liparophyllum* and *Villarsia* are found in the Southern Hemisphere.

Diagnostic features. Most species are perennial with tufted rootstocks or horizontal creeping rhizomes, but some species of *Nymphoides* and *Villarsia* are annual. The leaves are alternate, with sheathing petioles, simple, linear to orbicular, or trifoliolate, and without stipules. The flowers are unisexual or bisexual, regular and often heterostylous; they are borne in simple or branched cymes or racemes, or in dense heads or clusters. There are five sepals, united at the base, persistent in fruit and sometimes joined to the ovary below. The petals, also five and united at the base, are yellow, white or pink, and usually have hairs or crests on the inside. The five stamens are fused to the base of the corolla tube and alternate with the corolla lobes; the anthers are versatile. The ovary is

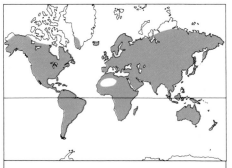

Number of genera: 5
Number of species: about 40
Distribution: almost cosmopolitan.
Economic uses: limited local uses as food and in medicine, and several aquatic weeds.

superior, of two fused carpels, with one locule containing two parietal placentas bearing few or numerous ovules. The style is simple and bifid. The fruit is a capsule and is regularly or irregularly dehiscent, or somewhat fleshy and indehiscent. The seeds may be winged, and have copious endosperm and a small embryo.

Classification. *Menyanthes* and *Nephrophyllidium* both have one species only. They are tough, rhizomatous herbs of wet places. *Menyanthes* has trifoliolate leaves and is widespread in the northern boreal zone, while *Nephrophyllidium* has simple, kidney-shaped leaves and is confined to the north Pacific from Honshu in Japan to Washington in northwest North America. *Liparophyllum* also has one species and it is a small, creeping herb with tufted linear leaves, occuring in Tasmania and New Zealand in mountain bogs. *Nymphoides*, with about 20 species, has the habit of the water lilies (*Nymphaea*) but in many species the flowers appear to arise directly from the petiole; the majority of the species are tropical. *Villarsia*, with about 16 species, is usually found as a terrestrial plant in wet places; the majority of the species are found in Australia and Southeast Asia but one species is found in South Africa. *Nymphoides* and *Villarsia* are distinguished largely by their habit and type of inflorescence, but in Australia, at least, these distinctions are somewhat unsatisfactory and a case could be made for a revision of the genera.

The Menyanthaceae is related to the Gentianaceae, differing in habit, alternate

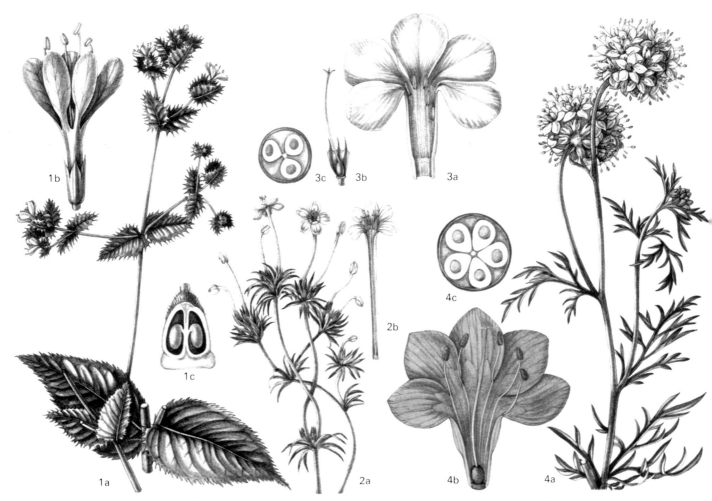

Polemoniaceae. 1 *Loeselia cordifolia* (a) shoot with toothed, opposite leaves and small cymose clusters of flowers ($\times\frac{2}{3}$); (b) flower ($\times4$); (c) vertical section of ovary showing basal disk and ovules on axile placentas ($\times12$). 2 *Linanthus androsaceus* (a) flowering shoot ($\times\frac{2}{3}$); (b) flower opened to show anthers inserted at apex of long corolla tube ($\times1$). 3 *Phlox paniculata* (a) corolla opened to show irregular insertion of stamens ($\times1\frac{1}{2}$); (b) part of calyx and entire gynoecium ($\times1\frac{1}{2}$); (c) cross section of ovary ($\times14$). 4 *Gilia achilleifolia* (a) flowering shoot ($\times\frac{2}{3}$); (b) flower opened out showing insertion of stamens between corolla lobes ($\times4$); (c) cross section of fruit ($\times6$).

leaves and valvate arrangement of the petals.

Economic uses. *Menyanthes* contains the bitter glucoside menyanthin which is used in medicine as a tonic and to bring down fever. In Scandinavia the leaves are occasionally added to beer or used as a tea substitute. In Russia they are eaten as an emergency food. Several species of *Nymphoides* are found as weeds in ricefields and irrigation channels and some are cultivated as ornamentals, eg *N. cordata*.   C.D.C.

LENNOACEAE

The Lennoaceae is a small family of fleshy herbs parasitic on the roots of shrubs.

Distribution. The family is found in deserts, desert scrub and sometimes coastal sand dunes, in southwestern North America; one species of *Lennoa* is recorded from Colombia.

Diagnostic features. The Lennoaceae are simple or branched herbs, lacking chlorophyll and brownish when dry. The leaves are reduced to bract-like scales. The flowers are bisexual, regular (rarely irregular), borne in heads or a compact thyrse. The calyx is deeply five- to ten-lobed, the corolla is salver-shaped and has a five- to ten-lobed limb. There are as many stamens as corolla lobes, inserted in one or two series in the throat of the corolla. The anthers have two locules dehiscing by longitudinal slits, and are usually essentially sessile. The ovary is superior, comprising six to fourteen fused carpels and six to ten locules. Each locule is divided into two parts by a false septum, each part with a single, anatropous, axile ovule. The solitary style is simple and the stigma is peltate, crenulate or obscurely lobed. The fruit is a capsule enclosed in the persistent perianth, finally breaking up into 12–28 one-seeded nutlets. The seeds have endosperm and a rounded, rather undifferentiated embryo.

Classification. In *Ammobroma* (one species) the inflorescence is a laterally extended head and the sepals have simple, moderately stiff hairs. The other two genera, however, have the flowers borne in axillary cymes to form a compact, spike-like thyrse and the sepals have capitate-glandular hairs: *Lennoa* (two to three species) has eight stamens with partially free filaments borne in two series, while *Pholisma* (one species) has five to seven anthers in one series and with the filaments joined by their whole length to the corolla.

This family was formerly included in the Ericales but on embryological and pollen data is now considered to be close to the Hydrophyllaceae and Boraginaceae.

Economic uses. Lennoaceae has no current economic uses, but the underground stems of *Ammobroma* were formerly an important food for the Indians of the southwestern North American deserts.   D.M.M.

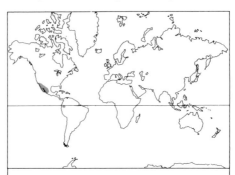

Number of genera: 3
Number of species: 4–5
Distribution: SW N America, Colombia.
Economic uses: none.

POLEMONIACEAE

Phlox

The Polemoniaceae, which includes the showy and familiar *Phlox* widely grown in gardens, is a smallish family with a great diversity of habit, ranging from trees and lianas to small leafless annuals. Of particular interest is the large variety of pollination mechanisms employed by different members.

Distribution. The family ranges from the tropics to high latitudes in both hemispheres but is predominantly New World, with most species occurring in North America, particularly the west.

Diagnostic features. Polemoniaceae are perennial or annual herbs, less commonly shrubs, lianas or small trees. The leaves are alternate or opposite, simple or compound, and are without stipules. The flowers are bisexual, usually regular and axillary or terminal, solitary or in small cymose clusters of dense heads. There are five sepals, fused into a tube, rarely only at the base. The petals, also five, are fused to form a flat and round, or bell-shaped or funnel-shaped corolla. The five stamens are fused to the corolla tube, alternating with the corolla lobes; the anthers have two locules, with longitudinal dehiscence. The ovary is superior, inserted on the basal disk, comprising three (rarely two or four) fused carpels and the same number of locules, each containing one to numerous anatropous ovules, on axile placentas. The simple style has a stigma with three (rarely two or four) lobes. The fruit is a capsule, usually splitting open along the midribs of the carpels and having one to numerous seeds, usually endospermic. The embryo is straight or slightly curved; the seed-coat is often sticky when wetted.

The family exhibits a notable array of pollination mechanisms. Pollination by bees is most widespread in North American Polemoniaceae, from which pollination by humming birds (eg *Gilia, Ipomopsis, Loeselia, Polemonium*), flies (*Gilia, Linanthus, Polemonium*) and beetles (*Ipomopsis, Linanthus*) seems to have arisen independently

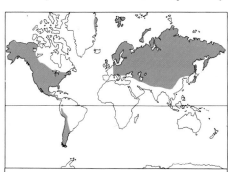

Number of genera: 18
Number of species: about 300
Distribution: mainly N America, but also Chile, Peru, Europe and N Asia.
Economic uses: many ornamentals, eg *Phlox, Polemonium* and *Gilia*.

in various genera. Butterfly and moth pollination is known as an advanced condition in several genera, while in the tropical tribes pollination by bats (*Cobaea*), hummingbirds (*Cantua, Loeselia, Huthia*) and hawkmoths (*Cantua, Cobaea*), as well as bees (*Bonplandia, Loeselia, Huthia*), is known.

Classification. The family is divided into five tribes:

COBAEEAE. Lianas with pinnate leaves, flowers solitary and calyx regular. Tropical America. Only genus *Cobaea*. This tribe is sometimes regarded as a separate family, the Cobaeaceae.

CANTUEAE. Small trees and shrubs with simple or pinnatifid leaves, flowers in axillary or terminal clusters and calyx regular. Confined to the northern Andes. *Cantua, Huthia*.

BONPLANDIEAE. Shrubs or herbs with simple to pinnatifid leaves, and flowers which may be solitary, in pairs or clustered; calyx slightly irregular. Tropical America. *Bonplandia, Loeselia*.

POLEMONIEAE. Perennial (rarely annual) herbs, with simple to pinnate leaves and calyx usually herbaceous; corolla regular and stamens inserted (often very irregularly) in the corolla tube or throat. Temperate America and Eurasia. *Polemonium, Allophyllum, Collomia, Gymnosteris, Phlox* and *Microsteris*.

GILIEAE. Annual or rarely perennial herbs, with simple, entire or much-dissected leaves; calyx with membranous sinuses which rupture in age; corolla regular or irregular and stamens inserted, usually regularly, in the throat of the corolla-tube or between lobes. Arid southwestern North America, extending to moister areas and into warm temperate South America. *Gilia, Ipomopsis, Eriastrum, Langloisia, Navarretia, Leptodactylon* and *Linanthus*.

The five tropical genera (tribes Cobaeeae, Cantueae, Bonplandieae) are mostly woody plants with large to medium corollas, winged seeds with little or no endosperm and large fleshy cotyledons. The 13 temperate genera (tribes Polemonieae, Gilieae), on the other hand, are mostly herbaceous with medium to small corollas, wingless, endospermic seeds and smaller cotyledons.

The Polemoniaceae is most closely related to the Hydrophyllaceae, the two families together constituting a group within the Polemoniales which in turn has affinities with a group comprising the Nolanaceae, Solanaceae and Convolvulaceae.

Economic uses. Many species of *Polemonium, Phlox* and *Gilia* are cultivated as garden ornamentals for their colorful flowers.   D.M.M.

EHRETIACEAE

The Ehretiaceae is a medium-sized family of trees and shrubs (and a few herbs) chiefly important economically for a number of trees that provide strong timber.

Distribution. Species are distributed through-

out the tropics and subtropics. The main centers of distribution are in Central and South America.

Diagnostic features. The leaves are simple, alternate, entire or with toothed margins and without stipules. The inflorescence is usually cymose and the flowers are regular and bisexual. The calyx consists of five sepals which are fused into a long or deeply divided tube. They are usually green and leaf-like, but sometimes membranous and enlarged, enclosing the fruit. In most species they are persistent. The petals are fused to form a corolla tube with five (occasionally four or six) lobes. The five stamens are attached to the corolla tube and alternate with the lobes. The ovary is superior, consisting of two to four fused carpels and two to four locules, each containing paired ovules generally attached basally to the axis. It is usually surmounted by a single terminal style with two or four branches or lobes at the tip; some species have two free styles each with a simple stigmatic tip. The fruit is a drupe often enclosed by the persistent calyx. The seeds may be endospermic or nonendospermic.

Classification. The genera can be separated on various vegetative and floral features, including the form of the calyx, style and fruit. For example, both *Cordia* and *Patagonula* have two-lobed stylar arms but the calyx of the former is only slightly enlarged in the fruit, while that of the latter is much enlarged. Both *Rochefortia* (spiny shrubs) and *Coldenia* (herbs or shrubs with hairy leaves) have two free styles. *Ehretia, Cortesia* and *Saccellium* all have flowers with a single style but only in the latter genus does the calyx become enlarged to envelop the fruit. *Halgania* has the anthers united into a cone around the style and in *Auxemma* the winged calyx surrounds the fruit.

There is no doubt about the affinity of this family to the Boraginaceae, and in fact some botanists include it within the latter.

Economic uses. A number of species of

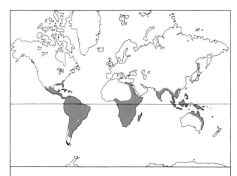

Number of genera: 13
Number of species: about 400
Distribution: tropics and subtropics with centers in C and S America.
Economic uses: valuable timber, some edible fruits, and a few medicinal decoctions of limited local value.

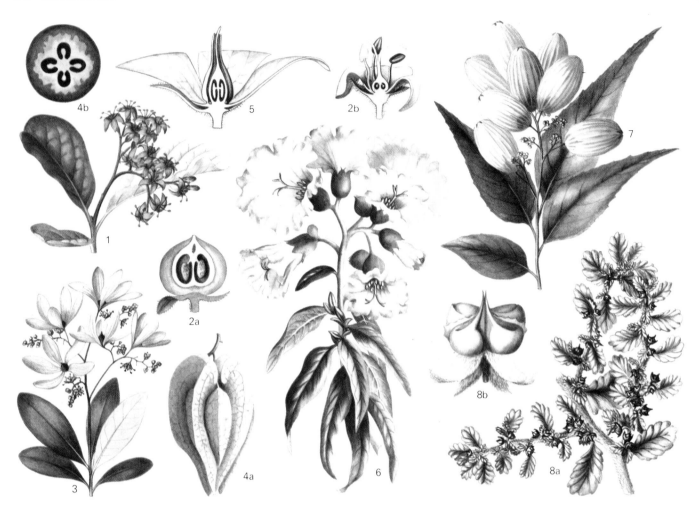

Ehretiaceae. 1 *Ehretia mossambicensis* leafy shoot and inflorescence (×⅔). 2 *Ehretia buxifolia* (a) vertical section of fruit (×4); (b) half flower (×4). 3 *Patagonula americana* leafy shoot with flower and fruit having a persistent star-like calyx (×⅔). 4 *Auxemma oncocalyx* (a) fruit surrounded by five-winged calyx (×⅔); (b) cross section of fruit (×1⅓). 5 *Halgania littoralis* half flower showing anthers united around the ovary (×2). 6 *Cordia decandra* leafy shoot and inflorescence (×⅔). 7 *Saccellium lanceolatum* leafy shoot with flowers and fruits that are surrounded by an inflated calyx (×⅔). 8 *Coldenia procumbens* (a) leafy shoot and fruit (×⅔); (b) fruit that separates into four nuts (×6).

Cordia (*Cordia gerascanthus*, *C. alba*, *C. dodecandra* and *C. alliodora*, native to tropical Central and South America) are valued for their timber which is used for making furniture and the beams and doors in houses. The fruit of some species (*C. gharaf* and *C. rothii* in Africa and India and *C. sebestina* in Mexico and the Caribbean) is edible. A decoction from the leaves and fruits of some species (eg *C. boisseri*) is used as a treatment for cold symptoms. The wood of *Ehretia elliptica* is used in Mexico for making the handles of agricultural implements, and the leaves of *E. philippensis* are used in the Philippines as a curative for intestinal disorders including dysentery. The South American genus *Patagonula* contains at least two species (*Patagonula americana* and *P. batensis*) valued for their timber which is used both for building and furniture.

S.R.C.

HYDROPHYLLACEAE

The Hydrophyllaceae is a smallish but widely distributed family of herbs and small shrubs containing several attractive temperate garden plants such as species of *Nemophila*, *Wigandia* and *Phacelia*.

Distribution. The family is almost cosmopolitan.

Diagnostic features. The members of the family are annual or perennial herbs or undershrubs. The leaves are alternate (rarely opposite), usually hairy or glandular, simple or compound, and without stipules. The usually blue to purple flowers are often borne in cymes or cincinni, and are bisexual and regular, with five free sepals with or

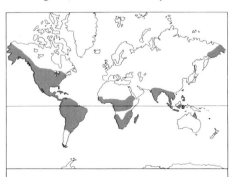

Number of genera: about 18
Number of species: about 250
Distribution: cosmopolitan.
Economic uses: several ornamentals.

without auricles between the lobes. The five-lobed corolla is fused at the base and is wheel- or bell-shaped or funnel-like, with five stamens inserted at the base of the corolla tube. The stamens often have a pair of small appendages at the base of each filament, and these protect nectaries which serve to attract pollinating bees. The ovary is superior, comprising two fused carpels and one or two locules, each containing two to many sessile or pendulous ovules, on parietal placentas when unilocular, or on axile placentas when bilocular. There are one or two styles. The fruit is a loculicidal capsule, and the many seeds have a small straight embryo and fleshy endosperm.

Classification. The family is a homogeneous one, being split into genera chiefly on the basis of technical fruit and seed characters. Its closest relation is the Polemoniaceae.

Economic uses. The Hydrophyllaceae contains a number of ornamental genera such as *Nemophila* and *Phacelia*, grown in gardens. Some of the more attractive phacelias are *Phacelia sericea* with silvery, silky foliage and bluish purple or white corollas; *P. campanularia* with deep blue corollas and *P. tanacetifolia* with hairy parts, fern-like

Hydrophyllaceae. 1 *Phacelia minor* shoot with leaves and flowers (×⅔). 2 *P. tanacetifolia* half flower showing appendages on bases of filaments (×4). 3 *P. franklinii* (a) cross section of ovary with ovules on parietal placentas (×18); (b) dehiscing capsule with many seeds (×1⅓). 4 *Hydrolea floribunda* stamen before (left) and after (right) dehiscence (×6). 5 *H. spinosa* (a) half flower (×4); (b) cross section of ovary showing ovules on placentas adnate to the septa (×10). 6 *Hydrophyllum virginianum* (a) shoot with pinnate leaf and flowers in a head-like cyme (×⅔); (b) dehiscing capsule with two seeds (×4).

compound leaves, and compact cymes of blue flowers; all are North American.

Hydrophyllum, from the Greek, *hydor*: water and *phyllon*: leaf – a reference to the watery appearance of the foliage of some species – is the type-genus of the family. They are chiefly perennials with mainly basal leaves, and greenish, white or violet flowers, with protruding stamens, borne in open or head-like cymes. *Wigandia* contains six species from the American tropics; several are planted for their bold foliage in bedding displays, eg *Wigandia caracasana*, with long leaves and violet and white flowers. *Nama* species include the perennial *Nama rothrockii*, a small attractive purplish-headed species with dentate leaves from dry sandy habitats in western Nevada and California. *Draperia systyla* from California is a softly hairy, diffuse perennial herb, with heads of pale violet flowers, and *Lemmonia californica*, also from California, makes an attractive annual with small white flowers and hairy leaves. B.M.

BORAGINACEAE
Forget-me-not and Alkanet

The Boraginaceae is a relatively large family of annual to perennial herbs, shrubs, trees and a few lianas. About 30 genera are used as ornamentals and several species are of medicinal value or used as dyes or herbs.

Distribution. The family is found throughout temperate and subtropical areas of the world with a major center of distribution in the

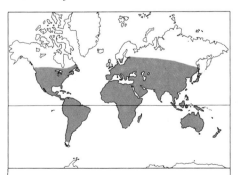

Number of genera: about 100
Number of species: 2,000
Distribution: throughout temperate and subtropical regions, but centered in the Mediterranean region.
Economic uses: ornamentals (eg heliotrope, forget-me-not) pot-herbs (alkanet, comfrey) and red dye.

Mediterranean region. It is less frequent in cool temperate and tropical regions.

Diagnostic features. The stems are usually covered in rough hairs which also occur on the leaves and in the inflorescences. The leaves are generally alternate, simple, usually entire, without stipules and often bearing cystoliths. The inflorescence is very characteristic of the family and usually consists of one or more determinate scorpioid or helicoid cymes (cincinni) which uncoil progressively as the flowers open. The flowers are regular (irregular in *Echium* and some related genera) and usually bisexual although female flowers borne on separate plants are quite frequent. There are five sepals, free or connate at the base, sometimes unequal in size. The corolla has five lobes and is salver-shaped to bell-shaped, the tube often with scales at the base or mouth. There are five stamens inserted on the corolla, sometimes unequal, often with basal appendages. The anthers have two locules and the filaments often have a nectariferous disk at the base. The ovary is superior, of two fused carpels, with two locules often becoming four by means of false septa. There is one erect, ascending or

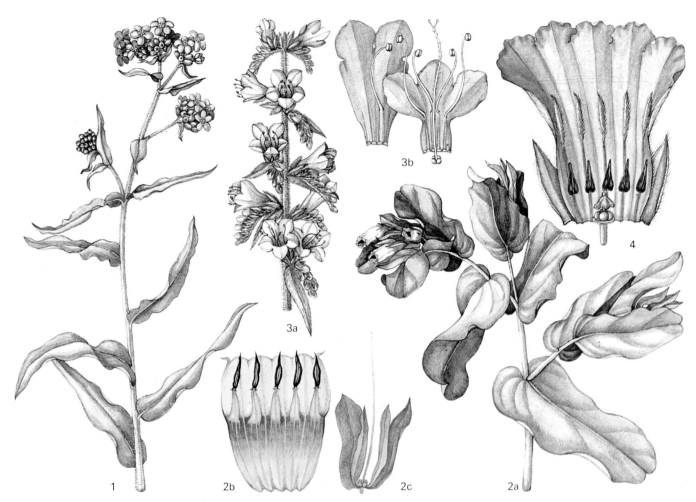

Boraginaceae. 1 *Anchusa officinalis* leafy shoot and inflorescence of regular flowers ($\times\frac{2}{3}$). 2 *Cerinthe major* (a) leafy shoot and inflorescence ($\times\frac{2}{3}$); (b) corolla opened out to show five epipetalous stamens ($\times 2$); (c) calyx and four-lobed gynoecium with a gynobasic style, ie arising from the base of the ovary between the lobes ($\times 2$). 3 *Echium vulgare* (a) inflorescence of irregular flowers ($\times\frac{2}{3}$); (b) flower dissected to show epipetalous stamens and four-lobed ovary with a thin, gynobasic style which is forked at its tip ($\times 2$). 4 *Heliotropium* sp. flower opened out with five arrow-shaped stamens and the ovary with a terminal style and an umbrella-shaped expansion below the stigma ($\times 2$).

horizontal, anatropous ovule in each locule. The single style is gynobasic or terminal, usually simple or capitate but two- or four-lobed in some genera. The fruit consists of four (rarely two) nutlets or is a drupe. The seeds are with or without endosperm and with a curved or straight embryo.

The flowers are predominantly insect-pollinated, with blue, white, pink or yellow flowers. Many have pendulous, bee-pollinated flowers, such as those of *Borago* and *Symphytum*, and several outbreeding mechanisms are to be found, such as heterostyly in *Pulmonaria* and separate female flowers in *Echium*; some species are self-incompatible.

Classification. The family can be divided into two subfamilies:

HELIOTROPIOIDEAE. Style terminal, simple or bilobed, with a ring of hairs near the tip; fruit a drupe; seed with endosperm (*Heliotropium*, *Tournefortia*).

BORAGINOIDEAE. Style gynobasic; fruit of two or four separate nutlets. This subfamily can be further subdivided into five tribes, mainly on style and fruit characters: CYNOGLOSSEAE (eg *Omphalodes*, *Cynoglossum*, *Rindera*); ERITRICHIEAE (eg *Echinospermum*,

Eritrichium, *Cryptanthe*); BORAGINEAE (eg *Symphytum*, *Borago*, *Anchusa*); LITHOSPERMEAE (eg *Myosotis*, *Lithospermum*, *Arnebia*) and ECHIEAE (*Echium*).

The family is included in the order Polemiales with other tubiflorous families such as the Hydrophyllaceae, Polemoniaceae and Convolvulaceae. The Ehretiaceae is often regarded as comprising two subfamilies of the Boraginaceae (Cordioideae and Ehretioideae). Other authorities treat all the subfamilies of the Boraginaceae as separate families.

Economic uses. Several genera are cultivated for ornament, for example *Heliotropium* (heliotrope), *Mertensia* (Virginia bluebells), *Myosotis* (forget-me-not), *Pulmonaria*, *Echium*. *Symphytum officinale* is commonly used as a pot-herb (comfrey) and *Alkanna tinctoria* (alkanet) is a source of red dye used to stain wood and marble and to color medicines, wines and cosmetics. The borage (*Borago officinalis*) is a traditional garden herb used since the Middle Ages for its reputed medicinal and culinary value, and to flavor drinks, but today is grown more for its attractive, bright blue flowers and as a source of nectar for bee-feeding.　D.B.

LAMIALES

VERBENACEAE
Teaks and Verbenas

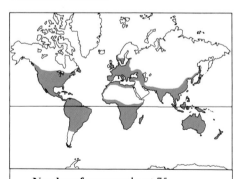

Number of genera: about 75
Number of species: over 3,000
Distribution: tropical and subtropical, a few temperate.
Economic uses: timbers (teaks), essential oils, teas, herbal medicines, fruits, gums, tannins and ornamentals.

This large family contains a number of useful plants (notably teak) and ornamentals. The Verbenaceae includes herbs, shrubs, trees

Verbenaceae. 1 *Clerodendrum thomsoniae* (a) shoot with cymose inflorescence of flowers which have an inflated, winged calyx ($\times\frac{2}{3}$); (b) fruit—a four-lobed drupe ($\times 1$). 2 *Verbena chamaedrifolia* (a) shoot bearing opposite leaves and a terminal raceme ($\times\frac{2}{3}$); (b) flower with irregular corolla ($\times 2$); (c) corolla opened out to show epipetalous stamens ($\times 6$); (d) gynoecium showing lobed ovary surmounted by a single style with a lobed stigma ($\times 3$). 3 *Vitex agnus-castus* (a) shoot bearing digitate leaves and cymose inflorescences ($\times\frac{2}{3}$); (b) flower ($\times 2$); (c) corolla opened out to show stamens of two lengths (didynamous) ($\times 3$); (d) fruit ($\times 4$); (e) cross section of fruit showing four locules ($\times 4$).

and many lianas; several members are thorny xerophytes.

Distribution. The family has an almost entirely tropical and subtropical distribution, with a few genera and species native to temperate zones.

Diagnostic features. The leaves are usually opposite, rarely whorled or alternate, entire or divided and without stipules. The flowers are usually irregular and bisexual, arranged in racemose or cymose inflorescences. The calyx is four- or five-lobed or toothed, the corolla is tubular and also four- to five-lobed. The stamens are four (rarely two or five), alternating with the corolla lobes, with bilocular anthers opening lengthwise. The ovary is superior, consisting of two (rarely four or five) fused carpels normally divided early into four (or more) locules by formation of false septa. Placentation is axile, with two erect, rarely pendulous, ovules per carpel, leading to one ovule in each locule after formation of the false septa. The style is terminal, occasionally arising from between the ovary lobes. The fruit is a drupe, less commonly a capsule or schizocarp. The seeds have a straight embryo and little or no endosperm is present.

Classification. The family is basically classified according to the type of inflorescence. The VERBENOIDEAE, with a racemose spicate inflorescence includes the genera *Verbena*, *Lantana*, *Lippia*, *Priva* and *Citharexylum*. The group with cymose inflorescences, which frequently occur as panicles and corymbs, or may even be reduced to a single axillary flower, is divided according to fruit structure into the VITICOIDEAE, the NYCTANTHOIDEAE and the CARYOPTERIDOIDEAE. The fruit of the Viticoideae is a drupe, and genera include *Tectona*, *Vitex*, *Callicarpa* and *Clerodendrum*. Those genera whose fruit is a capsule with two locules, valves and seeds, such as *Nyctanthes*, are included in the Nyctanthoideae. The Caryopteridoideae have a four-valved, capsule-like fruit, eg *Caryopteris*.

The woody Verbenaceae is generally considered to be closely related to the herbaceous Labiatae, although the Labiatae shows a constancy in pollen-type, while the Verbenaceae shows great variation.

Economic uses. The family includes many genera of economic value. The most important is *Tectona grandis* (Southeast Asia), the source of teak, a durable and water-resistant

timber much used in shipbuilding. *Citharexylum* (Mexico and South America), commonly called zither wood, is used to make musical instruments. *Vitex celebica* produces a fine timber and *V. agnus-castus* (chaste tree or monk's pepper tree) is the source of a valuable oil; other species yield edible fruits, gum and tannin. *Petitia* is another timber-producing genus, as is *Premna* (Malaya), which produces a beautifully veined wood used by the Japanese for knife handles. The South American shrub *Lippia citriodora*, lemon verbena, bears densely glandular, scented leaves which are used in herbal teas. Other species yield valuable essential oils.

A number of genera are cultivated for their ornamental value, including *Lippia citriodora*, with lemon-scented foliage; *Lantana camara*, a half-climbing shrub, the flowers of which open as pink and yellow and change to red and orange; *Holmskioldia sanguinea*, known as the Chinese hat plant for its large spreading calyx; *Verbena* species for their showy blooms; and species of *Petrea*, *Clerodendrum*, *Vitex*, *Caryopteris* and *Callicarpa*. *Verbena officinalis* (vervain) is used for a number of herbal remedies, eg to treat skin diseases. S.A.H.

LABIATAE
The Mint Family

The Labiatae (or Lamiaceae) is a large and natural family of mostly herbs and under-shrubs containing many useful plants such as sage (*Salvia*) and mint (*Mentha*).

Distribution. Few regions of the world lack labiates; they grow in almost all types of habitat and at all altitudes, from the Arctic to the Himalayas, Southeast Asia to Hawaii and Australasia, throughout Africa and in the New World from north to south; a few genera such as *Salvia*, *Scutellaria* and *Stachys* are almost cosmopolitan. One of the regions of greatest concentration of species is the Mediterranean basin, where such genera as *Micromeria*, *Phlomis*, *Rosmarinus*, *Sideritis* and *Thymus* are characteristic components of the maquis and the garrigue. In general, labiates are plants of open ground; only a few genera are found in tropical rain forest (eg *Gomphostemma*).

Diagnostic features. Most species are shrubby or herbaceous; trees are extremely rare but do occur in the huge South American genus *Hyptis*, where some species reach 40ft (12m). The stems often have a characteristic square shape. The leaves are mostly simple, opposite and decussate (each pair at right angles to the next) and are without stipules. The plants are often covered in hairs and glands that emit an aromatic fragrance.

The flowers of all labiates are essentially bisexual, but in many species of *Mentha*, *Nepeta* or *Ziziphora*, for instance, up to 50% of the plants may have flowers in which the male organs are reduced and sterile and the flower is functionally female. In these flowers, the corollas are often smaller and paler colored. The flowers are irregular and basically comprise: five fused sepals forming a funnel- or bell-shape, sometimes two-lipped; five fused petals; four or two epipetalous stamens, either of two lengths or all nearly equal; and a superior ovary of two fused carpels which form four distinct locules each with one basal ovule. A very characteristic feature of the family is the gynobasic style, arising from the base of and between the lobes of the ovary. The fruits consist of four one-seeded indehiscent achene-like nutlets. The seeds have little or no endosperm.

Labiatae. 1 *Stachys sylvatica* shoot with opposite leaves and terminal inflorescence (×⅔). 2 *Scutellaria indica* var *parvifolia* flowering shoot (×⅔). 3 *Salvia porphyrantha* flowering shoot (×⅔). 4 *Salvia* sp (a) section of flower showing stamen with much elongated connective (×2); (b) detail of stamens (×3). 5 *Coleus freederici* (a) flowering shoot showing the square stem characteristic of the family (×⅔); (b) detail of flower (×2). 6 *Teucrium fruticans* (a) flowering shoot (×⅔); (b) detail of flower (×2). 7 *Rosmarinus officinalis* flower with stigma and stamens projecting from the corolla (×⅔). 8 *Lamium marulatum* typical labiate four-lobed ovary (a) entire (×2) and (b) in vertical section (×9) showing style attached to base of ovary (ie gynobasic).

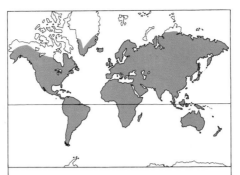

Number of genera: about 200
Number of species: about 3,000
Distribution: cosmopolitan, mostly on open ground.
Economic uses: ornamentals (salvia, lavender, coleus), herbs (mint, sage, thyme, marjoram) and essential oils.

There is a very wide range of corolla-shape and staminal position in the family. Usually, there is a clear division into an upper and a lower lip. In most of the temperate genera the upper, often hooded, lip consists of two lobes and the lower of three, forming a convenient landing platform for insects seeking nectar; the stamens are protected by, or included within, the upper lip. In most tropical genera (eg *Coleus*) there is a different organization: an upper lip of four lobes and a lower of one lobe; the stamens lie along the lower lip or ascend from it. In yet other genera (eg *Teucrium*) the upper lip is absent and the lower consists of five lobes, the stamens often being completely exposed. The corolla-tube also varies greatly: frequently there are protective devices, such as rings of hair or constrictions or folds in the throat of the corolla, which protect the nectar, secreted at the base of the ovary, from too-easy access by pollinators.

Various types of specialized pollination mechanisms occur; these are usually linked with insects, sometimes moths or butterflies, or with birds. The most advanced type is found in *Salvia*. A visiting insect knocks its head against one end of an elongated curved staminal connective which effectively prevents access to the nectar. As it does so, the other end of the staminal arm comes down by means of an articulating joint, tapping the insect's back with pollen. Although in most labiates pollination is accomplished by insects, there are many scarlet-flowered species in the New World, often with very long corolla-tubes, which are pollinated by long-tongued humming-birds. Explosive types of pollination mechanism are known in *Hyptis* and in *Aeollanthus* (tropical Africa). In these cases the mechanism consists of a tight juxtaposition of stamens and corolla lobes: the stamens are held under tension by the enfolding lobes of the corolla so that when an insect lands on the lower lip the stamens are abruptly released and a cloud of pollen dusts the pollinator.

Terpenes are present in many members of the family. Sometimes they act as growth inhibitors for other species: in the Californian *Salvia leucophylla* the presence in the air of terpenes exuded from its leaves prevents nearby grasses from germinating or growing.

Classification. The 200 or so genera are not readily grouped into higher natural units. Although some nine or ten subfamilies are currently recognized, many are unsatisfactory: numerous genera or closely allied groups of genera are very isolated in the family and do not fit happily into the existing hierarchy; the vast majority of temperate genera are in the subfamily STACHYOIDEAE (eg *Stachys*); most tropical genera are in subfamily OCIMOIDEAE (eg *Coleus*); *Scutellaria*, *Lavandula*, *Ajuga* and *Rosmarinus* are placed in independent subfamilies.

Generally regarded as one of the most highly evolved of all dicotyledonous families, the Labiatae is closely related to the Verbenaceae, primarily a woody tropical family, generally without essential oils and usually without a deeply four-lobed ovary. The small aquatic family Callitrichaceae is also considered to be an ally of the Labiatae.

Economic uses. A large number of labiates are cultivated either as ornamentals or as kitchen herbs. Upward of 60 genera are grown in temperate regions alone. Some of the best-known are *Mentha* (mint), *Monarda*, *Nepeta* (catmint), *Origanum* (marjoram or oregano), *Phlomis*, *Salvia* (sage), *Stachys*, *Thymus* (thyme) and *Ajuga* (bugle). Many are grown for their combined virtues of attractive flowers and pleasant fragrance: the essential oil from *Lavandula* (lavender) is mostly obtained from wild plants. In the tropics, *Coleus* and *Plectranthus*, better known as houseplants in cooler regions, are widely grown for their colorful and variegated foliage. So too are several showy species of *Salvia* and of *Leonotis*. *Ocimum sanctum*, a holy plant for Hindus, is frequently grown near temples.

Many species are cultivated commercially. Mostly these are the aromatic herbs of Mediterranean origin, such as mint, marjoram and thyme, so commonly used in flavoring food; but others which are important sources of essential oils used in perfumery and pharmacy are not infrequently cultivated in the tropics and subtropics. Various species of *Ocimum* (basil and sweet basil) are much grown; a species of *Pogostemon* is the source of patchouli, much used in perfumery in Southeast Asia; *Perilla* is grown in India for perilla oil, used in printing-inks and paints.

In different parts of the world, native species of Labiatae are much used by the local people: in Turkey and elsewhere, *Sideritis* leaves provide a tea-like drink; in Iran, *Ziziphora* is used to flavor yoghurt; and in India and Southeast Asia, tubers of *Coleus rotundifolius* (hausa potato) are eaten as a potato substitute.   I.H.

Callitrichaceae. 1 *Callitriche verna* (a) habit showing creeping submerged and erect aerial shoots ($\times\frac{2}{3}$); (b) male flower (left) comprising a single stamen and female flower (right) comprising an ovary with two styles ($\times 20$); (c) male and female flower in a single leaf axil (a rare occurrence) ($\times 20$); (d) cross section of ovary ($\times 34$); (e) fruit with winged lobes ($\times 23$). 2 *C. deflexa* habit showing solitary female flowers on long stalks ($\times 2\frac{2}{3}$). 3 *C. asagraei* (a) habit showing narrow submerged leaves ($\times 1\frac{1}{3}$); (b) habit showing spatula-shaped aerial leaves ($\times 1\frac{1}{3}$).

TETRACHONDRACEAE

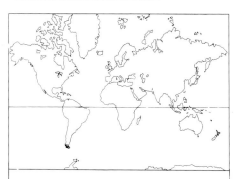

Number of genera: 1
Number of species: 2
Distribution: North Island, New Zealand, and Patagonia.
Economic uses: none.

This small family comprises a single genus of small creeping herbs.

Distribution. There is one species of *Tetrachondra* in New Zealand and another in Patagonia. This distribution illustrates the botanical affinities between Australasia and South America, seen also in other families such as the Winteraceae and Eucryphiaceae, and in the genus *Laurelia* (Monimiaceae).

Diagnostic features. In habit it is similar to *Crassula aquatica*. The leaves are simple, opposite and without stipules. The petioles connect across the stem, and are more or less fleshy with obscure glandular spotting. The stems root at the nodes. The flowers are bisexual, regular, solitary and terminal or axillary, with four fused sepals and four fused petals. There are four stamens which alternate with the petals and are inserted on the corolla. The ovary is superior, composed of four fused carpels, and is lobed to the base, from where the single gynobasic style arises. There is one erect ovule in each of the carpels. The fruits consist of four brown, one-seeded nutlets joined together at the base. The seeds have copious endosperm and a cylindrical embryo.

Classification. *Tetrachondra hamiltonii* occurs on North Island, New Zealand, in the Ruahine Range in wet open habitats such as damp meadow and carpeting river bottoms; *T. patagonica* occurs in South America.

The family is probably related to the Labiatae although *Tetrachondra* has been placed in the genus *Veronica* (Scrophulariaceae), in *Mentha* (Labiatae) and in the Boraginaceae by some authorities.

Economic uses. None are known. B.M.

CALLITRICHACEAE

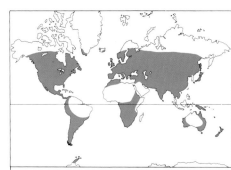

Number of genera: 1
Number of species: about 17
Distribution: cosmopolitan, centered in temperate zones.
Economic uses: none.

Most species in this family are submerged aquatics comprising one genus, *Callitriche*.

Distribution. *Callitriche* is almost cosmopolitan in occurrence, with most species found in the temperate zones of both hemispheres. Its distribution in the tropics is erratic: it is perhaps dispersed by migrating birds.

Diagnostic features. Some species are entirely submerged aquatics, with underwater pollination; others are amphibious; and a few are terrestrial with aerial pollination. All the species are small and delicate, annual or perennial herbs. The stems are usually erect above and creeping and rooting below. When submerged they are elongate and when emersed contracted. The leaves are decussate, but often rosette-forming at the tips of floating stems. The submerged leaves are usually linear and often have a forked apex. The floating or aerial leaves are linear, elliptic, oblong or spathulate. Stipules are absent.

The flowers are minute, unisexual and usually solitary or, rarely, one male and one female in the same leaf axil. There are no sepals or petals. The male flower consists of one stamen with a slender filament and an anther with two locules opening lengthwise, the slits joining at the top. The female flower consists of a single naked ovary with two elongate styles. The ovary has two carpels, each longitudinally divided into two locules. There is a single pendulous, anatropous ovule in each locule. The fruit is four-lobed, with each lobe winged or keeled. At maturity the fruit splits into four one-seeded nutlets. The seeds have a fleshy endosperm.

Classification. The relationships of the Callitrichaceae, like those of other reduced dicotyledonous aquatics, are disputed. The presence of four nutlets has often been cited as indicating a relationship to the Labiatae or Boraginaceae. In the latter families the septum is median but in the Callitrichaceae it is transverse. Most reduced dicotyledonous aquatics have single-seeded fruits so perhaps it is unwise to put too much stress on this character. In many ways *Callitriche* resembles the Tetrachondraceae.

Most species of *Callitriche* are very plastic in form, adapting to different conditions, and their identification is often very difficult.

Economic uses. *Callitriche* has no known economic use. Several species are very sensitive to specific pollutants. In southern Germany it is possible to predict the abundance of certain pollutants by the species composition and state of the *Callitriche* plants. C.D.C.

PHRYMACEAE

The Phrymaceae is a family of one genus of erect perennial herbs.

Distribution. The family is restricted to northeastern Asia and eastern North America.

Diagnostic features. The branches are quadrangular and bear simple, opposite, ovate leaves with coarsely toothed margins and without stipules.

The flowers are bisexual, irregular and borne in axillary or terminal spike-like racemes. The calyx is two-lipped, the upper with two and the lower with three lobes. There are five fused petals which also form a bilabiate structure, the lower lip of which is three-lobed and much larger than the upper

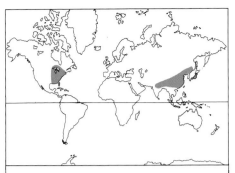

Number of genera: 1
Number of species: 1–3
Distribution: E N America and NE Asia
Economic uses: none.

two-lobed portion. There are four stamens (two longer than the rest) inserted above the middle of the corolla tube and projecting slightly beyond it. The ovary is superior, comprising a single carpel, and bears a terminal style with a forked stigma. There is a single erect ovule inserted at the base of the single locule. The fruit is enclosed by the persistent reflexed, ribbed calyx, and is a one-seeded nutlet with a membranous pericarp. The seed has no endosperm and the embryo is oblong with broad, folded cotyledons.

Classification. This family consists of a single genus (*Phryma*) and one, two or three species, depending on interpretation.

The family is closely related to the Verbenaceae. The main feature of distinction is the unilocular ovary containing a single ovule in *Phryma*. Otherwise, the two families are similar.

Economic uses. None are known. S.R.C.

PLANTAGINALES

PLANTAGINACEAE
Plantains

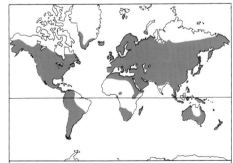

Number of genera: 3
Number of species: about 253
Distribution: temperate, and mountains in the tropics.
Economic uses: none.

The Plantaginaceae is a family of annual to perennial herbs. Most species belong to the genus *Plantago*, which has about 250 species.

Distribution. The family is widely distributed in temperate regions and on mountains in

the tropics. The bipolar temperate genus *Littorella* has two aquatic or shore species, while *Bougueria* has a single species (*Bougueria nubigena*) native to the Andes of southern Peru, Bolivia and northern Argentina.

Diagnostic features. The plants are herbaceous, but some have persistent woody stems. The entire or variously divided leaves are alternate, in basal rosettes or, rarely, opposite, with a basal sheath. They lack stipules. The flowers are small, usually bisexual and wind-pollinated, few or many in axillary spikes, rarely solitary. The calyx has four lobes which are usually imbricate. The corolla is scarious and regular, with a short tube and four lobes. There are four (rarely two or three) stamens alternating with the corolla lobes. The anthers are versatile, dehiscing inwards. The ovary is superior, of two fused carpels and two locules (rarely one), with one to several ovules on axile placentas in each locule. The style is solitary and the stigma simple. The fruit is a capsule with transverse (circumscissile) dehiscence, rarely indehiscent. The seed has a fleshy endosperm, and is mucilaginous when wet; the embryo is erect or curved.

Classification. *Plantago* has a dehiscent capsule with two to numerous seeds, while *Littorella* and *Bougueria* have indehiscent, single-seeded fruits, the former being aquatic or littoral herbs with separate male and female flowers, the latter small perennial herbs with bisexual flowers either alone or together with male and female flowers on the same plant.

The relationships of the family are not clear; it possesses affinities with the Polemoniaceae and allied families on the one hand and with the Scrophulariaceae and its relatives on the other.

Economic uses. The family has no economic value, except perhaps in a negative sense, since several species of *Plantago* are troublesome weeds. D.M.M.

SCROPHULARIALES

COLUMELLIACEAE

The Columelliaceae is a small family comprising a single genus, *Columellia*, with four species of evergreen trees and shrubs confined to the Andes of South America.

The leaves are opposite, simple and without stipules. The flowers are bisexual, slightly irregular and borne in terminal cymes. There are five sepals forming a five-lobed tube that is fused to the ovary, and the petals form a five-lobed corolla which is fused into a short tube. There are two stamens inserted near the base of the corolla and these alternate with the adaxial and lateral corolla lobes. The pollen sacs are contorted. The ovary is inferior, of two fused carpels and is imperfectly two-locular. There are numerous ovules on parietal placentas.

Myoporaceae. 1 *Myoporum viscosum* (a) shoot with flowers in leaf axils ($\times\frac{2}{3}$); (b) flower comprising a five-lobed fused calyx and corolla, four stamens and a simple style ($\times 1\frac{1}{3}$); (c) corolla opened out showing epipetalous stamens alternating with the corolla lobes ($\times 2$); (d) calyx and gynoecium ($\times 2\frac{2}{3}$); (e) fruit—a drupe ($\times 2$); (f) cross section of fruit ($\times 2$). 2 *Eremophila bignoniiflora* (a) shoot bearing linear leaves, flower with irregular two-lipped corolla, and fruits ($\times\frac{2}{3}$); (b) corolla opened out showing stamens of two lengths ($\times\frac{2}{3}$); (c) stamen with divergent anthers and longitudinal dehiscence ($\times 2$); (d) fruit ($\times\frac{2}{3}$); (e) vertical section of fruit ($\times\frac{2}{3}$). 3 *Stenochilus glaber* leafy shoot with flowers and fruits ($\times\frac{2}{3}$).

MYOPORACEAE
Emu Bushes

The Myoporaceae is a small family of chiefly trees and shrubs.

Distribution. The family is found mainly in Australia and the South Pacific area, with a few species scattered in South Africa, Mauritius, eastern Asia and the West Indies.

Diagnostic features. The leaves are alternate, rarely opposite, entire or toothed, without stipules and often glandular, scaly or woolly. The flowers are bisexual, usually irregular, axillary and either solitary or in cymose clusters. The calyx consists of five fused sepals, and the corolla of five fused petals forming a tube with five lobes. There are four stamens fused to the corolla tube and alternating with the lobes. The anther locules run into one another. The ovary is superior, of two fused carpels, forming two locules each with one to eight ovules, or three to ten locules by segmentation, each with only one ovule, these being pendulous. Placentation is axile. The style is simple. The fruit is a drupe, the seeds having little endosperm and a straight or slightly curved embryo.

Classification. *Myoporum* with about 32 species is the most widespread genus and the

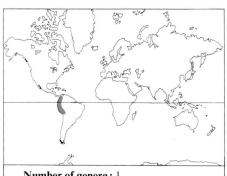

Number of genera: 1
Number of species: 4
Distribution: S America.
Economic uses: none.

The style is terminal with a two-lobed stigma. The fruits are capsular and contain numerous small seeds with fleshy endosperm and a tiny straight embryo. Perhaps the best-known species is *Columellia oblonga*, a small tree with silky downy shoots, oblong leaves and yellow flowers in terminal leafy clusters.

The affinities of this family are uncertain. It has been associated with the Gentianales and Rosales, but is here placed in the Scrophulariales. No economic uses for the family are known.   B.M.

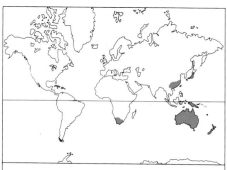

Number of genera: 4
Number of species: about 150
Distribution: mainly Australia and S Pacific area.
Economic uses: ornamentals and a few are useful timber trees.

type-genus of the family. In Australia, the genus consists of small trees or prostrate shrubs with alternate leaves, small creamy white to lavender flowers with a short corolla tube and a four- or five-lobed limb, and cream, yellow or purple drupes.

The emu bushes, *Eremophila*, are restricted to Australia. There are about 105 species. They differ from *Myoporum* in having more colorful flowers and tubular, often two-lipped, corollas. The 15 species of the closely related genus *Stenochilus* (here included in *Eremophila*) are also restricted to Australia.

Both species of *Oftia* are endemic to South Africa, the leaves of *Oftia africana* being flat, dentate and pubescent and those of *O. revoluta* having curled margins, but still dentate and pubescent. Both species have solitary, axillary, white flowers and globose drupes, and are placed in the Scrophulariaceae by some botanists.

The family is represented in the West Indies by *Bontia daphnoides*, the only species in its genus. It is a shrub or small tree with fleshy elliptical or lanceolate leaves, and solitary, rarely clustered, brownish-green flowers. The drupes are yellowish when mature. It is planted in places such as Barbados and Trinidad and is perhaps not native there but in northern South America.

The family is most closely related to the Scrophulariaceae and Gesneriaceae.

Economic uses. Creeping boobialla, *Myoporum parvifolium*, is a useful ground-cover plant in Australian gardens on account of its spreading prostrate habit. *Myoporum insulare*, a small tree with dense, bright green foliage which is fire- and wind-resistant, and *M. floribundum*, an aromatic shrub with narrow drooping leaves. *Eremophila* species have great horticultural potential in areas with hot, dry soils.

Several species, notably *Eremophila mitchelli* and *Myoporum sandwicense*, provide useful timber. B.M.

SCROPHULARIACEAE
The Foxglove Family

The Scrophulariaceae is a large family consisting mainly of north temperate herbs and a few shrubs and lianas. *Paulownia* is the sole tree genus. Some of the herbaceous genera are semiparasitic, taking part of their nourishment from the roots of their host plants, most frequently members of the Gramineae. Several genera provide attractive garden ornamentals.

Distribution. The Scrophulariaceae is a cosmopolitan family, most of the larger genera, eg *Pedicularis* (500 species), *Penstemon* (250 species), *Verbascum* (360 species), *Linaria* (150 species), *Mimulus* (100 species), *Veronica* (300 species), *Castilleja* (200 species), being mainly north temperate while *Hebe* (130 species) and *Calceolaria* (350 species) are southern genera from Australasia and South America respectively. As there are no large trees in the family, it is relatively poorly represented in densely forested regions of the world.

Diagnostic features. The leaves are usually alternate or opposite, and are evergreen in *Hebe*; they are without stipules, and both simple and pinnately lobed or incised shapes are represented. The inflorescence is racemose or cymose, and great variation can

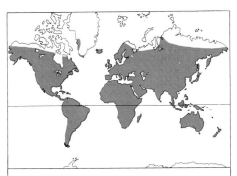

Number of genera: about 220
Number of species: about 3,000
Distribution: cosmopolitan, mainly north temperate.
Economic uses: the cardiac drugs digitalin and digoxin from the common foxglove; many ornamental garden genera, including *Antirrhinum, Veronica, Calceolaria, Penstemon, Mimulus* and *Verbascum*.

occur even within genera, as, indeed, can the size and shape of the bracts and bracteoles which reach their most spectacular in *Castilleja* where they are often brightly colored. The flowers are bisexual and usually irregular, sometimes markedly so as in the spurred *Linaria*; they are almost regular in some species of *Verbascum*. The most usual pattern is exemplified by *Antirrhinum*: the calyx is five-lobed, the corolla is five-lobed and two-lipped. The four stamens, two of which are longer than the others, are attached to the petals. The two-locular, introrse anthers split longitudinally by slits. There is a nectar-secreting disk at the base of the ovary, which is superior and consists of two united carpels and two locules aligned in the median plane. Numerous anatropous ovules occur on axile placentas in each locule. The style is single, often bilobed.

Numerous modifications to floral structure have occurred, some reflected in "reduction series" of floral parts, whereby organs exhibit several lower numbers than the assumed fundamental number – in this case five, at least for sepals, petals and stamens. *Verbascum* and *Capraria* have five fertile stamens, *Scrophularia* and *Penstemon* have four fertile stamens with a sterile staminode replacing the fifth posterior one, *Castilleja* and many species of *Linaria* have four with no staminode, *Stemotria* has three and *Calceolaria* and *Veronica* have two. Greatest reduction in combined floral parts is exhibited by *Veronica* and *Hebe* with four sepals, four petals and two stamens.

Further variation in floral structure, particularly corolla shape, reflects the evolution of specialized insect-pollination mechanisms. The commonest situation appears to be dichogamy, as in *Scrophularia*, where the ovule comes to maturity before the anthers. Cross-pollination is also encouraged in many species by the stigma extending beyond the anthers, so that the visiting insect

carrying pollen from another plant touches it first. In *Scrophularia* the female flowers have a relatively short style and are visited by wasps; an open flower with a relatively short tube in *Verbascum* and *Veronica* is suited to flies and bees, while a long tube with anthers and stigma arranged so as to touch the back of the visiting bee is exemplified by *Digitalis* and *Linaria*. *Pedicularis* and *Euphrasia* have "loose pollen" and spiny anthers which are protected by the upper lip of the corolla and shake the pollen on to the pollinator as it lands on the lower lip.

The fruit is usually a dry capsule with various types of dehiscence, depending on the position and plane of the split, and is rarely indehiscent, in which case it can be dry or succulent; the seeds may also be dispersed through pores. The seeds have endosperm and are smooth or have a variously and often intricately sculptured surface, and are sometimes angled or winged. The embryo is straight or slightly curved.

Classification. The family is usually divided into three subfamilies, based on the vernation of the corolla lobes and on the arrangement of leaves.

VERBASCOIDEAE (Pseudosolaneae). Two tribes and about 10 genera, which have the two posterior corolla lobes (equivalent to the upper lip) overlapping the lateral lobes in bud, and all the leaves alternate. There are often five stamens. The best-known genus is *Verbascum* (mullein).

SCROPHULARIOIDEAE (Antirrhinoideae). Seven tribes and over 100 genera, which have the lobes similarly overlapping, but at least the lower leaves are opposite, and the fifth stamen is staminodial or absent. This subfamily contains such well-known genera as *Calceolaria, Linaria, Antirrhinum, Scrophularia, Penstemon* and *Mimulus*. The tribe Selagineae, with up to eight genera, and with a single seed per locule, is sometimes considered as a separate subfamily or even family, the Selaginaceae, and has strong affinities with the Globulariaceae.

RHINANTHOIDEAE. Three tribes and over 100 genera, which differ from the other subfamilies in their vernation: the two posterior corolla lobes are overlapped by one or both of the lateral lobes in bud. This group includes *Veronica* and *Hebe* (always classified together because of their similarity in floral structure), *Digitalis* and the many semiparasitic genera of the family (such as *Castilleja, Euphrasia, Melampyrum, Odontites, Pedicularis, Rhinanthus,* and *Striga*).

The fused corolla and superior ovary of two fused carpels have led to the Scrophulariaceae being classified with a group of families of superficial resemblance often termed the Tubiflorae. The best-known of these are the Orobanchaceae, Gesneriaceae, Bignoniaceae and Acanthaceae. Some members of the Solanaceae are readily separable from the Scrophulariaceae only on the alignment of the ovary.

Globulariaceae. 1 *Globularia trichosantha* (a) leafy shoot with an erect capitulate inflorescence ($\times\frac{2}{3}$); (b) lower deeply three-lobed portion of corolla with four epipetalous stamens ($\times6$); (c) upper petal ($\times6$); (d) calyx opened out and gynoecium ($\times6$). 2 *G. salicina* flowering shoot ($\times\frac{2}{3}$). 3 *Poskea socotrana* (a) flowering shoot ($\times\frac{2}{3}$); (b) corolla opened out showing five petal lobes, four epipetalous stamens and ovary with a single style crowned by a forked stigma ($\times16$).

Economic uses. This large family is of limited economic use. Perhaps the best-known application are the drugs digitalin and digoxin extracted from certain species of *Digitalis*. Many genera are well known as garden ornamentals, such as species of *Antirrhinum* (snapdragons), *Veronica* (speedwells), *Hebe*, *Calceolaria* (slipper flowers), *Penstemon* (beard tongues), *Mimulus* (monkey flower), *Digitalis* (foxglove) and

Scrophulariaceae. 1 *Erinus alpinus* habit showing rosette of leaves and terminal inflorescence of irregular flowers ($\times\frac{2}{3}$). 2 *Verbascum betonicefolium* shoot with alternate leaves and inflorescence of irregular flowers ($\times\frac{2}{3}$). 3 *Rhinanthus minor* shoot with opposite leaves and inflorescence ($\times\frac{2}{3}$). 4 *Linaria vulgaris* (a) shoot with linear leaves and inflorescence ($\times\frac{2}{3}$); (b) half flower with spurred corolla and stamens of two lengths ($\times3$). 5 *Digitalis obscura* leafy shoot and inflorescence ($\times\frac{2}{3}$). 6 *Veronica fruticans* leafy shoot and inflorescence ($\times\frac{2}{3}$). 7 *Scrophularia macrantha* (a) lower lip of corolla opened out showing four stamens with anthers linked in pairs and a central, small staminode ($\times4\frac{2}{3}$); (b) cross section of ovary showing two locules and axile placentas ($\times6$). 8 *Sibthorpia europaea* dehiscing fruit—a capsule ($\times10$). 9 *Penstemon lyallii* leafy shoot with irregular flowers and young fruits ($\times\frac{2}{3}$).

Nemesia. Other cultivated genera include *Collinsia*, *Cymbalaria*, *Nierembergia*, *Torenia*, *Verbascum* and *Wulfenia*.

Some species, particularly semiparasites in subfamily Rhinanthoideae, are serious weeds, principally of cereal crops: *Rhinanthus minor* (yellow rattle) and *Pedicularis palustris* (lousewort) are common in north temperate regions, while *Centranthera humifusa* parasitizes grasses and sedges in India. The most destructive members of the family occur in the tropical genus *Striga* (witchweeds); they are root parasites with no root hairs and thus rely entirely on the host plant for water and mineral nutrition; *S. orobanchoides* can flower and seed entirely below ground.   I.B.K.R.

GLOBULARIACEAE

The Globulariaceae is a small family of two genera, *Globularia* with about 28 species and *Poskea* with two.

Distribution. The family is endemic to the Mediterranean region in a wide sense, with species in Macaronesia, Socotra, Somalia, northern Europe and the Alps as well as the Mediterranean basin. *Poskea* is endemic to Socotra and Somalia.

Diagnostic features. All members of the

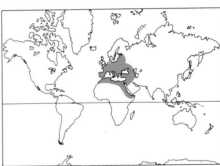

Number of genera: 2
Number of species: about 30
Distribution: Mediterranean, extending to Macaronesia, Socotra, Somalia, N Europe and the Alps.
Economic uses: rock garden ornamentals.

Globulariaceae are herbaceous or shrubby perennials with alternate, entire, smooth leaves without stipules. The flower heads are capitulate and surrounded by an involucre. They are arranged in paniculate (*Globularia*) or spicate (*Poskea*) inflorescences. The flowers are bisexual and somewhat irregular. The calyx is tubular and five-lobed, and the corolla of five fused petals is two-lipped with the upper lip two-lobed and the lower three-lobed. There are four stamens inserted on the upper part of the corolla tube. The anthers have a single locule and open by means of a single longitudinal slit. The ovary is superior, of one free carpel and one locule, with a single anatropous, pendulous ovule. There is a single style. The fruit is a one-seeded achene enclosed in the calyx. The seed has endosperm and a straight embryo.

Classification. The family Globulariaceae has been considered by some authorities to be related to the Scrophulariaceae, particularly to the southern African tribe Selagineae with which it has sometimes been united into a single family. Hutchinson, however, chooses to include the Globulariaceae within his order Lamiales, comprising the Labiatae, Myoporaceae, Globulariaceae and Selaginaceae (ie the Selagineae detached from the Scrophulariaceae). Recent pollen evidence, however, generally supports a close relationship between the Scrophulariaceae and the Globulariaceae and suggests that the latter family should be kept within the Scrophulariales. Globulariaceous pollen grains are isopolar and three-colporate with compound apertures; similar grains are found in some genera of Scrophulariaceae, but not in the Lamiales.

Economic uses. The family has no major economic use. A few species of the genus *Globularia* are occasionally cultivated as ornamental rock-garden plants.

D.B.

GESNERIACEAE
African Violets and Gloxinias

The Gesneriaceae is a large family comprising mostly tropical herbs and shrubs. It includes many popular cultivated ornamentals, the best-known being the gloxinias and African violets.

Distribution. The 125 genera and 2,000 or so species are mostly pantropical, but some are temperate, in the Americas from Mexico to Chile, East, West and South Africa, Madagascar, Southeast Asia, Polynesia, Australasia, China, Japan and southern Europe.

Diagnostic features. Gesneriads are often regarded as tropical counterparts of the essentially temperate family Scrophulariaceae, and are herbs and shrubs, rarely trees, with opposite or alternate, sometimes basal leaves (rarely a single leaf), which are simple, entire or toothed (rarely pinnatisect), and without stipules. The underground parts may be fibrous woody tubers, scaly rhizomes or aerial stolons. The flowers are bisexual, irregular and borne in racemes, cymes or singly. There are five sepals, usually tubular at the base, with five petals also fused into a basal tube, the free ends being oblique, two-lipped or rarely rotate. The two or four stamens often cohere in pairs and release pollen by longitudinal slits. The ovary is superior or inferior and has a single locule containing numerous ovules, usually on two

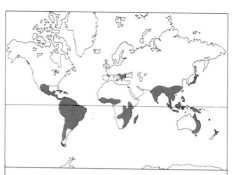

Number of genera: about 125
Number of species: about 2,000
Distribution: pantropical with some temperate species.
Economic uses: many popular cultivated ornamentals, including African violets and gloxinias.

parietal or intrusive placentas. The style is single, crowned with a two-lobed or mouth-shaped stigma. An annular, lobed or one-sided nectary lies between the ovary and petals. The fruits are rounded or elongated capsules or rarely berries, and contain many small seeds, with or without endosperm, and with straight embryos.

Evolution of about half of the New World gesneriads has been partly by co-adaptation with bird pollinators, notably the hummingbird family which is restricted to the Americas. Typical hummingbird flowers are two-lipped, often red as in *Columnea*, *Asteranthera* and some *Sinningia* species. Other pollinators such as bees, bats, butterflies, moths and flies have also been active in gesneriad evolution. In *Hypocyrta*, *Besleria* and *Alloplectus* some species have pouched corollas with constricted throats, the significance of which is still not clear. The Old World genus *Aeschyanthus* is considered a parallel development with *Columnea* in being bird-pollinated. Flowers are an important part of the pollination system in gesneriads but extra-floral attraction also exists in some species, such as strikingly colored leaf- and sepal-hairs, or leaf pigmentation with stained-glass-like optical properties when viewed against the light.

Classification. Notable New World genera include *Columnea*, 250 species of shrubs and climbers, often epiphytic; *Sinningia*, 60 species of herbs, some popularly known as gloxinias; *Achimenes*, 20 species of often hairy herbs with red to blue flowers; *Episcia*, 10 species of small trailing evergreens; *Gesneria* (46 species) and *Rhytidophyllum* (20 species), two related genera with yellow-green, white or red flowers; *Gloxinia* (not to be confused with the popular gloxinias), 15 species of herbs with lilac bell-flowers or cinnabar-red pouch flowers; *Smithiantha*, four Mexican species with green or purple-brown velvety leaves and pyramids of orange-red or yellowish tubular flowers; *Phinaea*, 10 species with whitish flowers; *Kohleria*, 20 species often with racemes of orange-red flowers

patterned inside with contrasting spots and with brown-green velvety hairy leaves.

Notable Old World genera include *Ramonda*, three species of stemless, hairy herbs from southern Europe with showy flowers on leafless scapes; *Saintpaulia*, 12 East African species mostly of rosette herbs; *Aeschyanthus*, 70 species of trailing or climbing shrubs from the Far East; *Streptocarpus*, 130 African species of evergreen herbs often with foxglove-like flowers; *Cyrtandra*, 350 species from Southeast Asia and Oceania; *Jankaea* (one species) and *Haberlea* (one species), rosette alpines with lilac or violet flowers native to southern Europe; *Chirita*, 80 species of tropical Asian herbs with fleshy, often transparent parts and large whitish, blue, purplish or yellow clustered flowers; *Titanotrichum*, with a single species from China and Taiwan, with tubular flowers bright yellow outside, blotched red-brown with a narrow yellow margin inside; *Conandron*, three Japanese species of alpine rosette herbs regarded as the counterpart of *Ramonda*; *Petrocosmea*, 15 species from Southeast Asia similar to *Saintpaulia*.

About half the genera are placed in the Old World subfamily Cyrtandroideae, with cotyledons of unequal length, unlike the New World Gesnerioideae with equal cotyledons. This division is supported by data from pigment chemistry and chromosome number patterns. Each subfamily is divided into tribes as follows, with representative genera given in parentheses.

CYRTANDROIDEAE: CYRTANDREAE (*Cyrtandra*), TRICHOSPOREAE (*Trichosporum* = *Aeschyanthus*), KLUGIEAE (*Rhynchoglossum*), LOXONIEAE (*Loxonia*), DIDYMOCARPEAE (*Ramonda*, *Chirita*, *Streptocarpus*).

GESNERIOIDEAE: GESNERIEAE (*Gesneria*), GLOXINIEAE (*Achimenes*, *Sinningia*), EPISCIEAE (*Episcia*, *Columnea*), BESLERIEAE (*Besleria*), NAPEANTHEAE (*Napeanthus*), CORONANTHEREAE (*Asteranthera*, *Mitraria*, *Sarmienta*).

The temperate Andean genera *Asteranthera*, *Mitraria* and *Sarmienta*, all climbers with red flowers, and *Rhabdothamnus*, a shrubby New Zealand genus with attractive red-striped yellow flowers, do not easily fit

Gesneriaceae. 1 *Chrysothemis pulchella* shoot with opposite leaves and inflorescences ($\times \frac{2}{3}$). 2 *Aeschyanthus microtrichus*, fruit—an elongate capsule ($\times \frac{2}{3}$). 3 *Columnea crassifolia* shoot with alternate leaves and solitary, two-lipped flower ($\times \frac{2}{3}$). 4 *Ramonda myconi* basal rosette of leaves and inflorescences ($\times \frac{2}{3}$). 5 *Gesneria cuneifolia* (a) basal rosette of leaves and solitary flowers ($\times \frac{2}{3}$); (b) flower with part of calyx and corolla cut away to show two stamens with anthers cohering together ($\times 2$). 6 *Aeschyanthus pulcher* flowering shoot ($\times \frac{2}{3}$). 7 *Streptocarpus caulescens* leafy shoot and inflorescences ($\times \frac{2}{3}$). 8 *Aeschyanthus pulcher* half flower showing corolla tube constricted at the base, four-lobed ovary crowned by a long style and stamens with curved filaments ($\times 1$).

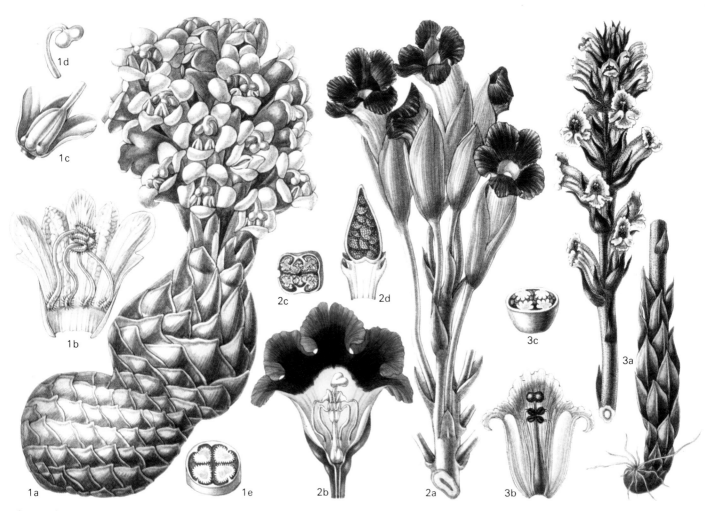

Orobanchaceae. 1 *Cistanche violacea* (a) habit showing swollen underground organ and flower spike ($\times\frac{2}{3}$); (b) flower opened out showing linked anthers ($\times 1$); (c) ovary and sepals ($\times 1$); (d) bilobed stigma ($\times 1$); (e) cross section of unilocular ovary ($\times 2$). 2 *Aeginetia pedunculata* (a) inflorescence ($\times\frac{2}{3}$); (b) flower opened out ($\times 1\frac{1}{2}$); (c) cross section of ovary ($\times 4$); (d) vertical section of ovary ($\times 4$). 3 *Orobanche major* (a) habit showing single, erect, stem with scale leaves, and terminating in a flower spike ($\times\frac{2}{3}$); (b) flower opened out showing stamens of two lengths with anthers linked in pairs ($\times 1\frac{1}{2}$); (c) section of ovary ($\times 5$).

into either Old or New World subfamilies, and their own subfamily MITRARIOIDEAE has been proposed by certain botanists.

Herbaceous families related to the Gesneriaceae are the Scrophulariaceae, Orobanchaceae, and Lentibulariaceae; the chiefly woody Bignoniaceae is also florally similar but has woody fruits that often have two locules, and winged seeds, as well as divided leaves. The gesneriad ovary may be superior, as in Scrophulariaceae, or inferior, but in contrast to the Scrophulariaceae the ovary usually has a single locule not two. The usually parietal placentas of gesneriads with superior ovaries differ from the basal placentas of butterworts (Lentibulariaceae). Orobanches are parasites and lack chlorophyll, so also differ from gesneriads.

Economic uses. Some species have been reported as being used in rural medicine, but the importance of the family lies in its cultivated ornamentals. Popular garden and house-plant genera include *Achimenes, Columnea, Episcia, Gesneria, Haberlea, Hypocyrta, Kohleria, Mitraria, Ramonda, Saintpaulia* (African violet), *Sinningia* (gloxinias), *Smithiantha, Streptocarpus* (Cape primrose) and *Aeschynanthus*.   B.M.

OROBANCHACEAE
Broomrapes and Toothworts

The Orobanchaceae is a family of total parasites almost completely lacking green coloration.

Distribution. The family is chiefly north temperate Eurasian. The largest genus, *Orobanche*, the broomrapes, with about 140 species, is quite common throughout temperate Eurasia. Elsewhere in the world the family is not at all well represented; there are a few tropical and American species.

Diagnostic features. Almost all the species are rooted in the soil, but few have any extensive rooting system. Instead there is either a congested mass of short, thick roots or a large, single or complex swollen organ. At one or more points on this underground structure there are connections, via swollen, clamp-like haustoria, with the root of the host plant, from which virtually all the nourishment of the parasite is obtained. Above the ground there is often a single erect stem bearing brownish scale leaves, terminating in the flower spike. The plants are mostly annuals, but some are perennial and in *Lathraea squamaria* there is a rhizome bearing fleshy, whitish scale leaves resembl-

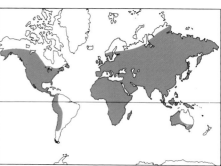

Number of genera: about 14
Number of species: about 180
Distribution: mainly temperate Eurasia.
Economic uses: none.

ing a set of dentures and giving the plant its common name of toothwort.

The flowers are irregular, bisexual and arranged in racemes or spikes. The calyx comprises two to five fused sepals forming a two- to five-toothed tube. The corolla is two-lipped, comprising five fused petals. There are four stamens (two of which are longer than the others) inserted below the middle of the corolla tube and alternating with the lobes.

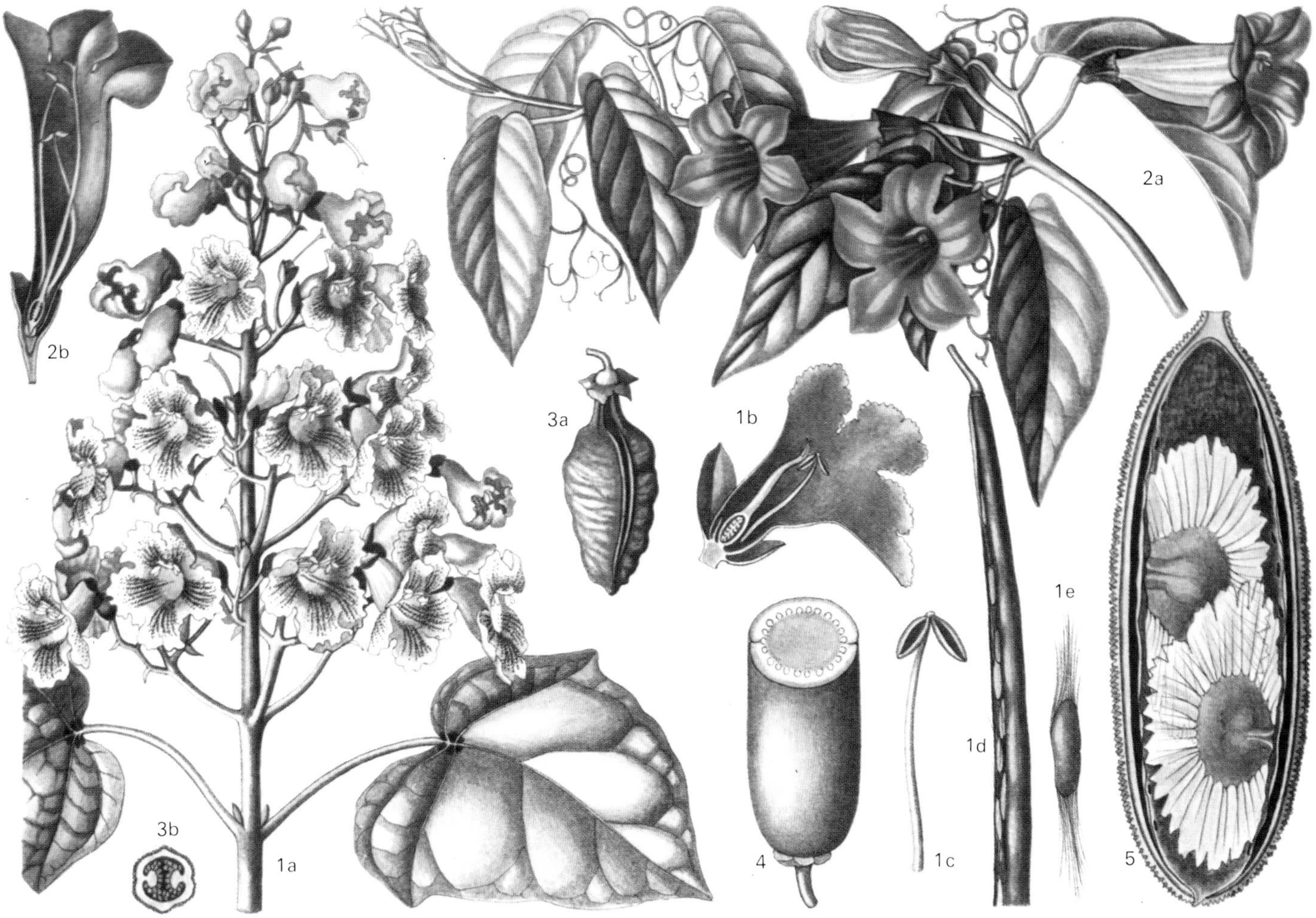

Bignoniaceae. 1 *Catalpa ovata* (a) shoot bearing flowers in a terminal panicle and simple opposite leaves ($\times\frac{2}{3}$); (b) half flower with fertile and infertile stamens ($\times 1\frac{1}{3}$); (c) stamen with divergent anthers ($\times 2\frac{2}{3}$); (d) part of fruit ($\times\frac{2}{3}$); (e) seed bearing tufts of hair ($\times 1\frac{1}{3}$). 2 *Bignonia capreolata* (a) flowering shoot with compound leaves in which the terminal leaflet is tendril-like ($\times\frac{2}{3}$); (b) half flower with all stamens fertile ($\times 1$). 3 *Eccremocarpus scaber* (a) dehiscing fruit ($\times\frac{2}{3}$); (b) cross section of ovary ($\times 5$). 4 *Parmentiera cereifera* base of fleshy indehiscent fruit in cross section showing numerous seeds ($\times\frac{2}{3}$). 5 *Pithecoctenium aubletii* vertical section of fruit ($\times\frac{2}{3}$).

A fifth stamen is either a staminode or absent altogether. The anthers open lengthwise. The ovary is superior, comprising two or rarely three fused carpels and a single locule with four parietal placentas bearing numerous ovules. The style is single. The fruit is a capsule opening by two valves, and the small, very numerous seeds have a fleshy endosperm and a minute embryo.

Some species are confined to a particular host, some to a related range (eg a family) of hosts, while others are more catholic. It is possible that in the last case there are different strains within the species which are adapted for parasitizing different species of host. This has not been substantiated, owing both to the difficulty often experienced in germinating the seeds experimentally and to the difficulty in tracing subterranean connections between the parasite and host roots in mixed vegetation.

The seeds of broomrapes (*Orobanche*) and most other genera are very small and light, but those of the toothworts are substantially larger. Since many of the broomrapes are annuals, the development of small, light seeds appears to be an adaptation allowing for large numbers to be produced, thus increasing the chances of some finding a suitable host plant. These seeds are very effectively spread by wind.

Classification. The family is very closely related to the Scrophulariaceae, many members of which are semiparasitic and with which it shares almost all its floral features. There is, in fact, no clear-cut difference between the two families, and there seems to be much in favor of uniting them. Indeed, some genera, including the toothworts (*Lathraea*), appear variously in one family or the other according to the judgment of different authors.

Economic uses. The family is of no economic importance except that in warm temperate climates some species may be serious pests of crop plants. In the Mediterranean region, for example, *Orobanche crenata* often infects fields of beans and peas and considerably decreases the yield. C.A.S.

BIGNONIACEAE

Catalpa

The Bignoniaceae is a family of trees and shrubs, the majority of which are lianas.

Distribution. The family is mainly tropical, and primarily centered in northern South America, with relatively few genera elsewhere. *Catalpa* and *Campsis*, from Southeast Asia, are also present in the New World.

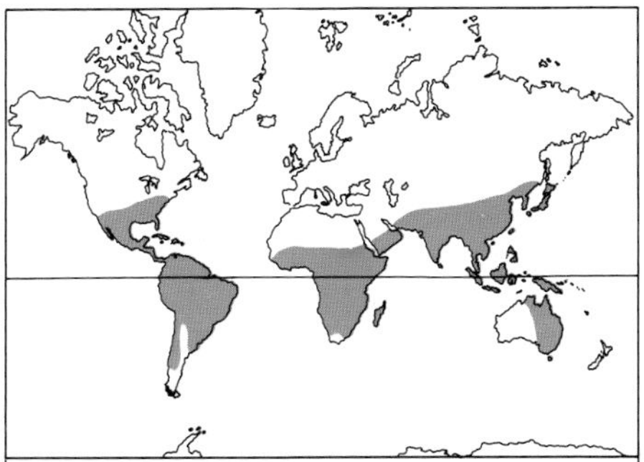

Number of genera: about 120
Number of species: about 650
Distribution: mainly tropical, centered on S America.
Economic uses: timber and many cultivated ornamentals.

Diagnostic features. Except for a few genera such as *Incarvillea*, the species of this family are nearly all woody, usually adapted in one way or another to climbing in the humid forests where they abound; often they have

Acanthaceae. 1 *Acanthus longifolius* (a) leaf, stem and terminal inflorescence ($\times\frac{2}{3}$); (b) flower with part of corolla cut away to show four stamens ($\times$1); (c) ovary entire and in cross section ($\times$1). 2 *Thunbergia grandiflora* flowering shoot ($\times$1). 3 *Reullia dipterocanthus* (a) corolla opened out to show epipetalous stamens ($\times$1); (b) calyx and gynoecium ($\times$1). 4 *Beloperone guttata* leaf and flower opened out showing two stamens with a broad connective ($\times$2). 5 *Justicia* sp flower opened out ($\times$3). 6 *Justicia patentiflora* vertical section of ovary with ovules on axile placentas ($\times$9).

twining stems, and frequently the terminal leaflet of pinnately-leaved species is modified into a tendril. The leaves are usually opposite, decussate, without stipules, and are usually compound; glands are often present at the base of the petiole. The showy flowers are clustered usually in a cymose arrangement, with relatively inconspicuous bracts and bracteoles; the calyx tube usually bears five lobes and is sometimes two-lipped; the larger, bell- or funnel-shaped corolla shows the same basic structure, and has four epipetalous stamens arched under the upper lip, holding the anthers in readiness for a suitable pollinating agent. Sometimes the number of stamens is reduced to two (eg *Catalpa*); often the missing stamens (assuming five to be the basic number, to agree with the number of calyx- and corolla-lobes) are represented as staminodes, as in the Scrophulariaceae. The two anther locules of each stamen are characteristically divergent, and dehisce by longitudinal slits. The single, superior ovary, with a longish style and two-lobed stigma, bears a nectariferous disk, and is composed of two fused carpels, usually bilocular with axile placentation, occasionally (eg *Eccremocarpus*) unilocular with two forked parietal placentas. The

ovules are numerous, anatropous, and usually develop into flat, winged seeds in a septicidal or loculicidal capsule. A few genera (eg *Kigelia*) have an indehiscent, fleshy fruit with unwinged seeds. The seeds have no endosperm and a straight embryo.

Classification. The family is usually divided into about five tribes, mostly on the basis of ovary structure, along with fruit and seed characters. It is closely related to the Scrophulariaceae.

Economic uses. The family is of some importance both for timber and for its ornamental species. *Tabebuia* (West Indian boxwood) and *Catalpa* (useful as a fencepost material) are the most commonly exploited timbers. Many genera provide often spectacular ornamental trees, particularly in the tropics: examples are *Spathodea*, *Kigelia* (the sausage tree), *Tabebuia* (the poui, gold tree or araguaney – the Venezuelan national tree), *Crescentia* (calabash tree) and *Jacaranda*. Climbers such as *Campsis* (trumpet vine), *Bignonia* and *Eccremocarpus* species are popular, as are the tender vines *Doxantha unguiscati* (cat's-claw), *Tecomaria* (Cape honeysuckle), *Pandorea* (Australian bower plant) and *Pyrostegia*. I.B.K.R.

ACANTHACEAE
Black-eyed Susan and Sea Holly

Number of genera: about 250
Number of species: about 2,500
Distribution: cosmopolitan, but centered in tropics.
Economic uses: mainly cultivated as ornamentals (*Aphelandra*, black-eyed Susan) with limited local medicinal uses.

The Acanthaceae is a family consisting mainly of tropical shrubs, but including some temperate species of which the best known is *Acanthus*, whose leaves are said to have provided the motif of the Corinthian capitals in classical Greek temples.

Distribution. There are about 250 genera and over 2,000 species mainly native to the tropics, although some extend into temperate regions. The main centers of distribution are Indomalaysia, Africa, Brazil and Central America.

Diagnostic features. Most species are shrubby or herbaceous, but there are a few trees. Drought-resisting, semi-aquatic and climbing habits are also found in this family. The leaves are opposite and decussate, simple, without stipules, and often have cystoliths which show up as streaks on the lamina.

The flowers are bisexual, usually irregular or two-lipped, solitary or arranged in cymes or racemes. The bracts and bracteoles subtending the individual flowers are often large and petaloid, enclosing the flower. There are four or five sepals and the same number of fused petals. There are two or four stamens attached to the petals, and sometimes one or more staminodes, Sometimes, one of the anther locules on the stamen is much smaller than the other. The ovary is superior, of two fused carpels forming two locules each with two to numerous ovules on axile placentas. The style is simple, usually long with two stigmas. The ovary ripens into a capsule in which the seeds are usually borne on small hook-like outgrowths. The seeds have no endosperm and usually large embryos. The testa of some genera (eg *Crossandra* and *Blepharis*) is covered with hairs or scales which become sticky or slimy on wetting.

Classification. The genera can be separated on a range of characters, including the size and nature of the bracts, form of the corolla, number and form of the stamens and staminodes, and the number of ovules in the ovary. For example, *Acanthus*, *Aphelandra*, *Crossandra* and *Thunbergia* all possess flowers with four stamens, while those of *Sanchezia*, *Eranthemum*, *Mackaya*, and *Odontonema* contain only two stamens. The latter two genera have inflorescences with small and inconspicuous bracts. *Filtonia* and *Graptophyllum* both have flowers with markedly two-lipped corollas, the latter possessing staminodes in addition to the stamens.

This family is closely related to the Scrophulariaceae. The irregular, five-part flowers, with reductions in stamen numbers and a bicarpellate superior ovary are common features to both families.

Economic uses. A number of the Acanthaceae are cultivated as ornamentals. For example *Aphelandra squarrosa*, native to Brazil, is a popular plant with its tubular yellow flowers and conspicuous bracts. *Crossandra*, a genus of about 50 species, includes a few suitable for greenhouse cultivation. *Crossandra nilotica* produces large showy red flowers over a period of about six weeks. *Thunbergia* produces several popular climbing plants, notably *Thunbergia alata* (black-eyed Susan). Some species of *Barleria*, *Beloperone*, *Eranthemum* and *Justicia* are also cultivated.

Some species of *Acanthus* are used medicinally. An extract of the boiled leaves of *Acanthus ebracteatus* (sea holly) is used as a cough medicine in parts of Malaya, while the roots of *A. mollis* (bear's breech) are used to treat diarrhoea in some parts of Europe. The leaves and flowers of *Blechum pyramidatum* are used as a diuretic and for the treatment of coughs and fevers in some parts of Central and South America.   S.R.C.

PEDALIACEAE
Sesame

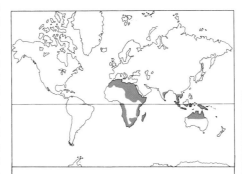

Number of genera: 12
Number of species: about 50
Distribution: dry and shore areas of Africa, Madagascar, Indomalaysia and Australia.
Economic uses: sesame seeds and oil, and occasional uses as vegetables.

The Pedaliaceae is a family of annual or perennial herbs and some shrubs.

Distribution. Members of the family are found in Africa, Madagascar, Indomalaysia and Australia, chiefly in desert or seashore habitats.

Diagnostic features. The leaves are opposite, or the uppermost may be alternate. They are simple, entire or lobed, without stipules, and often possess glandular hairs. The flowers are usually solitary, or borne in few-flowered axillary cymose clusters, with glands at the base of the stalks. They are bisexual and irregular with a calyx of five connate sepals and a tubular corolla of five fused petals. Apart from *Trapella*, which has two stamens, the androecium consists of four fertile epipetalous stamens two of which are longer than the rest; the fifth (posterior) stamen is replaced by a small staminode. The anthers are often contiguous in pairs and have two locules with longitudinal dehiscence. The ovary is superior and normally consists of two fused carpels bearing a long style with two stigmas. The ovary has two to four locules with one to numerous ovules borne on axile placentas. The fruit is a capsule or nut, often with hooks as in the South African *Harpagophytum procumbens* (the grapple plant). The seeds have a straight embryo and thin endosperm.

Classification. The chief genera are *Pedalium* one species), *Sesamum* (30 species), *Ceratotheca* (15 species), *Harpagophytum* (eight species) and *Uncarina* (five species). The family is related to the Martyniaceae and the Bignoniaceae.

Economic uses. The most important species economically is sesame (*Sesamum indicum*), an annual herb native to tropical Asia but widely cultivated, especially in India, for its seeds, which are used to coat bread and confections and from which sesame oil is expressed. The oil is used for cooking and in the manufacture of soap and margarine, and the residue is used for cattle feed. The seeds of *S. angustifolium* are used for similar purposes. The leaves of a number of African species, notably *Ceratotheca sesamoides* and *Pedalium murex*, are used as vegetables.
                    S.R.C.

HYDROSTACHYDACEAE

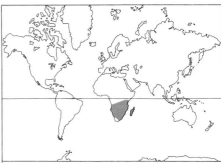

Number of genera: 1
Number of species: 22
Distribution: southern Africa and Madagascar, but most species in Madagascar.
Economic uses: none.

The Hydrostachydaceae is a small family of submerged freshwater aquatic herbs consisting of a single genus, *Hydrostachys*, with about 22 species.

Distribution. Most of the species are endemic to Madagascar. A few species are found in southern Africa from Tanzania and Zaire southwards to South Africa.

Diagnostic features. The plants are found attached to rocks and stones in flowing water. They come into flower as the water level drops. The roots are closely attached to rocks. The stems are flat and disk-shaped or thick and tuber-like. The leaves develop in tufts and have scales at the base. These scales probably represent intrapetiolar stipules. The leaves are very variable in shape, not only within the family but often within species. They are elongate and vary from simple to three times pinnate. The ultimate leaf segments are usually linear but occasionally scale-like. The compound leaves have been frequently misinterpreted as branched stems, particularly when the leaflets bear stipule-like scales at their bases. The flowers are unisexual (male and female on separate plants), and are borne in dense spikes which emerge above the surface of the

Martyniaceae. 1 *Proboscidea fragrans* leafy shoot covered with hairs and bearing irregular flowers in a terminal raceme ($\times\frac{2}{3}$). 2 *Proboscidea louisianica* half flower showing stamens of two lengths ($\times 1$). 3 *Martynia annua* (a) flowering shoot ($\times\frac{2}{3}$); (b) part of corolla with two fertile stamens with united anthers and two staminodes ($\times 2$); (c) young fruit ($\times\frac{2}{3}$). 4 *Martynia lutea* (a) cross section of ovary showing T-shaped parietal placentas ($\times 4$); (b) gynoecium ($\times 1$); (c) fruit (a capsule) showing horns that aid dispersal by animals ($\times\frac{2}{3}$).

water, each flower being borne in the axil of a bract. Sepals and petals are lacking. The male flower is reduced to a single stamen, while the female flower is reduced to a single ovary with two divergent styles. The ovary is superior, of two fused carpels and one locule containing numerous ovules borne on two parietal placentas. The fruit is a capsule opening by two equal valves. The seeds have no endosperm.

Classification. In habit the Hydrostachydaceae closely resembles the Podostemaceae and in many works these two families are considered to be related. Recent morphological and embryological work has shown that the Hydrostachydaceae should be assigned to the group of orders Polemoniales – Lamiales – Plantaginales – Scrophulariales (the Tubiflorae), and that they are probably closely allied to the Solanaceae and Plantaginaceae.

Economic uses. None are known.   C.D.C.

MARTYNIACEAE
Unicorn Plant

The Martyniaceae is a small family of herbs containing only three genera and about 13 species.

Distribution: Members of the family are re-

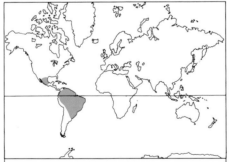

Number of genera: 3
Number of species: about 13
Distribution: chiefly drier parts of tropical and subtropical S America and Mexico.
Economic uses: limited use for fruits.

stricted to the New World. Two genera, *Proboscidea* (9 species) and *Craniolaria* (3 species) are found in tropical and subtropical South America, while the monotypic *Martynia* is confined to Mexico. They prefer dry and coastal regions.

Diagnostic features. All species are herbs, some annuals, the perennials often having tuberous roots. They are characteristically covered with sticky hairs, and the leaves are opposite or alternate, and without stipules.

The terminal inflorescence, which is sometimes subtended by bracts, bears racemes of usually showy bisexual flowers which are more or less two-lipped. The calyx is either spathe-like or composed of five free sepals. The corolla has a cylindrical, bell-shaped or funnel-shaped tube which has five lobes and is often curved. The stamens are attached to the petals; in *Proboscidea* and *Craniolaria* there are four, two longer than the rest, and the fifth is represented by a posterior staminode; *Martynia* has two fertile stamens and three staminodes. The anthers are bilocular, coherent in pairs and opening by slits. The ovary is superior and surrounded at the base by a nectariferous disk; there are two fused carpels, but a single locule with few to many anatropous ovules on parietal placentas. The single style is slender and the forked stigma is sensitive so that when the insect pollinator touches it its two flat lobes close up. The fruit is a loculicidal capsule with the persistent style forming a usually hooked projection at the end. Animal dispersal is further aided by the sticky outer wall which later splits from the apex, falling off to reveal the woody inner wall of the ovary which becomes more or less four-loculed by coherence of the two winged

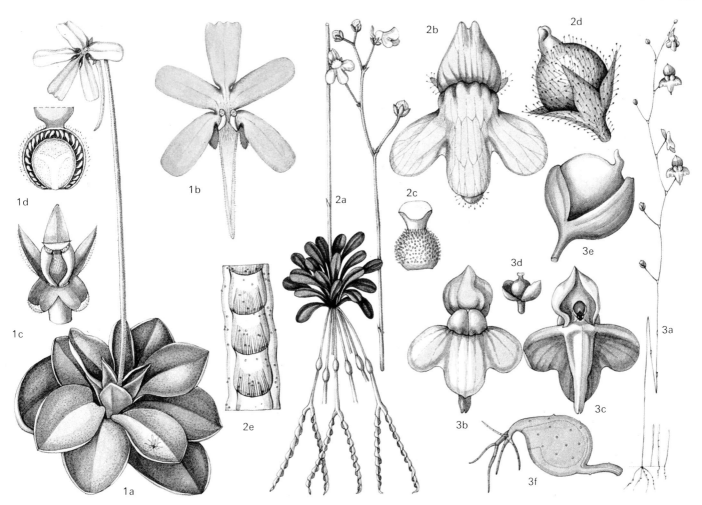

Lentibulariaceae. 1 *Pinguicula moranenis* (a) habit (×⅔); (b) spurred flower (×1); (c) calyx, ovary and stamens (×3); (d) vertical section of ovary showing the large free-central placenta (×8). 2 *Genlisea africana* (a) habit (×1); (b) flower (×4½), (c) gynoecium with sessile stigma (×12); (d) fruit—a capsule (×8); (e) section of pitcher (×14). 3 *Utricularia subulata* (a) habit (×1); (b) flower, front view (×6); (c) flower, back view (×6); (d) gynoecium and calyx (×6); (e) fruit (×12); (f) trap with projecting bristles around the entrance (×40).

placentas. The seeds are sculptured, somewhat compressed but not winged, with a straight embryo and no endosperm.

Classification. The Martyniaceae is closely related to the Bignoniaceae, but has its greatest affinities with another smallish family, the Pedaliaceae, in which it is sometimes included. However, the parietal placentation in the unilocular ovary distinguishes it. The Gesneriaceae, a large family often considered to be part of this complex of families, has a similar placentation, but in a usually inferior ovary; this and other differences in fruit structure separate it from the others.

Economic importance. Certain species are cultivated as "unicorn plants" on account of their horned fruits. Young fruits can also be pickled and eaten.   I.B.K.R.

LENTIBULARIACEAE
Bladderworts and Butterworts

The Lentibulariaceae is a small family of carnivorous and often rootless, occasionally epiphytic, herbs found in water and other moist habitats. It contains the bladderworts (*Utricularia*) and butterworts (*Pinguicula*).

Distribution. The tropical and temperate, aquatic and terrestrial bladderworts are

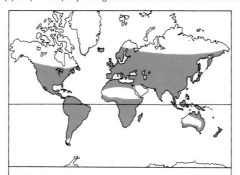

Number of genera: 4
Number of species: about 180
Distribution: cosmopolitan.
Economic uses: ornamental curiosities (bladderworts and butterworts).

represented by about 120 species and the 46 temperate species of terrestrial butterworts are found in Eurasia and the Americas. *Polypompholyx*, native to south and southwestern Australia, contains two species, while *Genlisea*, native to South and Central America and Africa, contains 15 species.

Diagnostic features. The leaves are simple, entire, alternate, sometimes arranged in rosettes and covered with glandular hairs (*Pinguicula*) or bearing bladders (*Utricu-*

laria). Digestive processes occur in contact with the glandular hairs or in the bladders. The distinction between stem and leaf is blurred in *Utricularia* where the morphology of the bladders has been variously interpreted. The traps consist of a hollow bag borne at the end of a stalk, with a small entrance near to or opposite the stalk. Around the entrance are usually some projecting bristles, so arranged that an insect or crustacean passing the bladder will tend to be guided towards its mouth. The entrance itself is closed by a hermetically sealed semicircular valve which bears four hairs. If these are touched the valve is triggered and the rush of water drags the animal inside.

The inflorescence is a raceme or a spike of irregular flowers with two to five calyx lobes, and a five-lobed, two-lipped corolla, the lower lip more or less spurred. Two stamens are borne on the petals. The ovary is superior, comprising two united carpels and a single locule, with one to numerous ovules on a free central placenta. The stigma is usually sessile, with two lobes. The fruit is a capsule which is indehiscent, or opens by two to four valves. The seeds lack endosperm.

Classification. *Utricularia* and *Polypompholyx* species bear bladders, but the latter has four calyx lobes, whereas *Utricularia* has two. *Genlisea* has rosettes of leaves and bottle-like pitchers containing bands of hairs and digestive glands, whilst *Pinguicula* is covered in glandular hairs and has no bladders or pitchers. *Pinguicula* and *Genlisea* have a five-lobed calyx. The Lentibulariaceae is allied to the Scrophulariaceae, but differs by the placentation and the carnivorous habit.

Economic uses. Some *Utricularia* species can become weeds in ricefields. The family is of great interest to biologists on account of the carnivorous habit. Several species of *Pinguicula* are in cultivation.   D.J.M.

CAMPANULALES

CAMPANULACEAE
The Bellflower Family

The Campanulaceae is a family that contains mostly herbs (annual, biennial or more often perennial), but rarely shrubs or undershrubs, which often produce large showy flowers that are predominantly blue in color. Species from genera such as *Campanula* (bellflowers), *Symphyandra* (pendulous bellflowers), *Phyteuma* (horned rampions), *Edraianthus* and *Jasione* are popular as garden ornamentals.

Distribution. The vast majority of the Campanulaceae have their native haunts in the north temperate zone. The Southern Hemisphere is exceedingly poor in the Campanulaceae, except for South Africa where seven small endemic genera are found. South America can show only certain species of *Wahlenbergia*, *Legousia* and *Cephalostigma*. The latter is the only genus of the family confined to the tropics; it is also represented in Africa and Asia. In Australia and New Zealand, only several species of *Wahlenbergia* occur.

Diagnostic features. The leaves are alternate, sometimes opposite or whorled, simple or rarely pinnate, and without stipules.

The flowers are regular and bisexual, with floral parts normally in fives. They are borne singly or more often in inflorescences (either racemes or cymes). The calyx tube is united with the ovary. There are small appendages present in the sinuses between the calyx teeth in *Michauxia* and certain species of *Campanula*, *Edraianthus* and *Symphyandra*. The petals are nearly always partially or wholly united (sympetalous) and the corolla is inserted at the line where the calyx becomes free from the ovary. The petals are not united in *Jasione*, *Asyneuma*, *Michauxia*, *Cephalostigma* and *Lightfootia*, and in *Phyteuma* when fully developed. There are as many stamens as corolla lobes. The anthers are free but tend to be united in certain genera and species; they show introrse dehiscence. The ovary is inferior to semi-inferior but in *Cyananthus*, *Codonopsis* and *Campanumoea* it is superior. It comprises five, three or two

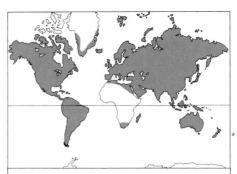

Number of genera: about 35
Number of species: about 600
Distribution: mainly found in the N Temperate Zone with a few in the S Hemisphere.
Economic uses: many species used as ornamentals, eg the bellflowers (*Campanula*).

fused carpels, with five, three or two locules (rarely one or six or 10), each containing a large number of ovules on axile placentas. The style is simple with as many stigmas as carpels.

The fruit is a capsule. It opens in a variety of ways but in some genera, such as *Peracarpa* of the Himalayas and *Merciera* of South Africa it is indehiscent. Only two genera, *Canarina* and *Campanumoea*, are known to produce berries. The seeds are numerous and small, with a straight embryo and fleshy endosperm. Anatomically, the members of the family are distinguished by the constant presence of latex-containing vessels in their tissues. The reserve material is not starch as in the majority of plants, but a polysaccharide called inulin.

The flowers are generally large and showy. The predominantly blue color is particularly attractive to bees but there are many other pollen carriers from various groups of insects. A glandular disk (in a few cases a cup) at the base of the style secretes honey. It is usually covered by the dilated bases of the stamens which allow the insertion of an insect's proboscis between them.

An interesting floral mechanism has been developed in the family, facilitating cross-pollination and hindering self-pollination. The flowers are distinctly protandrous, and pollen is shed upon the style (with the stigma lobes closed up against one another) in the bud. The style is either sticky (as in *Wahlenbergia*) or hairy, to hold the pollen. Technically, this is the male stage in the development of the flower and stamens wilt quickly as the corolla opens. After a time (usually several days) when the bulk of the pollen has been carried away by insects, the stigma lobes unfold and the female stage sets in. In some species the stigma lobes coil spirally and may touch the remnants of pollen deposited on the style, thus effecting self-pollination.

Species of *Legousia* produce, in addition to normal flowers, small, abortive ones which fail to open and are self-pollinated – a case of cleistogamy (pollination and fertilization before the flower has opened). *Campanula* has several cleistogamous species.

Classification. The family Campanulaceae, in its restricted sense (that is, excluding the aberrant genera *Cyphia*, *Pentaphragma* and *Sphenoclea*) is rather natural and homogeneous but its subdivision presents serious problems because there seems to be little correlation between the various diagnostic features. Based on the morphology of ovary and capsule, the following three subtribes may be distinguished which, however, do not necessarily represent separate phyletic (evolutionary) lines:

CAMPANULINAE. The ovary is inferior and carpels superposed on the calyx teeth. The fruit is a capsule opening laterally, sometimes indehiscent, in one genus a berry. Genera include *Campanula*, *Symphyandra*, *Adenophora*, *Legousia*, *Michauxia*, *Ostrowskia* and *Canarina*.

WAHLENBERGINAE. The ovary may be inferior or semi-inferior to superior. The carpels are superposed on the calyx teeth. The fruit is a capsule opening on the top, in one genus a berry. Genera include *Wahlenbergia*, *Campanumoea*, *Codonopsis*, *Cyananthus*, *Roella*, *Githopsis*, *Lightfootia*, *Edraianthus* and *Jasione*.

PLATYCODINAE. The ovary is inferior to semi-inferior. The carpels alternate with the calyx teeth, and the fruit is a capsule opening terminally or laterally. The type-genus is *Platycodon*.

The Cyphiaceae, Lobeliaceae, Pentaphragmataceae and Sphenocleaceae, often regarded as belonging to the Campanulaceae, are here treated as separate families.

The Cyphiaceae is a link between bellflowers and lobelias, having regular flowers, stamens fused into a tube and free anthers. There are four genera and about 70 species in South Africa. The Pentaphragmataceae is distinguished by the asymmetric leaves, regular flowers arranged in scorpioid cymes and baccate fruits. The only genus *Pent-*

Campanulaceae. 1 *Canarina eminii* shoot with opposite leaves and axillary, regular flowers ($\times\frac{2}{3}$). 2 *Trachelium rumelianum* shoot with alternate leaves and terminal inflorescences ($\times\frac{2}{3}$). 3 *Campanula rapunculoides* (a) leafy shoot and racemose inflorescence ($\times\frac{2}{3}$); (b) half flower showing free anthers to stamens, and inferior ovary surmounted by a single style with a lobed stigma ($\times 1$); (c) cross section of trilocular ovary with ovules on axile placentas ($\times 3$). 4 *C. rapunculus* dehisced fruit—a capsule ($\times 1\frac{1}{3}$). 5 *Phyteuma orbiculare* inflorescence ($\times\frac{2}{3}$). 6 *Lobelia cardinalis* cv "Red Flush" showing irregular flowers with stamens united around the style—features which differ from the Campanulaceae; note that in the upper flowers of the inflorescence the stigma is not protruding between the anthers, but it is in the lower flowers; these are the male and female stages of the flowering cycle ($\times\frac{2}{3}$). 7 *Pratia arenaria* (a) creeping stem ($\times\frac{2}{3}$); (b) flower ($\times 4$).

aphragma has about 30 species (mostly succulent) confined to Southeast Asia and Malaysia. Some authors relate it to the Begoniaceae. The Sphenocleaceae contains one species, *Sphenoclea zeylanica*, an annual herb that occurs in wet habitats in Central and Southeast Asia. The stem is hollow and flowers are regular, small, borne in dense spikes. Certain characters suggest affinity with the Lythraceae.

It seems possible that the Campanulaceae (or, rather, their evolutionary ancestors) are the basic stock from which the huge family Compositae evolved. This contention is supported by the morphological evidence (head-like inflorescences in *Jasione* and *Phyteuma*, connate anthers in certain species and genera), protandry, presence of latex and, last but not least, of inulin. This peculiar polysaccharide occurs in both the orders Campanulales and Asterales.

Economic uses. Many, if not all, species of *Campanula* (bellflowers), *Edraianthus*, *Symphyandra* (pendulous bellflowers), *Phyteuma* (horned rampions) and *Jasione* are valued ornamentals, being highly attractive and easy to grow; a number of them are extremely useful in rock gardens. *Adenophora*, *Michauxia*, *Ostrowskia* (giant bellflower), *Trachelium* (blue throatwort), *Codonopsis* and *Platycodon* (balloon flower) are also popular with gardeners. *Campanula rapunculus* or rampion is one of the very few species of (minor) nutritive value, the roots and leaves being used occasionally in salads.
M.K.

LOBELIACEAE
Lobelias

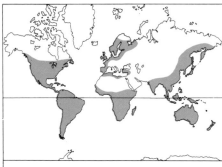

Number of genera: about 30
Number of species: about 1,200
Distribution: cosmopolitan, especially common in the Americas and tropics.
Economic uses: many ornamentals and *Lobelia inflata* yields medicinally important alkaloids.

The Lobeliaceae is a medium-sized family with life forms ranging from tiny annuals to trees, often of weird habit. Species of the Hawaiian genus *Cyanea* resemble palms. Desert species of *Lobelia* and *Monopsis* have developed needle-like leaves and the Australian *Lobelia gibbosa* is succulent. Certain representatives of *Clermontia* are epiphytes and several *Lobelia* species are aquatic.
Distribution. The family is worldwide, being particularly rich in the Americas and containing many tropical species and genera.
Diagnostic features. The leaves are alternate, simple and without stipules. The flowers are irregular, mostly blue, red or violet, normally bisexual (but several Australian species of *Lobelia* and *Pratia* are known to have male and female flowers on separate plants), and are inverted on their axis through 180°. They are arranged in racemes or panicles lacking the terminal flower; single-flowered species are rare. The calyx is five-lobed and joined to the ovary. The corolla has five fused petals (rarely free), which are two-lipped, with the lips either equal or unequal. The corolla tube is curved in most species. The five stamens are free from or joined to the corolla, and the anthers are fused into a tube. The upper three stamens are longer than the lower two. The ovary, of fused carpels, is inferior or rarely superior and has two or three locules (rarely one) with numerous ovules on axile placentas. The style is simple with two or three stigmas. The fruit is either indehiscent and pulpy or dry, or more often dehiscent, opening in various ways.

The flowers achieve cross-fertilization by being protandrous. The style pushes through the tube formed by the fused anthers and drives the pollen out at the top, where it is collected by insects. The style having emerged fully, the stigmas separate and the female stage of the flower begins. Exceptions are the African genus *Monopsis*, with anthers and stigmas ripening simultaneously, and *Lobelia dortmanna* (water lobelia), where the stigmas unfold within the anther tube and are self-fertilized by the pollen deposited there. Pollen carriers include a variety of aphids, bees and butterflies; some large-flowered species are pollinated by birds.

Many members of the family are strongly poisonous. For instance, *Laurentia longiflora* from South America supplies isotomin, a heart poison, and the mere smell of the Chilean *Lobelia tupa* may cause poisoning.
Classification. Two tribes of genera, based primarily on the morphology of the ovary and fruit, are currently recognized.
LOBELIEAE. Ovary conical at the top; fruit dehiscing; includes *Lobelia*, *Siphocampylus*, *Laurentia* and *Monopsis*.
DELISSEAE. Ovary flat at the top; fruit indehiscent, pulpy or dry; includes *Centropogon*, *Burmeistera*, *Hypsela*, *Pratia*, *Clermontia*, *Cyanea* and *Delissea*.)

The Lobeliaceae is an advanced type of the Campanulaceae from which it differs in its irregular flowers, connate anthers and the presence of different alkaloids. However, the relationships between the families are so close that some authorities include the Lobeliaceae as a subfamily of the Campanulaceae.

Economic uses. The genus *Lobelia* has many ornamental representatives which are much valued for their long flowering-period.

Perhaps the most familiar is *Lobelia erinus*, a native of South Africa, which has been in cultivation since the 17th century and is commonly used for bedding. *Lobelia cardinalis* (cardinal flower), *L. splendens*, *L. amoena* and *L. fulgens* are effective in the herbaceous border. Species of *Pratia*, *Centropogon*, *Downingia*, *Monopsis*, *Laurentia* and *Hypsela* are also grown for ornament.

Lobelia inflata, in addition to being the source of important alkaloids, yields a remedy for asthma and whooping cough. A decoction of the roots of *Lobelia syphilitica* was used by the American Indians to cure venereal diseases. The berries of *Centropogon* and *Clermontia* are edible.
M.K.

STYLIDIACEAE
Trigger Plant

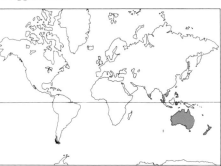

Number of genera: 6
Number of species: about 150
Distribution: centered in Australia.
Economic uses: some ornamentals.

The Stylidiaceae is a small family of subtropical and temperate annual or perennial herbs and a few shrubs. The largest genus, *Stylidium* (103 species) is sometimes called trigger plant or springback, in reference to the movable column in the flower, characteristic of the family.
Distribution. The family is confined to Australia except for a few species in New Zealand, South America, eastern Asia and India. They are usually somewhat adapted to drought conditions, but *Donatia* and *Phyllachne* are important in the wet bogs of New Zealand and southernmost South America.
Diagnostic features. The leaves are alternate or in a basal rosette, simple, and usually without stipules. The flowers are irregular and bisexual or unisexual. There are five persistent sepals, usually more or less united in two lips, and the corolla is usually deeply five-lobed, with one smaller downward-directed lobe (labellum) and the other four ascending, in pairs. There are two (rarely three) stamens, usually fused with the style to form a column; the anthers open outwards, often concealing the entire or two-lobed stigma. The column protrudes and curves in such a way that when an insect lands on the lower lip of the corolla, the column moves elastically up and down, and thus assists the transfer of pollen to and from the insect's back. The ovary is inferior, of two fused

carpels, and has one or two locules, with few or numerous anatropous ovules attached to the septum or a central placenta. The fruit is a two-valved capsule with small seeds containing endosperm and a minute embryo.

Classification. The family is usually subdivided into two subfamilies:

DONATIOIDEAE. Petals free and stamens two or three, also free. The only genus is *Donatia*, which is placed by some authorities in its own family, the Donatiaceae.

STYLIDIOIDEAE. Petals united at the base and stamens two, fused with the style as far as the apex. The tribe PHYLLACHNEAE has anther locules which are connate at the apex to form two curved anthers, each with a single cell (*Phyllachne* and *Forstera*). The tribe STYLIDEAE has anthers with two locules (*Oreostylidium*, *Levenhookia*, *Stylidium*).

The affinities of the Stylidiaceae are still open to debate, but the pollen of most of them is like that of the Campanulaceae and other characters do not contradict this.

Economic uses. A few species are cultivated for ornament. The most important are the western Australian evergreen shrubs belonging to *Stylidium* which are often referred to as *Candollea* by horticulturists.   D.M.M.

BRUNONIACEAE

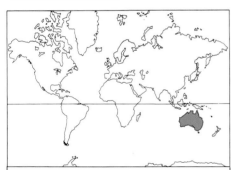

Number of genera: 1
Number of species: 1
Distribution: Australia and Tasmania.
Economic uses: none.

The Brunoniaceae is an Australian family containing a single genus of silky-haired perennial herbs, *Brunonia*.

Distribution. The single species of the genus, *Brunonia australis*, whose colloquial name, blue pincushion, is an apt description of the flowers, is restricted to Australia and Tasmania.

Diagnostic features. All leaves arise from the basal part of the plant, and are entire, without stipules, and up to about 4in (10cm) long. The flowers are bisexual, regular and arranged in dense hemispherical heads subtended by a series of bracts. There are five fused sepals, forming a tube which is not fused to the ovary, but the sepal lobes persist on the fruit. The corolla consists of five blue lobes, fused together at the base but free and spreading above. There are five stamens inserted at the base of the corolla tube and

the anthers cohere together around the style within the corolla tube. The ovary is superior and has a single locule with one erect ovule. There is a single style which is capped by a small stigma surrounded by a collar or indusium. The fruit is an achene with a single seed which lacks endosperm and has a straight embryo.

Classification. The family is thought to be related to Goodeniaceae in which it has often been included, both having an indusium around the stigma, but at the same time the family bears some similarity to the Dipsacaceae and Compositae in inflorescence structure.

Economic uses. None are known.   B.M.

GOODENIACEAE
Leschenaultias and Scaevolas

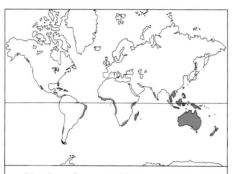

Number of genera: 14
Number of species: about 300
Distribution: centered in Australia.
Economic uses: several garden and greenhouse ornamentals.

The Goodeniaceae is a smallish family of herbs and some shrubs. It contains some outstanding ornamentals, cultivated in gardens in warmer climates and in greenhouses in temperate regions.

Distribution. The family is largely confined to Australia, particularly western Australia, with only a few species of *Scaevola* extending to New Zealand, Africa, eastern Asia, the West Indies, Central and South America and the Pacific Islands, and *Selliara radicans* occurring in Australia, New Zealand and central Chile.

Diagnostic features. The plants are herbs, sometimes woody at the base, or rarely shrubs. The leaves are alternate or radical, rarely opposite, and entire to pinnatisect; there are no stipules. The flowers are irregular, bisexual and axillary, either solitary or borne in axillary spikes, racemes or cymes. The calyx tube is usually attached to the ovary, and has five (rarely three) lobes or is reduced to a ring. The corolla tube is slit almost to the base on the upper side, sometimes fused to the ovary, the limb being unequally or equally five-lobed, and usually two-lipped, yellow or white to blue, rarely red to purplish. There are five stamens, free or slightly joined to the corolla, and alternating with the corolla lobes. The anthers are attached at their base to the filaments, and

are free or united in a ring round the style. The ovary is inferior or partly so, rarely superior, formed of two fused carpels and has two locules (rarely one), each with one to numerous erect or ascending, anatropous or rarely campylotropous ovules. The style has a terminal outgrowth (indusium) surrounding the usually two-lobed stigma. The fruit is an indehiscent drupe or nut, or a capsule, the seeds being usually flat and often winged, with endosperm and an erect embryo.

Classification. Most species belong to *Goodenia* and *Scaevola* (about 90 species each) and *Dampiera* (about 60 species). Like the related family Brunoniaceae, which is sometimes included in it, the Goodeniaceae is characterized by the cup-shaped or two-lipped indusium, often finely hairy, which contains the stigma at the apex of the style and which seems to be involved in aiding pollen capture from insect visitors.

Economic uses. Several species of *Goodenia*, *Dampiera*, *Leschenaultia* and *Scaevola* are grown for ornament in greenhouses or, in warmer climates, in gardens. *Leschenaultia* is considered to contain some of the most beautiful greenhouse shrubs, including *Leschenaultia biloba*, which is prized for its blue flowers. *Selliera radicans*, a hairless creeping perennial, is sometimes grown in moist rock gardens.   D.M.M.

RUBIALES

RUBIACEAE
Gardenias, Coffee and Quinine

The Rubiaceae is one of the largest flowering plant families. Most tropical species are trees or shrubs while all temperate ones are herbaceous. Coffee is the most important product of this family and is obtained mainly from *Coffea arabica* and *C. canephora*. *Cinchona* species yield the drug quinine. Among the many tropical species that are cultivated as ornamentals is *Gardenia jasminoides* (Cape jasmine), while the best-known European genera are *Galium* (the bedstraws) and *Asperula* (woodruff).

Distribution. This very widespread family is concentrated in the tropics and subtropics with some species represented in temperate regions. (See also p.878.)

Diagnostic features. The leaves are opposite or whorled, simple and usually entire. The presence of stipules is particularly characteristic; these are sometimes fused at each node, leaf-like (as in *Galium* and *Asperula*), or inserted in the axil of the petiole (intrapetiolar) or between the petioles. The flowers are borne in panicles or cymes or are aggregated into congested heads. They are usually bisexual and regular (although one of the sepals is often enlarged), with four or five free sepals, four or five fused petals and four or five stamens, the latter borne on the corolla tube whose mouth is frequently filled with flattened, ribbon-like hairs. The ovary

Rubiaceae. 1 *Ixora chinensis* (a) flowering shoot showing stipules between the petioles ($\times \frac{2}{3}$); (b) tubular corolla opened out to show epipetalous stamens and simple style with a lobed stigma and vertical section of ovary ($\times 1\frac{1}{2}$). 2 *Asperula suberosa* flowering shoot ($\times \frac{2}{3}$). 3 *Mussaenda luteola* flower with one calyx lobe much enlarged ($\times 1\frac{1}{2}$). 4 *Coffea arabica* (a) fruits ($\times \frac{2}{3}$); (b) cross section of fruit ($\times 1$). 5 *Nauclea pobeguinii* vertical section of fruit ($\times \frac{1}{2}$). 6 *Sherbournia calycina* (a) flowering shoot ($\times \frac{2}{3}$); (b) vertical section of ovary ($\times 2$); (c) cross section of ovary ($\times 3$).

is inferior (very rarely superior), with one to many carpels (normally two) and as many locules, each containing one to many anatropous ovules on axile, apical or basal (rarely parietal) placentas. The style is simple, and the stigma capitate or variously lobed. The fruit is a capsule, berry, drupe or schizocarp. The seeds are sometimes winged; they contain a straight or curved embryo, and endosperm may be present or absent.

Interesting examples of association with ants are found in the genera *Myrmecodia* and *Hydnophytum*, native to tropical Asia and Australia. All members of these genera are epiphytes which cling to branches of trees with their roots. Large swellings, containing a network of cavities, develop on the roots, and are inhabited by ants. Although it has been supposed that the plant and insects have developed a symbiosis of mutual benefit – the ant guarding the plant and providing it with extra nutrients, receiving shelter in return – it has not been proved that they are in fact interdependent.

Classification. Although the Rubiaceae forms a very clear-cut group, its intrafamilial classification is controversial and there has been disagreement about which characters are most suitable for delimiting tribes and

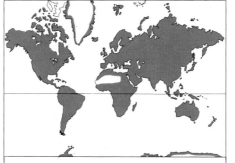

Number of genera: about 500
Number of species: about 7,000
Distribution: mainly in the tropics and subtropics with a few species in temperate and cold regions.
Economic uses: coffee and quinine, and some lesser-known drugs such as ipecacuanha, dyes from madder and gambier, and many ornamentals (eg *Gardenia*, woodruffs and bedstraws).

subfamilies. Older systems recognize two subfamilies, characterized, respectively, by one or many ovules per locule. Recently, however, three completely different subfamilies have been proposed, as follows:
RUBIOIDEAE. Calcium oxalate raphides (needle-shaped crystals) present in leaves;

hairs on stems and leaves often with cross-walls; heterostyly common; stipules often divided into many slender branches; seeds without endosperm. Predominantly herbaceous – 11 tribes.
CINCHONOIDEAE. Raphides absent; hairs without cross-walls; complete heterostyly absent; stipules rarely divided; seeds with endosperm. Predominantly woody – 17 tribes.
GUETTARDOIDEAE. Raphides absent; hairs without cross-walls; heterostyly absent; seeds lack endosperm. Woody – one tribe.

The affinities of the Rubiaceae seem to lie equally with the Gentianales and Dipsacales, both of which generally have opposite leaves and bicarpellate ovaries. Opinions vary as to whether the family is best placed in one or other, or kept as a distinct order. The Rubiaceae resembles members of the Gentianales (particularly the Loganiaceae) in having well-developed stipules which often bear special glands (colleters), and in possessing certain alkaloids; on the other hand, it differs in the absence of internal phloem and in its inferior ovary. These two features are typical of the Dipsacales, but the latter tend to lack stipules and do not synthesize alkaloids.

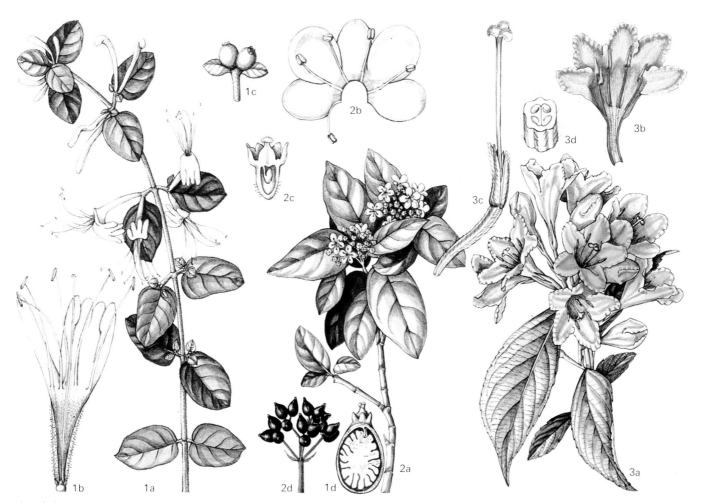

Caprifoliaceae. 1 *Lonicera biflora* (a) twining stem with opposite leaves and flowers in pairs ($\times\frac{2}{3}$); (b) flower opened out showing epipetalous stamens ($\times 2$); (c) paired fruit—berries ($\times 4$); (d) vertical section of fruit ($\times 3$). 2 *Viburnum tinus* (a) leafy shoot and inflorescences ($\times\frac{2}{3}$); (b) corolla and stamens ($\times 3$); (c) vertical section of gynoecium showing capitate stigma and pendulous ovule ($\times 3$); (d) fruits ($\times\frac{2}{3}$). 3 *Weigela amabilis* (a) leafy shoot and inflorescence ($\times\frac{2}{3}$); (b) corolla opened out ($\times 1$); (c) calyx, style and stigma ($\times 3$); (d) section of ovary ($\times 9$).

Economic uses. The best-known products of the Rubiaceae are coffee (*Coffea*) and quinine (*Cinchona* species). Members of the family also provide the drug ipecacuanha (*Cephaelis*) and the dyes madder (*Rubia*) and gambier (*Uncaria*). Of the large number of tropical flowering shrubs in the family, *Gardenia* is perhaps the most popular ornamental but others, such as *Bouvardia, Hamelia, Manettia, Randia* and *Rondeletia*, are also cultivated for their blooms. Other garden plants include *Asperula, Galium* and *Houstonia*. F.K.K.

DIPSACALES

ADOXACEAE

The Adoxaceae is a family consisting of one genus with one species of perennial, rhizomatous herbs, *Adoxa moschatellina*.

Distribution. *Adoxa* is widely distributed in Europe, North America, and northern and central Asia, on mountain rocks, and in hedges and woods.

Diagnostic features. The plants bear ternate radical leaves on long petioles, as well as a pair of opposite, shortly petiolate, trisected or ternate leaves on the erect, unbranched flowering stem. The inflorescence is a condensed cyme with each branch giving rise to two other branches. There are one terminal and four lateral regular, bisexual, greenish flowers. The terminal flower has a two-lobed calyx (or bracts) and a four-lobed greenish corolla, and four stamens alternating with the corolla lobes. However, the stamen filaments are deeply divided so that at first sight there appear to be eight stamens. The lateral flowers have a three-lobed calyx (or bracts) and a five-lobed greenish corolla and five (apparently 10) stamens. In both types of flower nectar is secreted by a ring round the base of the stamens. The flowers are visited by various small insects, particularly flies. The ovary is semi-inferior, of three to five fused carpels and three to five locules, each with a single pendulous ovule. The style is three- to five-lobed. The fruit is a drupe and the seed contains a small embryo surrounded by copious endosperm.

Classification. The affinities of the Adoxaceae are in some doubt. At one time *Adoxa* was included in the Caprifoliaceae but it differs from the members of this family in the longitudinal splitting of the stamen filaments almost to the base, and the semi-inferior ovary. Relationships have been suggested with the Araliaceae and the Saxifragaceae.

Economic uses. None are known. S.R.C.

CAPRIFOLIACEAE
Elders and Honeysuckles

The Caprifoliaceae is a smallish family mainly of small trees and shrubs, several of which are climbers and familiar ornamentals.

Distribution. Although generally distributed throughout the world, the family is richest in temperate parts of eastern North America

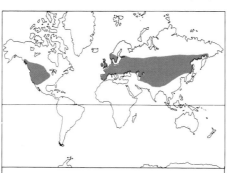

Number of genera: 1
Number of species: 1
Distribution: Europe, N America, northern and central Asia.
Economic uses: none.

and eastern Asia, and absent from the Sahara, southern and tropical Africa, but with one species in the East African mountains and Madagascar.

Diagnostic features. The Caprifoliaceae are mostly small trees or shrubs, with a number of lianas (as in some species of *Lonicera*). *Triosteum* is herbaceous, and *Sambucus* contains both shrubs and herbs. The leaves are usually opposite, simple and without stipules. An exception is *Sambucus* which has stipules and sometimes pinnate leaves, while in *Viburnum* and *Leycesteria* stipules are represented as nectar glands. The flowers are bisexual, and either regular or irregular. The inflorescence is basically cymose, often with pairs of flowers which are sometimes joined towards the bases of the ovaries. The calyx consists of four or five partly fused sepals. The calyx tube is fused to the ovary wall and is surmounted by usually five small teeth. The corolla, which rises above the ovary, usually has five spreading lobes and two lips. The shape of the tube is very variable, being very short in *Viburnum*, while in *Lonicera* it can be long and narrow or shortish and salver-shaped. The lobes are imbricate in bud, except in *Alseuosmia* and related genera and *Sambucus*. The stamens arise from the corolla tube, alternate with the lobes; occasionally one of the five is absent, as in *Linnaea*. The anthers have two locules and open by longitudinal slits, usually inwards. The ovary is inferior and formed usually of three to five united carpels, containing one to five locules. It is surmounted by a single style bearing a capitate or lobed stigma. There is a single pendulous ovule (numerous in *Leycesteria*) on an axile placenta in each locule. The fruit is most often a berry and the seeds typically have a small, straight embryo with copious endosperm. *Diervilla* and *Weigela* have a capsular fruit.

Classification. The chief genera are *Abelia* (30 species), *Diervilla* (three species), *Leycesteria* (six species), *Lonicera* (200 species), *Sambucus* (40 species), *Triosteum* (six species), *Viburnum* (200 species) and *Weigela* (12 species).

Alseuosmia, a genus of about eight species, from New Zealand, is sometimes separated as the family Alseuosmiaceae. Two other genera usually included in the Caprifoliaceae are transferred to this small family if recognized, namely *Periomphale* (two species) and *Memecylanthus* (one species), both from New Caledonia. They all have alternate leaves and valvate corolla lobes, and the pollen structure suggests that they may belong nearer to the Escallonioideae (a subfamily of the Saxifragaceae) and/or the Loganiaceae.

The other small genera, from Southeast Asia, *Carlemannia* (three species) and *Silvianthus* (two species), have also been split off as a further separate family, the Carlemanniaceae. Affinities with the Hydr-

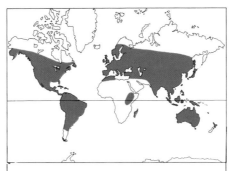

Number of genera: about 18
Number of species: about 450
Distribution: cosmopolitan, centered in E N America and E Asia.
Economic uses: many ornamentals (eg honeysuckle, snowberry) and elderberries used in wine-making.

angeoideae (a subfamily of the Saxifragaceae) are suggested by their two stamens with the anthers joined round the style and the numerous seeds in a two-chambered, four- to five-valved capsule.

The Caprifoliaceae as a whole is closely related to the Rubiaceae, from which the majority can be most readily distinguished by the absence of stipules.

Economic uses. Although a few species such as *Lonicera japonica* present a problem as weeds, the family is best-known for the numerous hardy ornamental shrubs it contains. Notable among these are *Lonicera* (honeysuckles), *Symphoricarpos* (snowberry, coralberry), *Sambucus* (elder) and species of *Viburnum*, *Abelia*, *Leycesteria* and *Weigela*. Elderberries are often used in winemaking.   I.B.K.R.

VALERIANACEAE
Spikenard and Valerians

The Valerianaceae is a medium-sized family, more than half of whose members are in the genus *Valeriana*. They are mostly herbs, but a few have a shrubby habit, while in parts of South America some are cushion plants.

Distribution. The Valerianaceae is primarily

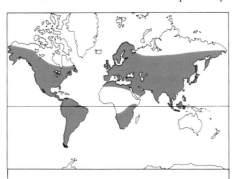

Number of genera: 13
Number of species: about 400
Distribution: mainly N Hemisphere and S America
Economic uses: limited uses as medicines, in perfumes, in salads and as ornamentals.

a Northern Hemisphere family, being absent from Australia and much of Africa. However, there is a diversity of genera in South America, particularly in the mountainous areas. The Mediterranean region is also a center of diversity with two genera, *Centranthus* (nine species) and *Fedia* (about three species), being endemic to this region.

Diagnostic features. The leaves are opposite, often pinnatisect, without stipules, and usually have clasping bases; when dry the plants give off a strong, characteristic odor, due to the presence of valerianic acid and derivatives, particularly in the roots.

The inflorescence is cymose, usually with numerous, bracteate, often crowded flowers, as in the part-inflorescences of *Valerianella*. The flowers are usually bisexual and irregular. The calyx, situated on the top rim of the ovary, is scarcely visible in flower, but shows great variation in structure in fruit. It is basically five-lobed but is considerably modified by unrolling into a "parachute" of up to 30 plumose segments in the fruit of *Valeriana* and *Centranthus*, while in *Valerianella*, a genus of about 80 species of small, annual weeds, it shows many variations in structure from being virtually absent in some species to being bladder-like or plumose in others. The petals are united, with usually five imbricate lobes and often with a long corolla tube which is particularly strongly developed in *Centranthus*, some species of which also have a long spur at the base containing nectar; pollination of such flowers is by moths. The stamens, which are attached to the upper part of the corolla tube, vary in number from four in *Patrinia* and *Nardostachys*, three in *Valeriana* and two in *Fedia* to one in *Centranthus*.

The ovary, of three united carpels, is inferior and has one locule by unequal development of the carpels, with a single pendulous, anatropous ovule. The style is simple and slender. The fruit is a cypsela, dry and indehiscent, parallel in many ways to the bicarpellate fruit of the Compositae.

Classification. The genera are mostly well delimited. The reduction in number of stamens and the highly modified calyx of some genera is an indication of how derived a particular genus is within the family. The Valerianaceae is in the order Dipsacales, generally recognized as an advanced group of families showing adaptations paralleled in the Compositae.

Economic uses. Species of *Valeriana* have medicinal properties, and both root and leaf extracts are used locally to treat nerve complaints. Some species of *Valerianella* provide corn salad or lamb's lettuce, used as a salad mainly in Continental Europe. A few species of the Valerianaceae produce perfumes and dyes; best-known is *Nardostachys jatamansi* from the Himalayan region, the spikenard of old. The best-known garden-ornamental is *Centranthus ruber*, red valerian.   I.B.K.R.

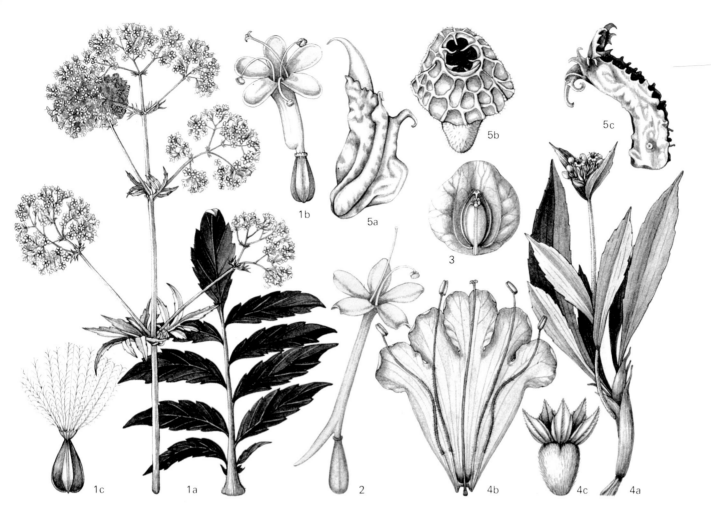

Valerianaceae. 1 *Valeriana officinalis* (a) pinnatisect leaf and cymose inflorescence ($\times\frac{2}{3}$); (b) flower with small corolla spur ($\times 6$); (c) fruit crowned by plumose calyx ($\times 6$). 2 *Centranthus lecoqii* flower with distinct spur and single stamen ($\times 4$). 3 *Patrinia villosa* fruit ($\times 4$). 4 *Nardostachys jatamangi* (a) leafy shoot and inflorescence ($\times\frac{2}{3}$); (b) flower opened out showing four stamens and one style ($\times 4$); (c) fruit ($\times 4$). 5 *Valerianella* species have very varied fruits due to the growth of the calyx; shown here are those of (a) *V. echinata*, (b) *V. vesicaria* and (c) *V. tuberculata*.

DIPSACACEAE
Teasel and Scabious

Number of genera: 11
Number of species: 350
Distribution: Europe to E Asia and central to southern Africa.
Economic uses: floriculture and teasel used in cloth industry.

The Dipsacaceae is a small family of herbs or subshrubs which provides some fine ornamentals as well as that rare product of the plant kingdom, a natural tool – the teasel.

Distribution. The family's center of diversity is in the Mediterranean region and the Near East, but extending to northern Europe, eastern Asia and central to southern Africa.

Diagnostic features. The Dipsacaceae are annual to perennial herbs and rarely shrubs. The leaves are opposite or in whorls and are without stipules. The flowers are in dense, cymose heads (capitula) subtended by involucral bracts, often with longer marginal flowers, and rarely in a spike of verticillasters. They are bisexual or female, and irregular, each with a basal epicalyx (involucel) of fused bracteoles which may be expanded into a "corona," often subtended by a receptacular scale.

The calyx is small, and cup-shaped or divided into four, five or numerous teeth or bristles. The corolla has four or five subequal lobes, or is two-lipped. There are two or four stamens, growing on the petals and alternating with the corolla lobes. The ovary is inferior, of two fused carpels and a single locule with a single pendulous ovule. The style is slender and the stigma either simple or two-lobed. The fruit is dry and indehiscent, enclosed in the epicalyx and often surmounted by a persistent calyx. It has a single seed with endosperm; the embryo is straight.

Perennial species occur in all genera but annuals have evolved several times in dry habitats as parallel lines of specialization, especially in *Cephalaria*, *Knautia*, *Pterocephalus* and *Scabiosa*. The capitula are generally conspicuous and insect-pollinated, with outbreeding assured by frequent self-sterility. Only some annual groups in, for example, *Pterocephalus* and *Scabiosa*, have inconspicuous capitula with reduced flowers which are predominantly self-pollinated.

Classification. The family is usually divided into two tribes: MORINEAE and DIPSACEAE. The Morineae has flowers in verticillasters in the upper leaf-axils, a leaf-like calyx and either two stamens, or four stamens two of which are longer than the others. The Dipsaceae has flowers in capitula (the outer flowers often enlarged), a scaly or bristly calyx and four (rarely two) similar stamens. Only *Morina* is included in the first tribe, which is sometimes separated as a distinct family, the Morinaceae.

Differentiation in the Dipsacaceae has been most evident in fruit characters. In less advanced species of *Cephalaria* and *Succisa* the involucel and calyx are inconspicuous and undifferentiated, the flowers are subtended by leafy bracts and the fruits are small

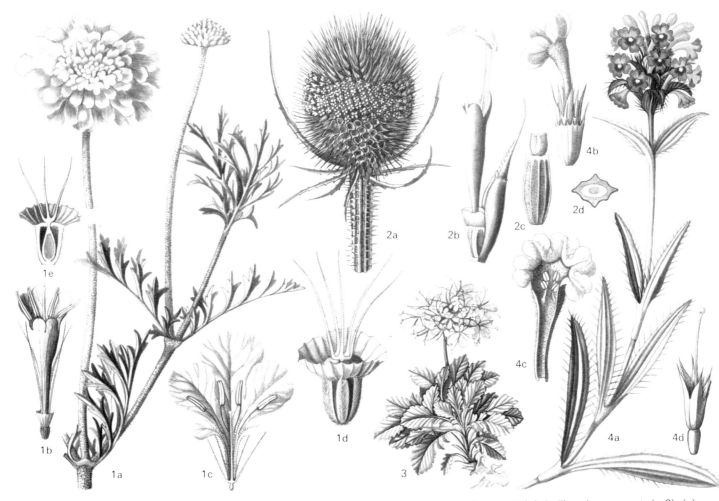

Dipsacaceae. 1 *Scabiosa anthemifolia* var *rosea* (a) leafy shoot and inflorescences ($\times\frac{2}{3}$); (b) inner flower with bristle-like calyx-segments ($\times 3$); (c) larger outer flower opened out ($\times 2$); (d) fruit with epicalyx (involucel) expanded into an umbrella-shaped extension and crowned by spines ($\times 3$); (e) vertical section of fruit ($\times 2$). 2 *Dipsacus fullonum* (a) dense flower head surrounded by spiny bracts ($\times\frac{2}{3}$); (b) flower ($\times 3$); (c) fruit ($\times 3$); (d) cross section of fruit ($\times 5$). 3 *Pterocephalus perennis* flowering shoot ($\times\frac{2}{3}$). 4 *Morina betonicoides* (a) leafy shoot and inflorescence ($\times\frac{2}{3}$); (b) flower ($\times 2$); (c) corolla tube opened to show stamens of two lengths ($\times 2$); (d) gynoecium and calyx ($\times 2$).

hard grains. The subtending bracts are elongated and rigid in *Dipsacus* to provide a catapult mechanism for dispersal as animals brush against the thistle-like fruiting heads. The bracts are reduced in other genera that develop adaptations to wind dispersal, which is achieved in *Scabiosa*, for example, by a thin, translucent umbrella produced by extension of the involucel limb, and in *Pterocephalus* by the numerous long calyx bristles which bear feather-like hairs. Adaptations to animal dispersal are seen in several genera. *Knautia* has a fatty outgrowth at the fruit base that attracts ants which carry off the fruit, while annual species of *Cephalaria* and *Scabiosa* develop, from the involucel and calyx respectively, rough, often branched, spines.

This family bears a superficial resemblance to the Compositae, in that the inflorescence usually forms a head surrounded by a calyx-like involucre of bracts. It is, however, readily distinguished by the stamens, with free anthers protruding from the corolla, and by the fruit being enclosed in an involucel of united bracteoles and crowned by the calyx composed of four, five or more bristles or teeth.

Economic uses. Many species of *Cephalaria*, *Morina*, *Pterocephalus* and *Scabiosa* (scabious) are cultivated for ornament, while teasel (*Dipsacus sativus*) is used on a limited scale for raising the nap on cloth.

D.M.M.

CALYCERACEAE

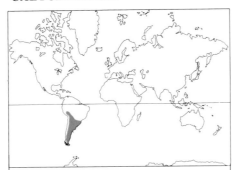

Number of genera: 6
Number of species: about 52
Distribution: S America.
Economic uses: none.

The Calyceraceae is a small family of annual and perennial herbs.
Distribution. The family is entirely South American, being most abundant in the Andes south from Bolivia, but extending eastwards through Paraguay to Uruguay and southern Brazil and throughout much of Argentina to southern Patagonia. Most species occur in dry soils supporting open scrub or steppe vegetation.

Diagnostic features. The leaves are alternate, entire to pinnatisect, in a basal rosette and without stipules. The flowers are bisexual or rarely unisexual, regular or irregular, clustered in a head with the receptacle surrounded by one to two series of involucral bracts. The heads of flowers may be solitary or in cymes, and are stalked or sessile. The receptacular bracts are free, united into groups of two or three, or absent. There is a calyx of four to six teeth or lobes, persisting in the fruit. The corolla is cylindrical, with a four- to six-lobed limb. The stamens are four to six, alternate with the corolla lobes and joined into a · tube around the style, the filaments being partially free and inserted at various levels in the corolla tube. The anthers are free, with inward dehiscence. The ovary is inferior and has one locule with a solitary, anatropous, apical, pendulous ovule. The style is protruding and thread-

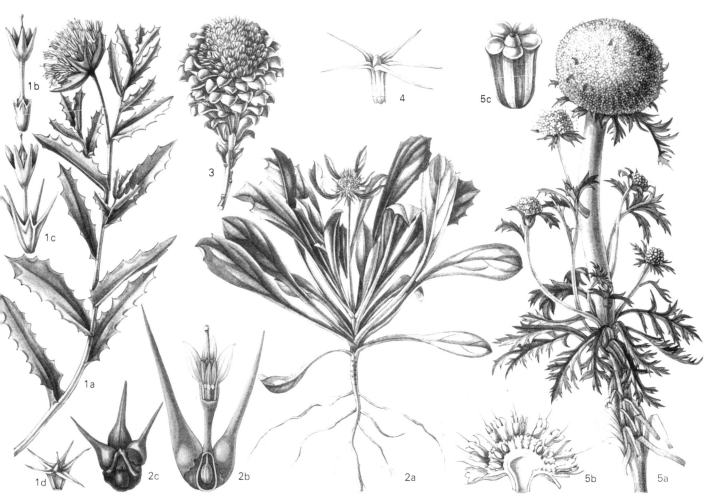

Calyceraceae. 1 *Calycera crassifolia* (a) leafy shoot and flowers in a head surrounded by involucre of bracts (×⅔) ; (b) floret immediately after opening (×2) ; (c) old floret (×2) ; (d) fruit—a ribbed achene with a persistent calyx (×⅔). 2 *Acicarpha spathulata* (a) habit (×⅔) ; (b) fertile marginal floret with spiked calyx-lobes and parts of the corolla tube and ovary wall removed to show stamens in tube around the style and single pendulous ovule (×4) ; (c) vertical section of achene (×4). 3 *Moschopsis rosulata* shoot (×⅔). 4 *Calycera herbacea* var *sinuata* achene (×2). 5 *Nastanthus patagonicus* (a) habit (×⅔) ; (b) vertical section of capitulum (×2) ; (c) achene (×6).

like with a rounded stigma. The fruits are achenes with persistent calyx lobes at the apex, and may be free or united with each other. They contain a pendulous seed with fleshy endosperm and a straight embryo.

Classification. The six genera can be distinguished as follows: in *Moschopsis* the involucre is not well developed; in *Acicarpha* the heads of flowers have sterile central and fertile marginal florets, the outer achenes being joined in their lower part; *Gamocarpha* has the receptacular bracts united into groups of two to three; *Calycera* has dimorphic achenes, the outer being spiny; *Nastanthus* has winged achenes and a large receptacle, while *Boopis* has ribbed achenes and a small receptacle.

Because the flowers are borne in heads subtended by involucral bracts, this family bears an obvious resemblance to the Compositae and Dipsacaceae, while the pollen form and arrangement of anthers are similar to those found in the Goodeniaceae and related families. The floral morphology is similar to that of the Compositae but the ovule is apical in the Calyceraceae, not basal, so that it is usually treated as an aberrant relative of the Dipsacaceae, which it further

resembles in the attachment of the filaments and in certain embryological features.

Economic uses. None are known.

D.M.M.

ASTERALES

COMPOSITAE

The Sunflower Family

The Compositae or Asteraceae is one of the largest families of flowering plants, with about 1,100 currently accepted genera and 25,000 species. Most of its members are evergreen shrubs or subshrubs or perennial rhizomatous herbs, but tap-rooted or tuberous-rooted perennials, and biennial and annual herbs are also frequent; large trees are infrequent, as are epiphytes, and true aquatics are rare. Some tropical island and montane species are giant tree-like herbs, the so-called cabbage trees; many are scramblers, some are true climbers and not a few are succulents, with fleshy leaves or stems. The family includes lettuces, artichokes and sunflowers, as well as chrysanthemums, dahlias and numerous other popular garden flowers, not to mention

weeds like dandelions, thistles and sow thistle.

Distribution. The family is of worldwide distribution, being absent only from the Antarctic mainland, and is particularly well represented in semiarid regions of the tropics and subtropics, such as the Mediterranean region, Mexico, the Cape Province of South Africa, and the woodland, wooded grassland, grassland and bushland formations of Africa, South America and Australia. Compositae are also abundant in arctic, arctic-alpine, temperate and montane floras throughout the world. Only in the tropical rain forests are they poorly represented.

Diagnostic features. The leaves are alternate or opposite, rarely whorled, and without stipules; they are simple (rarely compound), pinnately or palmately veined, and sessile or with petioles, often with an expanded, sheathing or auricled base; they are usually lobed or toothed, sometimes succulent, rarely ending in a tendril, sometimes reduced to scales and quickly falling. Anatomically, Compositae are characterized by the presence of resin canals (in all except most members of the tribe Lactuceae) or latex ducts (in all Lactuceae and a few genera of

Cardueae and Arctotideae). Characteristic biochemical features include the presence of the polysaccharide inulin, instead of starch, in the subterranean parts and fatty oils in the seeds.

The familiar daisies, thistles and dandelions exemplify one of the most characteristic features of the Compositae – the head-like inflorescence, known as a capitulum, made up of numerous small individual flowers called florets, and surrounded by an involucre of protective bracts. The whole resembles a single flower, and is usually taken as such by the layman; indeed, biologically it functions as a single flower. This type of inflorescence is constant throughout the family, though sometimes much modified in various ways.

Further characteristic floral features include the inferior ovary with one locule and one basal ovule; the modified calyx, known as a pappus, made up of hairs, scales, bristles or awns (sometimes more or less fused), which acts as an aid to the distribution of the fruit, although it is sometimes completely lacking; the corolla of fused petals, with the five stamens inserted on the corolla tube and united by their anthers into a cylinder surrounding the style; and the two style arms, which bear hairs or papillae on their tips and external surfaces while the receptive stigmatic surfaces are on the inner sides.

This arrangement of anthers and style arms is associated with a particular mode of pollen presentation. The anthers ripen before the stigmas, and discharge their pollen into the tube formed by the cylinder of fused anthers. At this stage, the style is short and the style arms are pressed together. The style then elongates up the anther tube, from which the pollen is swept by the hairs of the style arms and presented at the apex of the anther tube to any visiting pollinator. Only later do the style arms separate to expose the stigmatic surfaces. Each floret thus goes through a staminate (male), then a pistillate (female) stage. Finally, the style arms may

Compositae. 1 *Gazania linearis* a low-growing perennial herb producing a basal rosette of leaves and terminal radiate (ie outer ray and inner disk florets) flower heads (capitula) that are subtended by a series of green bracts ($\times \frac{2}{3}$). 2 *Mutisia oligodon* (a) a scrambling perennial herb showing alternate leaves with tendrils and the terminal capitulum ($\times \frac{2}{3}$); (b) bisexual bilabiate floret with a three-toothed outer lip and a two-toothed inner lip ($\times$ 3). 3 *Cichorium intybus* (endive) (a) flowering shoot with capitula of ligulate florets only ($\times \frac{2}{3}$); (b) ligulate floret ($\times$ 2); (c) ligulate floret with corolla removed to show stamens inserted in the corolla tube and anthers united in a tube around the style ($\times$ 4). 4 *Liatris graminifolia* (a) flowering shoot bearing discoid capitula (ie only with disk florets) ($\times \frac{2}{3}$); (b) disk floret with a regular five-lobed corolla ($\times$ 4). 5 *Centaurea montana* leaf and terminal capitulum of disk florets, the outer ones being sterile and enlarged ($\times \frac{2}{3}$).

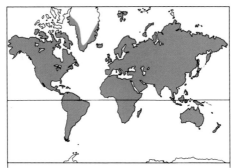

Number of genera: about 1,100
Number of species: about 25,000
Distribution: cosmopolitan.
Economic uses: food plants (eg lettuce, artichokes, sunflower), ornamentals (chysanthemums, dahlias), insecticide (pyrethrum) and medicines and drugs.

recurve sufficiently for the stigmas to make contact with pollen from the anthers of their own floret. In this way, in self-compatible species, self-pollination may be effected should cross-pollination for some reason have failed to occur. Some florets, however, are exclusively staminate or pistillate.

Florets in the individual capitula are arranged in a racemose or indeterminate manner, with the outer ones opening first. The capitula themselves, however, are cymosely disposed in the total overall inflorescence, which is very variable in size, shape, construction, number of capitula and disposition on the plant. Commonly, the capitula are arranged in terminal or terminal and upper axillary corymboid or paniculoid cymes or thyrses. In some genera, the capitula are secondarily aggregated into spikes or compound capitula; sometimes, as in *Echinops*, each individual capitulum in such a compound cluster is reduced to the one-flowered condition and the whole is sometimes surrounded, as in *Lagascea*, *Elephantopus* and some *Sphaeranthus* species, by a secondary involucre of its own.

The most common type of floret is the disk floret, which is usually bisexual, sometimes staminate or sterile, and has a tubular corolla with five (rarely four) apical lobes or teeth. Other types are the bilabiate floret, which is two-lipped with a three-toothed (or four-toothed) outer (lower) lip and a two-toothed (or one-toothed) inner (upper) lip; the ray floret, usually pistillate or sterile, and strap-shaped with three or fewer apical teeth; the ligulate floret, which is bisexual and strap-shaped with five apical teeth; the reduced ray floret, which is pistillate and has a short, usually narrow ray; and the filiform floret, which is pistillate, with a narrow corolla tube and oblique or truncate apex. Rarely, the corolla is highly reduced or even absent.

Capitula may be homogamous, with all the florets bisexual, or heterogamous, in which case the inner florets are usually bisexual and the outer florets pistillate or

sterile. Less commonly, other arrangements may be found, and in some cases the capitula are unisexual, either pistillate (with all florets pistillate) or staminate (with all florets staminate). Unisexual capitula may be borne on the same plant (the monoecious condition) or on different plants (the dioecious condition). Homogamous capitula may be discoid (with all florets disk), ligulate (with all florets ligulate) or bilabiate (with all florets bilabiate). Heterogamous capitula are usually radiate (with outer ray florets and inner disk florets), disciform (with outer filiform florets and inner disk florets) or radiant (with inner bisexual disk florets and outer enlarged, sterile disk florets).

In common use, as in *Bellis* or in *Helianthus*, the central regular florets are collectively called the "disk" and the outer irregular florets are termed the "rays".

The involucre may be of one or more rows of overlapping bracts; only rarely is it absent. On the receptacle, between the florets, there may occur chaffy bracts, scales, bristles or hairs; most often, however, the receptacle is naked. The anthers may be dorsifixed (fixed to the filaments by their upper surface), with pollen grains within the anthers below the level of attachment, or basifixed (fixed at their bases), with all the pollen grains above the insertion. At the apex of the anther, there is usually a sterile appendage; the base of each anther lobe may be rounded, acute or lobed, short or long; when long and attenuate, it is referred to as tailed. The style arms vary in shape, length and distribution of the hairs or papillae, configuration of the stigmatic surfaces, and in the shape of the apex, which may be truncate, rounded, tapered or variously appendaged.

The fruit is one-seeded, indehiscent, nearly always dry, and is termed a cypsela. It may be angular, rounded, variously compressed, or curved, ornamented or winged in various ways; rarely it is a drupe, with fleshy endocarp. It is often furnished with an apical pappus (a ring of fine hairs which can act as a parachute for wind-dispersal). The seed has no endosperm and a straight embryo.

Classification. The classification of the Compositae is in a state of transition. The arrangement into twelve tribes, which has been generally accepted for the last 20 years, is now seen to be in need of modification, in the light of recent discoveries in biochemistry, pollen analysis, micromorphology, anatomy and cytology. Not a few genera have been shown to be misplaced, while others require segregation into distinct tribes. Below tribal level, the classification into subtribes and genera is likely to be much modified in the light of new knowledge, and the number of accepted species is likely to undergo reduction. The following arrangement recognizes two subfamilies and 17 tribes. The tribes Eupatorieae and Senecioneae are intermediate between the two

subfamilies in some respects, and might warrant segregation together into a third subfamily.

SUBFAMILY LACTUCOIDEAE

Capitula homogamous, ligulate, bilabiate or discoid, less often heterogamous, radiate or disciform; disk florets usually with long, narrow lobes, purplish, pinkish or whitish, less often yellow; anthers dorsifixed; style arms usually with single stigmatic area on inner surface; pollen ridged, ridged and spiny, or spiny.

1. LACTUCEAE. Capitula ligulate; latex ducts present; resin canals mostly absent; pollen usually ridged and spiny or spiny; mostly herbs; leaves alternate. Nine subtribes, 70 genera, 2,300 species, worldwide, mainly in the Northern Hemisphere. *Catananche* (Mediterranean), *Chondrilla* (Eurasia), *Cichorium* (Mediterranean), *Crepis* (Northern Hemisphere, Africa), *Hieracium* (temperate, except Australasia), *Hypochoeris* (Northern Hemisphere and South America), *Lactuca* (mostly Northern Hemisphere, Africa), *Lapsana* (Eurasia), *Picris* (Eurasia and Mediterranean), *Prenanthes* (temperate Northern Hemisphere), *Scolymus* (Mediterranean), *Scorzonera* (Eurasia), *Sonchus* (Old World), *Taraxacum* (mostly Northern Hemisphere), *Tragopogon* (Eurasia).

2. MUTISIEAE. Capitula bilabiate or ligulate, rarely radiate or discoid; latex ducts absent; anthers usually tailed; pollen and style arms various; woody or herbaceous; leaves alternate, rarely opposite. Three subtribes, 90 genera, 1,000 species, mostly South American. *Barnadesia* (South America), *Gerbera* (Africa and Asia), *Mutisia* (South America), *Perezia* (New World), *Stifftia* (tropical South America).

3. EREMOTHAMNEAE. Capitula radiate; latex ducts absent; anthers shortly tailed; pollen spiny; style arms elongate, acute; shrubs; leaves alternate. One subtribe, one genus, one species, South Africa. *Eremothamnus*.

4. ARCTOTIDEAE. Capitula radiate, rarely discoid; latex ducts usually absent; anthers obtuse to acute, not tailed; pollen spiny; style arms short with swollen papillose zone below the style arms, usually with collar of hairs at its base; herbs or shrubs; leaves alternate. Three subtribes, 15 genera, 200 species, mostly South African. *Arctotis* (including *Venidium* (South Africa), *Gazania* (South Africa).

5. CARDUEAE. Capitula discoid, homogamous or with sterile outer florets; latex ducts usually absent; anthers acute, often tailed; pollen spiny, not ridged; style arms usually short, often with papillose zone below them as in Arctotideae; herbs or rarely shrubs; leaves alternate. Three well-marked subtribes, 80 genera, 2,600 species, mostly Eurasian. *Arctium* (temperate Eurasia), *Carduus* (Eurasia), *Carlina* (Eurasia), *Carthamus* (Mediterranean), *Centaurea* (mostly Eurasia and Africa), *Cirsium* (temperate Northern Hemisphere), *Cnicus* (Mediterranean), *Cousinia* (Asia), *Cynara* (Mediterranean, southwest Asia), *Echinops* (Eurasia, Africa), *Jurinea* (Eurasia), *Onopordum* (Mediterranean, southwest Asia), *Saussurea* (mostly temperate Asia), *Silybum* (Mediterranean), *Xeranthemum* (Mediterranean).

6. VERNONIEAE. Capitula discoid, rarely ligulate, homogamous; latex ducts absent; anthers obtuse to acute, rarely tailed; pollen spiny, ridged and spiny, or ridged; style arms elongate, gradually attenuate, acute or obtuse, hairy; herbs or shrubs, rarely trees; leaves alternate or opposite. One subtribe, 50 genera, 1,200 species, mostly tropical. *Stokesia* (southeast United States of America), *Vernonia* (pantropical).

7. LIABEAE. Capitula radiate or discoid; latex ducts absent; anthers acute or shortly tailed; pollen spiny; style arms as in Vernonieae; herbs, shrubs or small trees; leaves opposite or whorled. One subtribe, 15 genera, 120 species, New World, mostly tropical. *Liabum* (Central and South America).

8. EUPATORIEAE. Capitula discoid, homogamous; latex ducts absent; anthers obtuse to acute, not tailed; pollen spiny; style arms elongate, club-shaped, papillose; herbs or shrubs; leaves opposite or alternate. Perhaps three subtribes, 120 genera, 1,800 species, mostly New World. *Ageratum* (New World), *Ayapana* (New World), *Chromolaena* (New World), *Eupatorium* (temperate Northern Hemisphere), *Liatris* (North America), *Mikania* (mostly New World tropics), *Piqueria* (Central and South America), *Stevia* (New World).

SUBFAMILY ASTEROIDEAE

Capitula heterogamous, radiate or disciform, less often discoid; disk florets usually with short, broad lobes, usually yellow; anthers basifixed; style arms usually with two distinct stigmatic areas; pollen spiny; latex ducts absent.

9. SENECIONEAE. Involucral bracts usually in one row, often with an outer series of reduced bracts; receptacle naked; anthers rounded to acute, sometimes tailed; style arms usually truncate, apically minutely hairy, less often variously appendaged; herbs or shrubs, sometimes more or less succulent; leaves alternate. Three subtribes, 85 genera, 3,000 species, worldwide. *Cacalia* (temperate Northern Hemisphere), *Cineraria* (Africa), *Crassocephalum* (Africa), *Doronicum* (Eurasia), *Emilia* (Old World tropics), *Euryops* (Africa and Arabia), *Gynura* (Africa and Asia), *Kleinia* (mostly Africa), *Ligularia* (mostly eastern Asia), *Othonna* (South Africa), *Petasites* (Eurasia), *Senecio* (worldwide), *Tussilago* (Eurasia).

10. TAGETEAE. Involucral bracts in one or two series, free or united, usually with pellucid glands; receptacle naked; anthers obtuse to acute, not tailed; style arms truncate or variously appendaged; herbs or shrubs; leaves opposite or alternate, usually with pellucid glands containing strongly scented essential oils. Two subtribes, 20 genera, 250 species, New World, mostly Mexico and Central America. *Tagetes* (New World), *Pectis* (New World).

11. HELIANTHEAE. Involucral bracts in several series; receptacle naked or scaly; anthers obtuse to acute, not tailed; style arms various, tapered and hairy throughout or truncate with apical hairs or hairy appendages; pappus usually of awns or scales; herbs, less often shrubs; leaves opposite, less often alternate, frequently roughly hairy. Perhaps 26 subtribes, 250 genera, 4,000 species, worldwide but mostly New World. *Acanthospermum* (South America), *Ambrosia* (mostly New World), *Argyroxiphium* (Hawaii), *Arnica* (northern temperate and arctic), *Bidens* (including *Coreopsis* and *Cosmos*) (worldwide), *Dahlia* (Central America), *Echinacea* (North America), *Eriophyllum* (North America), *Espeletia* (South America), *Flaveria* (mostly Central America), *Gaillardia* (New World), *Galinsoga* (Central and South America), *Guizotia* (Africa), *Helenium* (North America), *Helianthus* (mostly North America), *Heliopsis* (North America), *Lagascea* (New World tropics), *Layia* (North America), *Madia* (New World), *Parthenium* (New World), *Polymnia* (New World), *Ratibida* (North and Central America), *Rudbeckia* (North America), *Sanvitalia* (North America), *Silphium* (North America), *Spilanthes* (pantropical), *Tithonia* (Central America), *Tridax* (Central and South America), *Wyethia* (North America), *Xanthium* (New World), *Zinnia* (New World).

12. INULEAE. Involucral bracts in several series; receptacle naked, sometimes scaly; anthers usually tailed; style arms truncate and apically hairy, rounded or variously appendaged; herbs or shrubs; leaves alternate. Perhaps three subtribes. 180 genera, 2,100 species, worldwide. *Anaphalis* (mostly temperate Northern Hemisphere), *Antennaria* (mostly arctic and temperate Northern Hemisphere), *Blumea* (Old World tropics), *Buphthalmum* (Eurasia), *Gnaphalium* (worldwide), *Helichrysum* (Africa, Madagascar, Australasia, Eurasia), *Helipterum* (southern Africa, Australia), *Inula* (Eurasia and Africa), *Leontopodium* (Eurasia), *Raoulia* (Australasia), *Sphaeranthus* (Old World tropics).

13. ANTHEMIDEAE. Involucral bracts in several series, usually with thin, dry, transparent tips or margins; receptacle naked or scaly; anthers obtuse to acute, not tailed; style arms truncate, fringed with short hairs;

Compositae (continued). 6 *Ursinia speciosa* shoot bearing pinnatisect (deeply cut) leaves and radiate capitulum (×⅔). 7 *Bellis perennis* showing basal rosette of leaves and solitary radiate capitula (×⅔). 8 *Helianthus giganteus* (a) female ray floret (×4); (b) bisexual disk floret (×6); (c) disk floret opened out (×6). 9 *H. angustifolius* flowering shoot (×⅔). 10 *Argyranthemum broussonetti* flowering shoot (×2). 11 *Leontopodium haplophylloides* flowering shoot (×2).

herbs or less often shrubs; leaves alternate, vary rarely opposite, often much divided, strongly scented. Perhaps four subtribes, 75 genera, 1,200 species, mostly Northern Hemisphere. *Achillea* (temperate Northern Hemisphere), *Anacyclus* (Mediterranean), *Anthemis* (Europe, Mediterranean, southwest Asia), *Argyranthemum* (Macaronesia), *Artemisia* (mostly Northern Hemisphere), *Chrysanthemum* (Europe, Mediterranean), *Dendranthema* (mostly eastern Asia), *Leucanthemum* (Europe, Mediterranean, southwest Asia), *Lonas* (Mediterranean), *Matricaria* (Eurasia), *Santolina* (Mediterranean), *Tanacetum* (Europe, southwest Asia).

14. URSINIEAE. Involucral bracts in several series, often with thin, dry transparent tips or margins; receptacle scaly; anthers obtuse to acute, not tailed; style arms truncate, fringed with short hairs; shrubs or herbs; leaves alternate or opposite. Perhaps three subtribes, eight genera, 120 species, South African. *Lasiospermum* (South Africa), *Ursinia* (mostly South Africa).

15. CALENDULEAE. Involucral bracts in one or two series; receptacle naked; anthers acute, more or less tailed; style arms truncate, with apical hairs; pappus absent; cypselas often curiously shaped; herbs or shrubs; leaves alternate or opposite. One subtribe, seven genera, 100 species, Africa, Europe and southwest Asia. *Calendula* (mostly Mediterranean), *Dimorphotheca* (South Africa), *Osteospermum* (Africa and southwest Asia).

16. COTULEAE. Involucral bracts in one or two series; receptacle naked; anthers obtuse to acute, not tailed; style arms truncate, fringed with short hairs; mostly herbs; leaves alternate. One subtribe, 10 genera, 120 species, mostly Southern Hemisphere. *Cotula* (Australasia, subantarctic islands, South Africa, South America).

17. ASTEREAE. Involucral bracts in two or more series; receptacle naked, or rarely scaly; anthers obtuse, not tailed; style arms with a shortly hairy triangular to lanceolate apical appendage; herbs, shrubs or rarely small trees; leaves alternate or less often opposite. Perhaps three subtribes, 120 genera, 2,500 species. *Aster* (mainly Northern Hemisphere), *Baccharis* (New World), *Bellis* (Eurasia), *Brachylaena* (Africa, tribal position uncertain), *Brachycome* (Australasia), *Callistephus* (eastern Asia), *Conyza* (mostly tropical), *Erigeron* (mostly Northern Hemisphere), *Felicia* (Africa), *Grindelia* (temperate North and South America), *Haplopappus* (New World), *Olearia* (Australasia), *Solidago* (Northern Hemisphere, mostly New World).

The relationships of the Compositae are uncertain, a fact recognized in classification by their allocation as the only family in a distinct order, the Asterales. Certain features exhibited by the Compositae are also known in other families, but their occurrence is insufficiently correlated to permit the selec-

tion of any one of these as indicating a close relationship. Some of the basic features of the Compositae probably evolved very rapidly very early in the history of the family, thus setting it apart very clearly from any other. They include the involucrate capitulum, the receptacle without bracts, the inferior ovary with a single locule, the capillary pappus, the pollen-presentation mechanism and the cypsela. The tribe Mutisieae is most heterogeneous in many respects, such as the pollen grain wall structure and corolla form, and gives the appearance of a rather loosely allied assemblage of archaic (though often highly specialized) forms. The bilabiate corolla is most frequent in this tribe, and certain considerations of the floral biology of racemose inflorescences indicate that this is the least specialized of the various types exhibited by the Compositae.

Amongst the families often postulated as allied to the Compositae – Rubiaceae, Caprifoliaceae, Dipsacaceae, Valerianaceae, Stylidiaceae, Goodeniaceae, Brunoniaceae, Calyceraceae, Campanulaceae – the first four have basically cymose, not racemose, inflorescences, and regular, not irregular, flowers; they also differ widely from the Compositae in biochemical features, in which they resemble more such families as the Cornaceae. The Stylidiaceae, Goodeniaceae and Brunoniaceae resemble the Compositae in being mostly racemose and irregular and in possessing inulin; on the other hand, they resemble the previous families, and differ from the Compositae, in some other biochemical features commonly held to be of taxonomic significance. The Calyceraceae is too poorly known biochemically to be assessed, but the Campanulaceae, whilst differing from the Compositae in embryological details, resembles it biochemically in the presence of inulin and the absence of tannins and iridoid compounds. On the other hand, there are many biochemical similarities between the Compositae and the Umbelliferae, Araliaceae and Pittosporaceae, and, more remotely, the Rutaceae and eventually the Magnoliales.

Economic uses. The Compositae are of incalculably great indirect economic importance to Man as major contributors to the diversity, and therefore the stability and sustainable productivity, of the drier (wooded grassland, grassland, bushland and semidesert) vegetation types throughout the world, especially in tropical and subtropical areas. In proportion to its size, however, the direct economic importance of the family is comparatively small. It includes food plants, sources of raw materials, medicinal and drug plants, ornamentals and succulents, and, on the debit side, weeds and poisonous plants.

The most commercially important food plant is *Lactuca sativa* (lettuce); others include *Cichorium endivia* (endive), *C. intybus* (chicory), *Scorzonera hispanica* and

Tragopogon porrifolius (salsify), *Cynara scolymus* (globe artichoke), *Helianthus tuberosus* (Jerusalem artichoke), and the culinary herb tarragon (*Artemisia dracunculus*).

Helianthus annuus (sunflower), *Carthamus tinctorius* (safflower) and *Guizotia abyssinica* (niger seed) are grown for their seeds, which are important sources of edible and drying oils. *Tanacetum cinerariifolium* is the main commercial source of natural pyrethrum, used as an insecticide. *Parthenium argentatum* (guayule) and *Taraxacum bicorne* have been utilized as minor sources of rubber. *Brachylaena huillensis* yields a commercial timber (muhugu) of high durability. Many members of this chemically rich family have long been used in folk medicines. Certain *Artemisia* species, such as *Artemisia cina* and *A. maritima*, yield santonin, used as a vermifuge; *A. absinthium* is the source of the essential oil used to flavor absinthe. *Anthemis nobilis* produces chamomile.

The Compositae contribute largely to gardens throughout the world as ornamental plants. They include species and/or hybrids of the following genera: *Gerbera, Mutisia, Arctotis, Gazania, Echinops* (globe thistle), *Stokesia* (Stokes' aster), *Ageratum, Senecio* (*S.* × *hybridus*, florists' cineraria), *Tagetes* (African and French marigolds), *Bidens* (cosmos), *Dahlia* (*D.* × *hortensis*, dahlia), *Gaillardia, Helianthus* (sunflower), *Zinnia, Helichrysum* (everlastings), *Dendranthema* (florists' chrysanthemum), *Leucanthemum* (ox-eye daisy), *Ursinia, Calendula* (marigold), *Aster* (Michaelmas daisy), *Callistephus* (florists' aster), *Olearia* (daisy bush) and *Solidago* (golden rod). Of these, *Dahlia, Dendranthema* and *Callistephus* are the most important, each with many thousands of cultivars. Many species of *Kleinia, Senecio* and *Othonna* are grown by succulent plant enthusiasts.

Several Compositae have become widespread, sometimes noxious, weeds, frequently in areas far removed for their original homes. They include *Chondrilla juncea* (skeleton weed), *Sonchus oleraceus* (sow thistle), *Taraxacum* species (dandelions), *Cirsium arvense, C. vulgare* and *Carduus nutans* (thistles), *Ageratum conyzoides, Chromolaena odorata, Mikania micrantha, Crassocephalum crepidioides*, a number of *Senecio* species, *Ambrosia artemisiifolia, Tridax procumbens, Acanthospermum hispidum, Xanthium spinosum* and *X. strumarium* (cocklebur), *Bidens pilosa* (black Jack) and *Helichrysum kraussii*. Poisonous *Senecio* species are especially serious weeds of pasture as they are responsible for more deaths of domestic stock than all other poisonous plants together. The wind-borne pollen of the ragweeds *Ambrosia artemisiifolia* and *A. trifida* is one of the main causes of hay fever in the regions of North America where these species occur.

C.J.

Monocotyledons

ALISMATIDAE

ALISMATALES

BUTOMACEAE
Flowering Rush

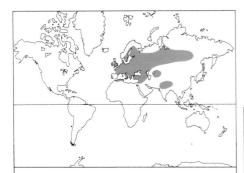

Number of genera: 1
Number of species: 1
Distribution: Europe and temperate Asia, in aquatic and marshy habitats.
Economic uses: cultivated as an ornamental and the rhizomes are eaten in parts of Russia.

The Butomaceae is a family consisting of a single herbaceous aquatic species, *Butomus umbellatus*, widely cultivated under its common name, the flowering rush.

Distribution: *Butomus* usually occurs in swamps, ditches and along pools, lakes and rivers. It is widespread in Europe and temperate Asia, and has become naturalized in North America.

Diagnostic features. *Butomus* is a rhizomatous perennial with linear leaves up to 3ft (1m) long or more. The leaves are triangular in transverse section and arise in two rows along the rhizome. The inflorescence is umbel-like, consisting of a single terminal flower surrounded by three cymes. The flowers are regular and bisexual. There are three petal-like sepals which are pink with darker veins, and persist in the fruit. The three petals are like the sepals, but somewhat larger. There are six to nine stamens. The pollen grains have a single distal aperture. The carpels are superior, six to nine in number and slightly united at the base; when ripe they are obovoid and crowned by a persistent style. The ovules are numerous and found scattered over the inner surface of the carpel wall, except on the midrib and edges. The fruit is a follicle. The seeds have no endosperm and a straight embryo.

Classification. In floral anatomy, development and structure, the Butomaceae is in many ways very similar to the dicotyledonous family Nymphaeaceae. However,

Butomus undoubtedly belongs to the Monocotyledons and is related to the Alismataceae, Limnocharitaceae and Hydrocharitaceae, and possibly also the Aponogetonaceae.

Economic uses. *Butomus* is frequently cultivated as a decorative plant. In parts of Russia the rhizomes are used as food.

C.D.C.

LIMNOCHARITACEAE
Water Poppy

Number of genera: 3
Number of species: about 12
Distribution: tropics and subtropics, in aquatic habitats.
Economic uses: *Limnocharis* is cultivated for food and *Hydrocleis* (water poppy) as an ornamental.

The Limnocharitaceae is a small family of annual and perennial aquatic herbs.

Distribution. The monotypic genus *Tenagocharis* is found in tropical Africa, India, Malaysia and northern Australia. *Hydrocleis* and *Limnocharis* are found in tropical and subtropical America. *Limnocharis flava* has become naturalized in India and Southeast Asia.

Diagnostic features. All species have secretory ducts containing latex. The juvenile leaves are linear and usually submerged, the mature leaves differentiated into petiole and blade. The leaf blades are ovate to cordate with distinct, curved, parallel nerves. The inflorescence is usually umbel-like; occasionally the flowers are solitary. The flowers are showy, regular and bisexual. There are three sepals which are green and persistent in fruit, and possess latex tubes. There are three petals alternating with the sepals and these are white or yellow, delicate and not persistent. There are six to nine or numerous stamens; staminodes are often present. The pollen has four or more pores. The carpels are superior, three to numerous, free, in one or rarely two whorls. The ovules

are numerous and scattered over the inner surface of the carpel wall. The fruit is a follicle which opens by the adaxial (ventral) suture to release numerous seeds that have no endosperm and a curved or folded embryo.

Classification. *Tenagocharis* has relatively small white petals, lacks staminodes and in some respects resembles *Damasonium* in the Alismataceae. The New World genera have large, showy, yellow petals and usually some staminodes.

On the basis of the diffuse parietal placentation of the ovules the Limnocharitaceae is often considered to be allied to the Butomaceae. In older works both families are combined. However, recent phytochemical, embryological and anatomical studies indicate a close relationship with the Alismataceae and not with the Butomaceae.

Economic uses. *Limnocharis flava* is cultivated for food in India and Southeast Asia, the leaves being eaten as an alternative to spinach or endive or used as fodder for pigs. *Hydrocleis nymphoides* (water poppy) has large decorative blossoms which are shining yellow with a reddish-brown center; it has been grown in heated greenhouses in Europe since 1830.

C.D.C.

ALISMATACEAE
Water Plantains

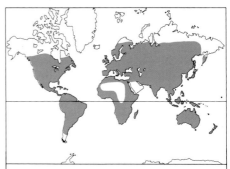

Number of genera: 11
Number of species: about 100
Distribution: cosmopolitan, centered in New World, in aquatic and marshy habitats.
Economic uses: important food for wildlife, some species decorative and *Sagittaria* cultivated for its edible tubers.

The Alismataceae is a small family of aquatic or amphibious plants widely distributed throughout the world. Very few are cultivated, but many provide food for wildlife.

Distribution. The family as a whole is cosmopolitan. The majority of species are found in the New World.

Diagnostic features. Most species are robust perennials, but some may be annual or perennial depending on the water regime;

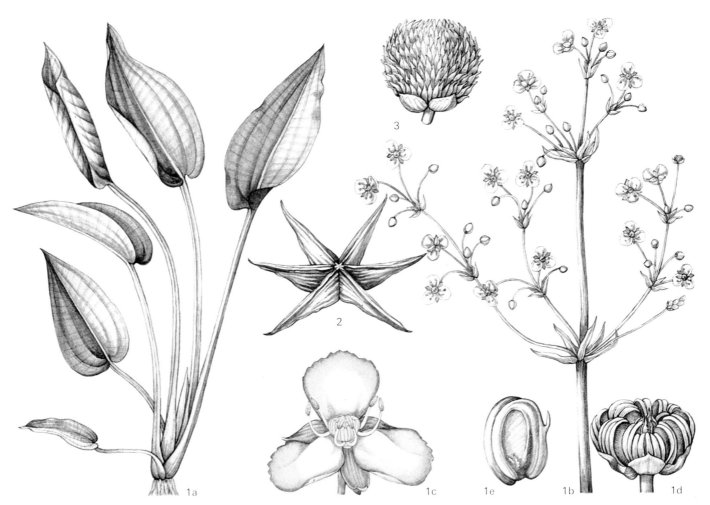

Alismataceae. 1 *Alisma plantago-aquatica* (a) habit showing leaves with sheathing bases, long petioles and leaf blade with main veins parallel to the edges (×⅔) ; (b) inflorescence with flowers arranged in whorls (×1) ; (c) flower with three green sepals, three pink petals, six stamens and gynoecium of numerous free carpels (×8) ; (d) fruit—a head of nutlets, each with longitudinal ribs (×6) ; (e) single nutlet with a persistent style (×8). 2 *Damasonium alisma* star-shaped whorl of dehiscent fruits which are united at their bases (×4). 3 *Sagittaria sagittifolia* fruiting heads composed of numerous nutlets (×3).

generally speaking, in permanent water they are perennial and in seasonal water they behave as annuals. The stems are corm-like or stoloniferous. Most species have two forms of leaf: the juvenile leaves are linear and usually submerged while the mature leaves vary from linear to ovate or occasionally sagittate, and are usually emergent. Most species have a distinct petiole. with an expanded, sheathing base. Secretory ducts are present. The inflorescence is usually compound with whorls of branches, but some species have umbel-like inflorescences and others have solitary flowers. The flowers are regular, bisexual or unisexual (male and female on separate plants in *Burnatia*). There are three sepals which usually persist in fruit. The petals are three, usually conspicuous, white, pink, purple, occasionally with yellow or purple spots, but they rarely last for more than one day. In *Burnatia* and *Wisneria* the petals are minute and occasionally absent in female flowers. The stamens are three, six, nine or numerous. The ovary is superior, comprising three to numerous free carpels in one whorl or in a clustered head; each carpel contains one (rarely two) anatropous ovules. The fruit is a

head of nutlets (except in *Damasonium* which has six to ten dehiscent or semi-dehiscent, several-seeded fruits in one whorl which are more or less united at the base or adnate to the elongated receptacle and spread star-like in fruit). The seeds have no endosperm and a curved or folded embryo.

Classification. The generic delimitation in the Alismataceae is somewhat unsatisfactory. The Old World genera *Baldellia*, *Caldesia* and *Ranalisma* are somewhat artificially separated from each other and the New World genus *Echinodorus*. *Limnophyton* and *Wisneria* are found in tropical Africa and Asia. *Wisneria* shows a remarkable superficial resemblance to *Aponogeton* (Aponogetonaceae). *Burnatia* is monotypic and found in tropical and southern Africa. *Luronium* is also monotypic but is endemic to Europe; it is probably related to *Caldesia*. *Damasonium*, as noted above, has an unusual fruit and a somewhat disjunct distribution: about four species in Europe, North Africa and the Orient, one in southern Australia and one in western North America. It has been suggested that it should be recognized as a distinct family. *Alisma* has nine species, and is almost cosmopolitan

through introductions, although probably indigenous in the Northern Hemisphere. *Sagittaria* has 20 or perhaps more species, the majority being found in the New World.

The Alismataceae, at least superficially, resembles the dicotyledonous family Ranunculaceae but there are considerable anatomical and embryological differences. There is no doubt that the Alismataceae belongs to the monocotyledons and that it possesses many primitive characteristics. It is probably more closely related to the Limnocharitaceae than the Butomaceae. The genera *Tenagocharis* (Limnocharitaceae) and *Damasonium* (Alismataceae) are very similar.

Economic uses. *Sagittaria sagittifolia* is cultivated in China and Japan for its edible corms. The roots of *Sagittaria latifolia* were used as food by North American Indians, and today are eaten by the Chinese in North America. Most genera are important for providing food for wildlife. Several species of *Sagittaria*, *Echinodorus* and *Alisma* are cultivated as decorative poolside plants, eg *Sagittaria sagittifolia*, *S. lancifolia*, *S. latifolia* and *S. montevidensis*. *Sagittaria subulata* and *S. latifolia* are sometimes used as aquarium plants. C.D.C.

Hydrocharitaceae. 1 *Vallisneria spiralis* (a) habit showing stolons bearing new plants, ribbon-shaped leaves and long-stalked female flowers that reach the surface of the water ($\times\frac{2}{3}$); (b) male flower which separates from the parent and floats to the water surface ($\times 12$); ovary (c) in cross section ($\times 8$) and (d) in vertical section ($\times 4$); (e) female flower ($\times 4$). 2 *Elodea canadensis* (a) habit showing female flowers on long stalks ($\times\frac{2}{3}$); (b) vertical section of ovary ($\times 5$); (c) female flower with three, forked styles ($\times 5$). 3 *Hydrocharis morsus-ranae* (a) general habit of this free-floating plant. shown here with male flowers ($\times\frac{2}{3}$); (b) cross section of fruit ($\times 2$); (c) female flower ($\times\frac{2}{3}$).

HYDROCHARITALES

HYDROCHARITACEAE
Canadian Waterweed and Frog's Bit

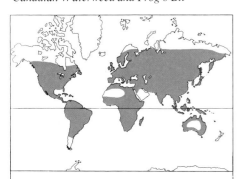

Number of genera: 15
Number of species: about 106
Distribution: cosmopolitan but mainly tropical, in marine and freshwater habitats.
Economic uses: pernicious weeds and some aquarium plants.

The Hydrocharitaceae is a family of marine and freshwater aquatics which produces some fine aquarium ornamentals and has specialized pollination mechanisms.

Distribution. This family is found in a wide variety of aquatic habitats throughout the world, though the majority of species are tropical.

Diagnostic features. The family consists of annual or perennial aquatic herbs, having either a creeping monopodial rhizome with leaves arranged in two vertical rows, or an erect main shoot with roots at the base and spirally arranged or whorled leaves. The leaves are simple, usually submerged, or sometimes floating or partly emergent. They are very variable in shape: from linear to orbicular, with or without a petiole and with or without sheathing bases. The flowers are arranged in a forked, spathe-like bract or between two opposite bracts. They are usually regular though occasionally slightly irregular (eg *Vallisneria*), and either bisexual or unisexual (male and female then being borne on separate plants). The perianth segments are in one or two series of three (rarely two) free segments; the inner series when present are usually showy and petal-like. The stamens are one to numerous, in one or more series; the inner ones are sometimes sterile (in *Lagarosiphon* the staminodes function as sails for the free-floating male flowers). The pollen is globular and free but in the marine genera *Thalassia* and *Halophila* the pollen grains are liberated in chains like strings of beads. The ovary is inferior with two to fifteen united carpels containing a single locule with numerous ovules on parietal placentas which either protrude nearly to the center of the ovary or are incompletely developed. There are as many styles as carpels. The fruits are globular to linear, dry or pulpy, dehiscent or more usually indehiscent and opening by decay of the pericarp. The seeds are usually numerous with straight embryos and no endosperm.

The family has a remarkable variety of specialized pollination mechanisms. Some genera such as *Egeria*, *Hydrocharis* (frog's bit) and *Stratiotes* have relatively large showy flowers that are insect-pollinated but some species are reported to be self-pollinating before the flower has opened (cleistogamous). In *Hydrilla*, *Lagarosiphon*, *Maidenia*, *Nechamandra* and *Vallisneria* the male flowers become detached from the mother plant and rise to the surface where they

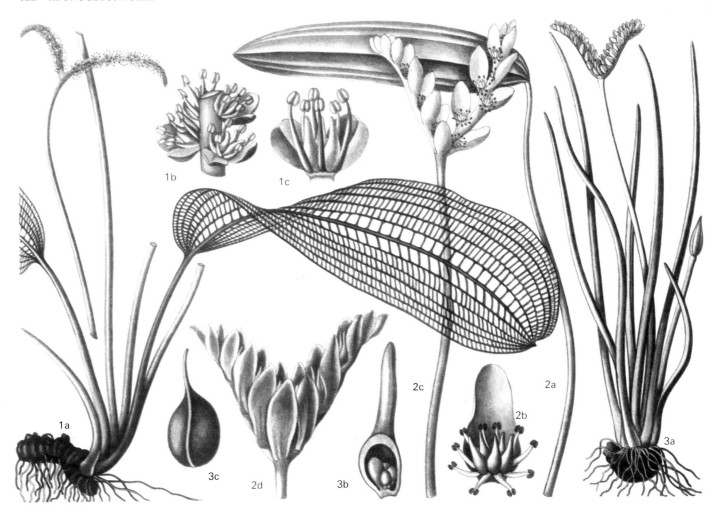

Aponogetonaceae. 1 *Aponogeton madagascariensis* (a) habit showing rhizome bearing leaves in which the blade is merely a lattice of veins and nerves, and a forked inflorescence born on a long stalk (×⅔) ; (b) portion of inflorescence (×4) ; (c) flower consisting of two perianth segments, six stamens and three sessile carpels (×6). 2 *Aponogeton distachyos* (a) aerial leaf (×⅔) ; (b) flower (×2) ; (c) inflorescence (×⅔) ; (d) infructescence with persistent perianth segments (×⅔). 3 *Aponogeton spathaceus* (a) habit showing tuber-like corms, tufts of strap-like leaves and forked inflorescence (×⅔) ; (b) vertical section of carpel showing sessile ovules (×16) ; (c) fruit—a leathery follicle (×6).

expand and then drift or sail to the female flowers. In *Elodea* the male flowers may become detached or remain on the mother plant but in either case the anthers explode and scatter pollen grains over the surface of the water.

Classification. The Hydrocharitaceae is usually divided into three subfamilies: HYDROCHARITOIDEAE, THALASSOIDEAE and HALOPHILOIDEAE. The latter two subfamilies are monogeneric (*Thalassia, Halophila*) and grow in tropical seas; the male spathe contains one flower, pollination takes place underwater and the pollen is liberated in chains. The genera of the Hydrocharitoideae are pollinated at or above the water surface with globular pollen grains. They occur in fresh water except for *Enhalus*.

The Hydrocharitaceae does not possess secretory ducts and frequently contains anthocyanin pigments. These characters, along with the pollen morphology and numerous embryological features, indicate a relationship with the Butomaceae and more remotely with the Nymphaeaceae. In most systems the Hydrocharitaceae is given a central position in the group known as the Helobiae, which includes the orders Alis-

matales, Hydrocharitales and Najadales, but today it looks as if they may represent a very primitive group within the monocotyledons.

Economic uses. Many species are attractive or interesting aquarium plants. Several introductions, however, have become serious weeds in their new habitats, eg *Hydrilla* in the United States of America, *Elodea canadensis* (Canadian waterweed) in Europe and *Lagarosiphon* in New Zealand. C.D.C.

NAJADALES

APONOGETONACEAE

Water Hawthorn

The Aponogetonaceae comprises a single genus of freshwater aquatic or amphibious perennial herbs with corms or rhizomes.

Distribution. The family is found in the warm and tropical regions of the Old World and in northern Australia; most species are found in Africa and Madagascar. *Aponogeton distachyos* (the water hawthorn or Cape pondweed), a native of South Africa, has become naturalized in southern Australia, western South America and Western Europe.

Diagnostic features. The stems are reduced to

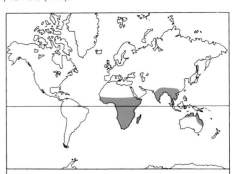

Number of genera: 1
Number of species: about 45
Distribution: warmer and tropical regions of the Old World, in aquatic or marshy habitats.
Economic uses: tubers eaten by Man and livestock.

tuber-like corms or elongated and branched rhizomes. The roots are fibrous. Many species grow in temporarily still or flowing water and live through the dry period as a dormant tuber. The leaves are borne in tufts at the tips of the stems. The majority of *Aponogeton* species have two forms of leaf: the juvenile leaves are usually strap-like, while the mature leaves are usually stalked with an expanded, linear, elliptic or oblong blade mostly with a distinct midrib and one or more pairs of parallel main nerves connected by numerous cross veins. In the Madagascan lace plant, *A. madagascariensis* (*A. fenestralis*) the whole blade often consists of no more than a lattice of veins and nerves. Submerged leaves are usually thin and are often undulate or contorted. Several species develop thick, leathery floating leaves. In some species, such as *A. junceus*, the leaves are reduced to elongated midribs and resemble rushes.

The flowers are usually bisexual or occasionally unisexual; some species are agamospermous (forming seeds without fusion of gametes). The inflorescences are spike-like and are borne on long stalks that emerge above the water surface. In bud, each spike is enveloped in a spathe. In all the Asian and most of the Australian species the spikes are single; in the majority of the African species they are paired and in some species from Madagascar there are up to ten spikes on a single stalk. The number and form of the floral parts is very variable. The perianth segments may be absent or up to six, they may be petal-like or bract-like and they may be persistent or caducous. The stamens are in two or more whorls, usually six or more in number. The ovary is superior with two to nine free, mostly sessile carpels each with two to numerous anatropous ovules on a basal placenta. The top of each carpel narrows into a style with an adaxial stigmatic ridge. Each carpel matures into a free, leathery follicle containing one to numerous seeds. The seeds have a straight embryo and no endosperm; the testa is usually single but sometimes is split into two, an inner one closely fitting the embryo and a loose transparent outer one.

Classification. The Aponogetonaceae is considered to be allied to the Potamogetonaceae-Najadaceae complex of families.

Economic uses. The tubers of several species are eaten by humans and their livestock. Many species make decorative aquarium plants, notably *A. distachyos*. As a result of large-scale trade the Madagascan lace plant (*A. madagascariensis*) has become extinct in many localities in Madagascar.

C.D.C.

SCHEUCHZERIACEAE

Arrowgrass

The Scheuchzeriaceae consists of a single genus (*Scheuchzeria*) of marsh plants, with inconspicuous flowers and a graceful, grasslike appearance, hence their common name, arrowgrass.

Distribution. *Scheuchzeria* is restricted to cold north temperate zones, being especially common in cold sphagnum bogs.

Diagnostic features. The plants are slender perennial herbs with alternate, linear leaves, with a sheath at the base which embraces the

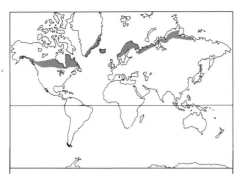

Number of genera: 1
Number of species: 2
Distribution: cold north temperate zone, especially sphagnum bogs.
Economic uses: none.

stem and terminates in a ligule. The flowers are regular, bisexual and borne in terminal racemes with bracts. The perianth is of two similar whorls each of three free segments. There are two whorls of three free stamens with basifixed anthers. The ovary is superior, comprising three to six carpels, united only at their bases, with three to six locules, each containing two or few basal, erect, anatropous ovules. Each carpel bears a sessile stigma. The fruit is composed of a number of one- or two-seeded follicles, the seeds having no endosperm. The embryo has a rounded cotyledon and a small plumule.

Classification. Some botanists consider that the family should also include *Triglochin*, which here is placed in a separate family, the Juncaginaceae. However, there is no doubt about the close relationship between *Scheuchzeria* and *Triglochin* as they have many features in common, both vegetatively and floristically. The six carpels in two whorls and the free perianth segments are regarded as primitive and may indicate a relationship with the Alismataceae.

Economic uses. None are known.   S.R.C.

JUNCAGINACEAE

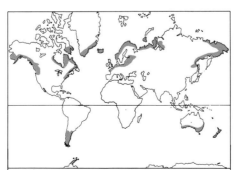

Number of genera: 3
Number of species: 14
Distribution: temperate and cold regions of the N and S Hemispheres, in marshy habitats.
Economic uses: limited, local uses as food.

The Juncaginaceae is a small family of annual and perennial marsh herbs.

Distribution. The family is found in temperate and cold regions of the Northern and Southern Hemispheres, mainly around the coasts.

Diagnostic features. The rhizome produces fibrous or tuberous roots and flat linear leaves, which are sheathing at the base, and usually radical (sometimes floating).

The inflorescence is a raceme or spike. The flowers are regular, without bracts, bisexual or unisexual (male and female on separate plants or male, female and bisexual on the same plant). They have a green or red perianth of two series of three free segments. There are four or six stamens with subsessile anthers. The ovary is superior and consists of four or six free or partly united carpels, each containing a single basal, anatropous ovule (rarely apical and orthotropous). The styles are short or absent, and the stigmas often feathery. The fruit is a follicle and the seeds have a straight embryo and no endosperm. The flowers are wind-pollinated, and in one species of *Triglochin* there are boat-shaped pockets under the anthers which first collect the pollen before it is dispersed by the wind.

Classification. The genera *Triglochin* (12 species), *Maundia* (one species) and *Tetroncium* (one species) are closely related to each other and to the Lilaeaceae. They show similarities with other monocotyledonous aquatic and marsh plants of the families Aponogetonaceae and Najadaceae. The possession of a double whorl of carpels is regarded as a primitive feature and possibly indicates evolutionary links with the Alismataceae and the Butomaceae.

Economic uses. The leaves of *Triglochin maritima* of the north temperate zone are edible, and the Australian aborigines use the rhizome of *T. procerum* as food.

S.R.C.

LILAEACEAE

The Lilaeaceae is a family of aquatic and marsh herbs having only a single genus with a single species. The plants are notable for their strikingly unusual inflorescences.

Distribution. *Lilaea* is found in permanent or temporary shallow water in western North America and western South America southwards to Chile and Argentina. It is also found in Victoria, Australia, but is probably introduced.

Diagnostic features. *Lilaea* is a tufted, grasslike annual. The leaves are basal, simple, linear and cylindrical with membranous, sheathing bases that converge across the top to form a short ligule. The inflorescence is very complex; each leaf axil bears one or two female flowers and a stalked spike bearing bisexual and male flowers. The female flowers are enclosed in the sheathing leaf base and consist of a completely naked carpel with a thread-like style up to 12in (30cm) long that arises laterally at the top of the carpel but at length ascends. The fruit is an

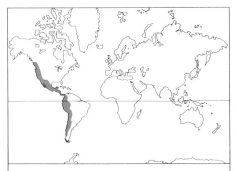

Number of genera: 1
Number of species: 1
Distribution: temperate western N and S America, in aquatic and marshy habitats.
Economic uses: none.

occasionally auriculate base. The flowers are unisexual, small, axillary, solitary or in small clusters; male and female are borne on the same plant in some species, on different plants in others. The male flowers are enclosed in a perianth-like, membranous sheath (spathe) which terminates in two thickened lips; the stamen is solitary and the anther subsessile. Pollination takes place under water, the pollen grains being ellipsoidal and without apertures. The female flowers are either naked or surrounded by a spathe. The ovary is superior and consists of a single carpel tapering into a short style with two to four linear stigmas. There is a single basal, anatropous ovule. The fruit is a single-seeded nutlet. The seeds have a straight embryo and no endosperm.

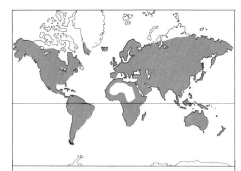

Number of genera: 2
Number of species: about 100
Distribution: cosmopolitan, in aquatic habitats.
Economic uses: important food plants for many animals.

angled nutlet, often with hooks or horns at the apex. The bisexual flowers have a single, bract-like perianth segment arising from the base of the solitary and sessile anther and one naked carpel with a single style that is very variable in length from flower to flower. Female and bisexual flowers have a single, basal, erect, anatropous ovule in each carpel. The fruits of the bisexual flowers are flattened nutlets with a dorsal ridge and wavy lateral wings. The male flowers consist of a single, bract-like perianth segment arising from the base of a solitary, stalkless anther. The seeds have a straight embryo and no endosperm.

The single species, *Lilaea scilloides*, is found in shallow water and usually starts to flower as the water level drops. It passes through the dry period as a seed and is a characteristic plant of vernal pools.

Classification. The structure of the flower and inflorescence of *Lilaea* is disputed. Some authors consider that the bisexual flowers are partial inflorescences consisting of one male and one female flower and that the perianth is an outgrowth of the connective. In spite of the confusion in the interpretation of the flower there is little doubt that the Lilaeaceae are helobian monocotyledons. They can be considered to represent a bridge between the Zannichelliaceae and the Najadaceae.

Economic uses. None are known.

C.D.C.

NAJADACEAE
The Najadaceae is a family of small submerged aquatic annual or perennial plants containing one genus, *Najas*.

Distribution. *Najas* species occur throughout temperate and warm regions of the world.

Diagnostic features. The stems are slender, either sparsely branched and diffuse or much-branched and condensed. The leaves appear to be opposite but are usually crowded in leaf axils and thus may be described as pseudo-whorled or in bunches. Each leaf is simple, linear and usually toothed at the margin with a sheathing and

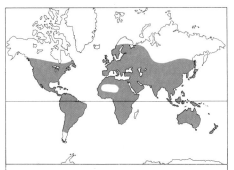

Number of genera: 1
Number of species: 50
Distribution: cosmopolitan, in aquatic habitats.
Economic uses: food for fish, green fertilizer and as a packing material.

Classification. The affinities of the Najadaceae are obscure. The family is usually placed in the superorder Alismatidae, which includes the orders Alismatales, Hydrocharitales as well as the Najadales. Its nearest relatives are probably the Aponogetonaceae and Potamogetonaceae. About 50 species are recognized but identification is difficult.

Economic uses. In warmer regions *Najas* species can be problematical weeds in ricefields and irrigation ditches. However, *Najas* provides a valuable fish food, and being relatively easily gathered, is also frequently used as a green fertilizer and as packing material.

C.D.C.

POTAMOGETONACEAE
Pondweeds
The Potamogetonaceae is a family of aquatic herbs which are a familiar sight all over the world, often inhabiting ditches and ponds.

Distribution. All species grow in fresh or somewhat brackish water. *Potamogeton* is cosmopolitan and occurs in a wide variety of aquatic habitats. *Groenlandia* is found in Western Europe and northern Africa to southwestern Asia; it shows a preference for water which is rich in nutrients but is sensitive to organic pollution.

Diagnostic features. The plants are usually perennial but some are annual. The stems are elongate, flexible, erect, creeping or floating. Some species develop specialized winter buds (turions) on the creeping stems. The leaves are alternate in *Potamogeton* and opposite or whorled in *Groenlandia*. They are simple, entire and often have two forms: the floating leaves are broad and the submerged ones narrower and often linear or capillary. Sheathing bases are usually present in *Potamogeton* but except for the leaves subtending the inflorescence absent in *Groenlandia*. The inflorescence is a stalked spike. The flowers are bisexual, regular and somewhat inconspicuous. The perianth consists of four free, bract-like, clawed scales inserted opposite each stamen (the perianth segments are often considered to be outgrowths of the connective). There are four stamens, each of which is joined to a perianth segment; the anthers are sessile and have two locules. The ovary is superior and consists of four (rarely fewer) free or partly united carpels, each containing a single campylotropous ovule. The stigmas are sessile or on short styles. The fruit is a drupe with a bony endocarp and a fleshy exocarp in *Potamogeton* or a nutlet with a thin pericarp in *Groenlandia*. The seeds have a well-developed hypocotyl and no endosperm.

Classification. *Groenlandia* differs from *Potamogeton* in having opposite or whorled leaves without sheathing bases, and a thin pericarped nutlet as fruit. There is only one species (*Groenlandia densa*). *Potamogeton*, with about 100 species, is the largest exclusively aquatic genus of flowering plants. Most of the species have aerial pollination but the subgenus *Coleogeton* is pollinated underwater.

The family Potamogetonaceae takes a somewhat central position in the superorder Alismatidae, the helobian group. It is usually positioned between the more or less terrestrial families Juncaginaceae and Scheuchzeriaceae and the very reduced aquatic families Ruppiaceae and Zannichelliaceae. The Potamogetonaceae is probably very

Zannichelliaceae. 1 *Althenia filiformis* (a) habit showing narrow leaves with sheaths joined to their bases ($\times\frac{2}{3}$); (b) female flowers ($\times 4$). 2 *Zannichellia palustris* (a) habit showing leaf sheaths free from the leaves ($\times\frac{2}{3}$); (b) male flower of one stamen and female flower of five carpels ($\times 6$); (c) carpel ($\times 16$); (d) vertical section of carpel ($\times 16$); (e) fruits ($\times 4$); (f) fruit ($\times 8$). 3 *Lepilaena preissii* (a) shoot with female flowers ($\times\frac{2}{3}$); (b) shoot with male flowers ($\times\frac{2}{3}$); (c) female flowers ($\times 2$); (d) gynoecium of three free carpels with spoon-shaped stigmas ($\times 6$); (e) male flowers ($\times 2$); (f) stamens ($\times 6$).

closely allied to the marine families Posidoniaceae and Zosteraceae.

Economic uses. Several species of *Potamogeton* have been reported to be a nuisance in canals and ditches. However, they are very important food plants for many animals. The starchy rootstock of *Potamogeton natans* and the turions have been used as a source of human food.   C.D.C.

ZANNICHELLIACEAE
Horned Pondweed

The Zannichelliaceae is a small family of submerged aquatic plants usually with graceful, slender leaves and stems, and inconspicuous flowers.

Distribution. The family is found throughout the world in fresh and brackish water.

Diagnostic features. The stems are thin and flexible, the upper parts usually floating above and the lower parts creeping and rhizomatous below. The leaves are alternate, opposite or in bunches; they are simple, entire and linear or reduced to a sheath. The leaf base is sheathing, with the sheath free from or partly joined to the leaf. These sheaths can be morphologically interpreted as sheath-like stipules, free or partly joined to the leaf. The

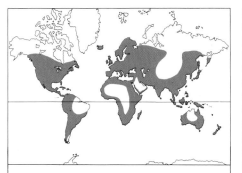

Number of genera: 4
Number of species: about 7
Distribution: cosmopolitan, in freshwater or brackish habitats.
Economic uses: some species stabilize mud and purify polluted water.

flowers are unisexual, solitary or clustered in the leaf axils; male and female are either on the same (monoecious) or on separate plants (dioecious). The perianth is either a small cup-like sheath, or a few scales, or absent. The stamens are solitary, or two or three united. The pollen is more or less spherical and pollination takes place under water. The ovary is superior and consists of one to nine free carpels, each with a single, pendulous ovule. The styles are simple and usually persist in fruit. The stigma is conspicuous, usually irregularly flattened or spoon-shaped, and the margin of the stigma is either entire or fringed. The fruit is a nutlet and the seeds are without endosperm.

Classification. The cosmopolitan *Zannichellia* has one species (*Z. palustris* – the horned pondweed) which has the leaf sheath free from the leaf and the leaves usually opposite or in false whorls. The plants are monoecious. *Althenia* and *Lepilaena* have the leaf sheaths joined to the leaves for most of their length, the leaves being alternate and the plants dioecious. *Althenia* is found in the Mediterranean, Persia and South Africa, usually in brackish water; there are one or two species. *Lepilaena* has four species in Australia and New Zealand. *Althenia* and *Lepilaena*, although geographically isolated should perhaps be totally or partially united. A new genus *Vleisia* has recently been described from South Africa.

The Zannichelliaceae belongs in the super-order Alismatidae, the helobian group of monocotyledons. There are convincing arguments to support the theory that it has evolved from the marine family Cymodoceaceae, and certainly it has close affinities with this family. The two families are often united and are, in turn, probably allied to the Potamogetonaceae.

Economic uses. None are known, but *Zannichellia* can be considered a beneficial plant as it stabilizes mud and contributes to the purification of the water. C.D.C.

RUPPIACEAE
Ditch Grasses

The Ruppiaceae consists of a single genus (*Ruppia*) of submerged aquatic herbs commonly known as ditch grasses.

Distribution. *Ruppia* is found throughout the world. It usually grows in brackish water in coastal areas but a few species are found inland in freshwater in South America and New Zealand. Plants have been collected at 13,000ft (about 4,000m) in the Andes.

Diagnostic features. The stems are slender, the upper parts floating and the lower parts creeping, with alternate or opposite leaves which are simple, hair-like and somewhat toothed at the apex. The leaf bases are enlarged and sheathing, and the inflorescence is a short terminal raceme which appears umbel-like. The flowers are bisexual, small and borne in pairs on slender axillary stalks. These axillary stalks are at first short and enveloped in a spathe-like leaf base but at the opening of the flower bud or following pollination they elongate and sometimes become coiled. The perianth is lacking or vestigial. There are two stamens with sessile bilocular anthers. The ovary is superior with four, or rarely more, free carpels, each with a single, pendulous, campylotropous ovule. The carpels are at first sessile but become stalked in fruit. The style is lacking and the stigma is a small disk on top of the carpel. The fruit is usually a nutlet but occasionally a drupe with a somewhat spongy exocarp. The seeds have no endosperm.

Classification. The Ruppiaceae probably represents a family that has evolved from the Potamogetonaceae by reduction. Pollination takes place under water in some races, while in others the pollen floats on the water

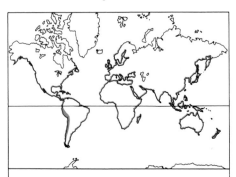

Number of genera: 1
Number of species: about 7
Distribution: cosmopolitan, in brackish water.
Economic uses: none.

surface and contacts floating stigmas. As with many other aquatics, the flowers are reduced and the plants are very plastic in form so there is little agreement as to how many species exist. It seems likely that there are about seven species but some authorities recognize only one or perhaps two polymorphic species.

Economic uses. None are known. C.D.C.

ZOSTERACEAE
Eel Grasses

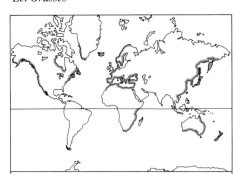

Number of genera: 3
Number of species: 18
Distribution: mainly in temperate seas of N and S Hemispheres.
Economic uses: dried leaves and stems used as packing material, also mixed with plaster or cement to add strength.

The Zosteraceae is a marine family of grass-like herbs which live entirely submerged.

Distribution. These plants are found in salt water only, distributed in the temperate seas of the N and S Hemispheres. A few species extend into tropical seas. (See also p.885.)

Diagnostic features. The stem is a creeping rhizome, monopodial in *Phyllospadix* and *Zostera* (eel grass) or sympodial in *Heterozostera*. The leaves are linear and grass-like with distinctly sheathing bases. The inflorescence is a flattened spadix, enclosed at flowering time in the spathe (the sheath of the uppermost leaf). The flowers are unisexual, the male and female being borne either on separate plants or on the same plant; in the latter case male and female are arranged alternately along the spadix. Each male consists of one stamen with two free, bilocular anthers joined by a ridge-like connective. The pollen grains are long threads of the same specific gravity as sea water so when discharged they float freely and have a good chance of adhering to the stigmas. In most species a curious hook-like process (retinaculum) is found beside each stamen or in the female spadixes of *Phyllospadix* where they alternate with the female flowers. The female flower consists of a single, naked carpel with a short style and two relatively long stigmas. The ovule is solitary, straight and pendulous. The fruit is ovoid or ellipsoidal with a dry, thin pericarp or it is crescent-shaped with the pericarp differentiated into a soft exocarp and a hard,

fibrous endocarp. The seed has no endosperm.

Classification. *Zostera* (12 species) is widely distributed, but *Heterozostera* (one species) occurs on coasts of Australia and Chile and *Phyllospadix* (five species) occurs on the coasts of Japan and Pacific North America.

The family is probably related to the Posidoniaceae and Potamogetonaceae. In several treatments they are all included within the Potamogetonaceae.

Economic uses. The dried leaves and stems of *Zostera* are used as a packing material, particularly for Venetian glass. They are also mixed with plaster or cement as a strengthening material. *Zostera* also has considerable indirect economic importance by supporting flora and fauna which themselves provide food for many bird and fish species. C.D.C.

POSIDONIACEAE

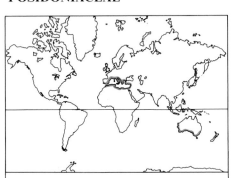

Number of genera: 1
Number of species: 3
Distribution: Mediterranean sea and S Australian coast.
Economic uses: the fibers are used in textiles and packing materials.

The Posidoniaceae is a family of submerged marine perennials with a single genus, *Posidonia*.

Distribution. *Posidonia* shows a wide disjunction. Two species are found in the extratropical waters of Australia and the third occurs in the Mediterranean; there are some doubtful records from the western Atlantic coast of Europe.

Diagnostic features. The stem is a creeping monopodial rhizome. The leaves are linear with a distinct auriculate and ligulate leaf sheath which surrounds the stem. The leaf blade and sheath have numerous dark spots and stripes resulting from local accumulations of tannin.

The inflorescence is a stalked cyme. The flowers are bisexual or male and the perianth is lacking. The three stamens are sessile; the anthers are bilocular and have a broad connective that is somewhat produced beyond the locules; the anthers are extrorsely dehiscent. The pollen is thread-like and pollination takes place under water. The carpel is superior, solitary and naked, containing a single, campylotropous, ventrally attached ovule. The stigma is sessile and irregularly lobed. The fruit has a fleshy pericarp, and the seed is filled completely by the embryo.

Classification. The Mediterranean species *Posidonia oceanica* differs from the Australian ones in that the leaf sheaths are incompletely wrapped around the stem, the ligule is very short, the bracts of the inflorescence are larger than its sheaths and the seed coat is without a wing. The Australian species are relatively simple to distinguish; *P. australis* has membranous leaves, 0.2in to 0.5in (6mm to 14mm) wide with about 11 nerves and two to seven terminal flowering spikes, while *P. ostenfeldii* has leathery leaves, 0.04in to 0.2in (1mm to 4mm) wide with about seven nerves and 6–14 terminal flowering spikes.

The Posidoniaceae certainly belongs to the helobian group (ie the superorder Alismatidae), and is usually considered to be allied to the Potamogetonaceae and Zosteraceae.

Economic uses. *Posidonia australis* is the source of posidonia fiber, cellonia or lanmar. Either alone or mixed with wool it is used for making sacks and coarse fabrics. It is also used for packing and stuffing.   C.D.C.

CYMODOCEACEAE

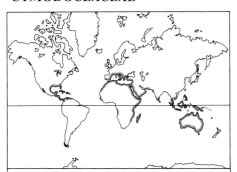

Number of genera: 5
Number of species: 16
Distribution: mainly tropical and subtropical seas.
Economic uses: none.

The Cymodoceaceae is a family of sea-grasses, which grow submerged in seawater, where they provice both food and shelter for fish.

Distribution. The Cymodoceaceae are marine plants found in tropical and subtropical seas with a few species in warm temperate waters. The genus *Amphibolis* is limited to the temperate seas of Australia.

Diagnostic features. The stem is creeping, either herbaceous and monopodial or woody and sympodial. The leaves are arranged in two vertical rows, linear or awl-shaped with a sheathing base and a leaf tip that is very variable in outline. The flowers are unisexual, naked, and either terminal on a short branch or, in *Syringodium*, arranged in a cymose inflorescence. Male and female are borne on separate plants. The male flower consists of two dorsally united stamens (some authorities consider the male flower to be an inflorescence of two one-stamened flowers). The pollen is thread-like and pollination takes place in water. The female flower consists of two free carpels with a long (*Halodule*) or short style and two or three stigmas. Each carpel contains a solitary pendulous ovule. The fruit is indehiscent and one-seeded, either with a hard or fleshy exocarp (eg *Amphibolis*) or consisting of a fleshy bract enclosing the fertilized ovaries (eg *Thalassodendron*). The seeds have no endosperm.

Classification. The genera are *Cymodocea* (four species), *Syringodium* (two species), *Amphibolis* (two species), *Halodule* (six species) and *Thalassodendron* (two species). The family is allied to the Zannichelliaceae.

Economic uses. The beds of sea-grasses are of no direct use to Man, but many fish use them both as food and as spawning grounds.
                         C.D.C.

TRIURIDALES

TRIURIDACEAE

The Triuridaceae is a small family of small tropical herbs which live on dead or decaying matter.

Distribution. The family is native to tropical America, Africa and Asia.

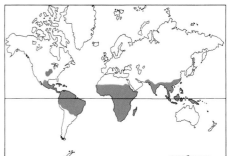

Number of genera: 7
Number of species: 80
Distribution: tropical America, Africa and Asia.
Economic uses: none.

Diagnostic features. The plants are small, colorless or reddish-purple saprophytes with scale leaves. The small flowers are regular and bisexual, or unisexual with male and female flowers on the same or separate plants, and are borne in racemes. The perianth consists of one series of three to ten segments which may be equal or unequal in size, and which become reflexed after flowering. In a number of species the segments are terminated by a tuft of hairs. There are two to six free stamens with short filaments and anthers with two or four locules, which sometimes dehisce transversely. The connective is sometimes extended into a long appendage (as in *Andruris*). In the male flowers there may be three fertile stamens and three staminodes; female flowers may possess staminodes. The gynoecium consists of numerous, superior, free carpels immersed in the receptacle, each carpel containing a single erect basal ovule with one integument. Each carpel has its own style which may be inserted terminally, laterally or basally. The fruit is a crowded mass and the erect seeds contain white oily endosperm.

Classification. The chief genera are *Triuris* (one species), *Sciaphila* (50 species), *Seychellaria* (three species) and *Andruris* (16 species). The relationships of the Triuridaceae are obscure, its closest relative being the Alismataceae.

Economic uses. None are known.   S.R.C.

COMMELINIDAE

COMMELINALES

XYRIDACEAE
Yellow-eyed Grasses

The Xyridaceae is a small family of herbaceous marsh plants.

Distribution. The family is mainly tropical and subtropical in distribution in marshy areas, especially in the southeastern United States, tropical America, and southern Africa.

Diagnostic features. The plants are some-times annual, but mostly perennial, rush-like herbs with leaves normally arising in tufts from the top of the rootstock. The leaves are linear, either flat and slender or circular in cross-section, and distinctly sheathing at the base.

The flowers are bisexual, slightly irregular and arranged in globose or cylindrical heads. Each flower is in the axil of an overlapping stiff or leathery bract. There are three sepals, of which the inner initially forms a hood-shaped structure over the petals, while the two lateral sepals are small and keel-shaped.

The corolla consists of three (normally yellow) petals fused to form a short or long tube, opening out into three lobes at the top. There are three fertile stamens opposite the corolla lobes and in some species there are three small staminodes alternating in position with them. The stamens are attached to the corolla tube by their short, flat filaments, and the anthers have two locules, opening lengthwise. The ovary is superior, made up of three fused carpels forming a single locule with numerous ovules inserted basally or on three parietal placentas. It is surmounted by

Rapateaceae. 1 *Rapatea pandanoides* habit showing oblong leaves with large sheathing leaf bases (×$\frac{1}{3}$). 2 *R. paludosa* (a) inflorescence with involucre of two bracts (×$\frac{2}{3}$) ; (b) half flower showing stiff outer perianth-segments, inner petaloid perianth-segments, epipetalous stamens with basifixed anthers, and superior ovary containing a single ovule in each locule and crowned by a simple style (×$5\frac{2}{3}$) ; (c) capsule dehiscing by three valves to reveal one seed in each locule (×$5\frac{2}{3}$). 3 *Schoenocephalium arthrophyllum* (a) habit showing linear leaves and inflorescences (×$\frac{1}{3}$) ; (b) dehiscing capsule with two seeds in each locule (×4).

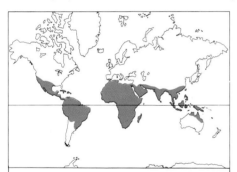

Number of genera: 2
Number of species: about 240
Distribution: chiefly in SE US, tropical America and southern Africa, in marshy habitats.
Economic uses: aquarium ornamentals and local medicinal uses.

a simple or three-lobed style. The corolla tube is persistent on the fruit, which is a capsule containing numerous seeds each with a small apical embryo surrounded by copious endosperm.

Classification. The genus *Xyris* (yellow-eyed grass—about 240 species) has a much wider distribution than *Achlyphila* (one species

tropical South America) and can be separated largely on the basis of floral characteristics. For example, *Xyris* has no appendages at the style base, and the inner sepal is distinctly hooded.

The family is related to the Commelinaceae and the Eriocaulaceae.

Economic uses. The leaves and roots of two North American species, *Xyris ambigua* and *X. caroliniana*, have been used as domestic remedies in treating colds and skin diseases respectively. A few species of *Xyris* are used as aquarium plants.   S.R.C.

RAPATEACEAE

The Rapateaceae is a small tropical family of perennial herbs.

Distribution. The family is native to tropical South America, with one genus (*Maschalocephalus*) in West Africa, often in swampy habitats.

Diagnostic features. The leaves arise from a thick rhizome or fleshy rootstock. They are narrow or linear, usually twisted and sheathing at the base, and may attain a length of 5ft (1.5m), as in *Rapatea paludosa*. The flowers are regular and bisexual, borne in heads of spikelets enclosed in two large

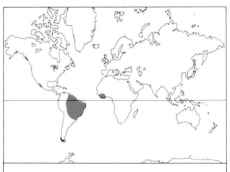

Number of genera: 16
Number of species: about 80
Distribution: swamps, habitats in tropical S America with one genus in Liberia.
Economic uses: none.

spathes. The perianth consists of two whorls, the outer of three rigid lobes, the inner of three petal-like segments fused at the base and spreading out into three broad ovate lobes. The six stamens are adnate to the corolla tube with anthers basifixed and opening by one, two or four apical pores, or by terminal slits. The ovary of three fused carpels is superior, with one to three locules, each containing one or several ovules on basal or axile placentas. It is surmounted by a simple style. The fruit is a capsule containing several seeds, each with copious, mealy endosperm.

Classification. One system of classification groups the genera into two subfamilies according to features of the carpels.

SAXOFRIDERICIOIDEAE. Carpels with several ovules which are either axile or on the septa; seeds prismatic or pyramidal; includes *Saxofridericia*, *Stegolepis* and *Schoenocephalium*.

RAPATEOIDEAE. Carpels with one ovule inserted at or near the base; seeds oval or oblong; includes *Rapatea*, *Cephalostemon* and *Monotrema*.

Alternatively the genera can be classified on a number of other characters including the nature of the inflorescence and details of the anthers. For example, *Rapatea* (flowers with pedicels), *Cephalostemon* (flowers sessile, anthers dehiscing by a terminal slit), *Schoenocephalium* (flowers sessile, anthers dehiscing by two terminal pores) and *Amphiphyllum* (flowers sessile, anthers dehiscing by one terminal pore) all have clusters of flowers subtended by a common involucre of bracts. On the other hand, *Windsorina* (flowers with pedicels), *Stegolepis* (flowers sessile) and *Maschalocephalus* (flowers subsessile) all have clusters of flowers without a common involucre.

The distinct calyx and corolla, lack of nectaries or nectar, superior ovary and capsular fruit place the Rapateaceae close to the other families in the Commelinales (Commelinaceae, Xyridaceae, Mayacaceae). The Rapateaceae is most closely related to the Xyridaceae.

Economic uses. None are known.

S.R.C.

MAYACACEAE

The Mayacaceae is a monogeneric family of small, mat-forming aquatic or amphibious herbs, some of which are used as ornamental aquarium plants.

Distribution. The family is primarily American, extending from the southwestern United States to Paraguay. One species, *Mayaca baumii*, is found in Angola. The plants grow on mud or in shallow water.

Diagnostic features. The stems are usually branched, the lower parts creeping and rooting and the upper parts erect or floating, often densely packed together in mats. The leaves are spirally arranged and clothe the stem; they are simple, linear, up to about 1.2in (3cm) long, and notched at the apex. The flowers are regular, bisexual, borne singly on long stalks and subtended by membranous bracts which usually become reflexed after flowering. The perianth is in two whorls, the outer sepal-like with three elongate segments persistent in fruit, the inner petal-like with three broad white, pink or violet segments. Three stamens alternate

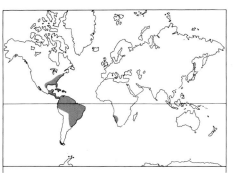

Number of genera: 1
Number of species: about 10
Distribution: chiefly America, from SW USA to Paraguay, with one species in Angola, in aquatic and marshy habitats.
Economic uses: some species used as decorative aquarium ornamentals.

with the petal-like segments; the anthers open by an apical pore or pore-like slit. The ovary is superior, of three fused carpels forming a single locule with numerous orthotropous ovules attached in two rows to three parietal placentas. There is a single style, simple or slightly three-lobed. The fruit is a three-valved capsule. The seeds have a pitted or net-like surface; they contain endosperm and the small embryo is situated under an embryostega, as in the Commelinaceae.

Classification. *Mayaca*, the only genus, contains 10 species. The Mayacaceae is allied to the Commelinaceae, from which it differs in having parietal placentation, anthers opening by pores or pore-like slits and non-sheathing leaves.

Economic uses. Some species are cultivated as decorative aquarium plants.

C.D.C.

COMMELINACEAE
The Spiderwort Family

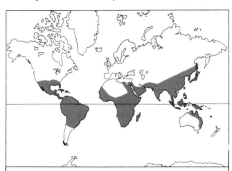

Number of genera: 38
Number of species: about 600
Distribution: tropical, subtropical and warm temperate.
Economic uses: garden ornamentals, greenhouse and house plants: *Commelina*, *Tradescantia* (spiderwort, wandering Jew), *Rhoeo*, *Cyanotis* and *Zebrina*

The Commelinaceae is a medium-sized family of succulent annual or perennial herbs, many of which are popular as garden, greenhouse and house ornamentals.

Distribution. The Commelinaceae in general prefer damp conditions and are mostly found in tropical, subtropical and warm temperate regions. A few are found in the southern United States of America, China, Japan and Australia.

Diagnostic features. The plants are either stemless or have jointed, succulent aerial stems with alternate leaves. The leaves are flat, entire, and with a closed basal sheath. The adventitious roots on the underground stem are fibrous or occasionally swollen and tuberous.

The inflorescence is essentially a cyme and is borne either at the end of the stem or in the axil of a leaf. The flowers are bisexual, usually regular but occasionally irregular. The perianth consists of two series of three segments, the outer series of three generally free, imbricate green sepals, the inner series of three free, usually equal petals. In a few species the petals are fused into a tube while rarely one of the three petals is reduced in size. The stamens are in two series of three with the filaments generally free. In some genera only three of the stamens bear anthers, the other three being sterile and modified as staminodes. One genus (*Callisia*) possesses only one functional stamen and no staminodes. In several genera the filaments are adorned by brightly colored hairs. An unusual feature in a few species is that the anthers liberate their pollen through an apical pore instead of through lengthwise slits. The ovary is superior, of three fused carpels with three locules (rarely two), each containing one to several orthotropous ovules on axile placentas. It is surmounted by a single style terminating either in a flattened stigmatic head or in three stigmatic branches. The fruit is a thin-walled dehiscent capsule, but rarely may be fleshy and indehiscent. The seeds usually have a rough or ridged surface covered by an aril. They contain copious, mealy endosperm, the embryo being situated under a disk-like structure (embryostega) on the seed coat.

Classification. There are various systems used in classifying the genera of this family. One system divides the family into two subfamilies — the TRADESCANTOIDEAE (regular flowers) and the COMMELINOIDEAE (irregular flowers). Further divisions are made by splitting the former group into subgroups dependent on the presence of either three or six fertile stamens and the latter into subgroups dependent on the orientation of the flower buds toward the axis (stem).

In the other primary division of the family, the genera can be grouped according to whether or not the inflorescence perforates and emerges near the base of the leaf sheath which subtends it. Those in which it does include *Forrestia* (petals free) and *Coleotrype*

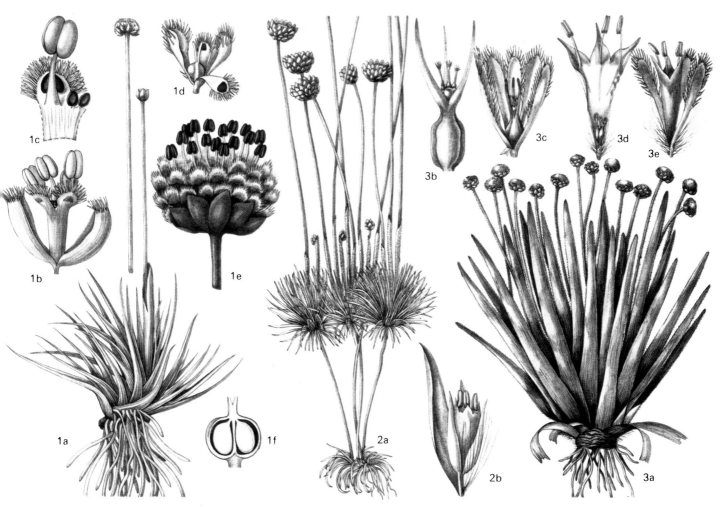

Eriocaulaceae. 1 *Eriocaulon aquaticum* (a) habit showing dense head of flowers and basal rosette of leaves (×⅔) ; (b) male flower with free outer and fused inner perianth segments (×8) ; (c) inner perianth segment from male flower showing vestigial stamen and fertile stamen with gland behind (×12) ; (d) female flower (×8) ; (e) head of male and female flowers (×3) ; (f) vertical section of fruit (a capsule) showing pendulous seeds (×12). 2 *Syngonanthus laricifolius* (a) habit (×⅔) ; (b) male flower (×15). 3 *Paepalanthus riedelianus* (a) habit (×⅔) ; (b) gynoecium (×16) ; (c) female flower (×8) ; (d) inner perianth of male flower opened out to show three stamens and vestige of ovary (×10) ; (e) male flower (×8).

(petals fused), while those which have the inflorescence emerging from the top of the leaf sheath include *Callisia* and *Cochliostema* (one to three stamens), *Cyanotis* (six stamens and sepals fused at the base) and *Rhoeo* (six stamens and sepals free).

The family shows a number of similarities to the Flagellariaceae and the Mayacaceae with respect to such vegetative characters as leaves bearing a closed sheath, regular or irregular flowers with biseriate perianth differentiated into sepals and petals, and stamens usually three or six in number, a

Commelinaceae. 1 *Commelina erecta* shoot showing sheathing leaf bases, flowers with three petals, three stamens and three staminodes (×⅔). 2 *Gibasis graminifolia* (a) leafy shoot and inflorescence, each flower with six stamens (×⅔) ; (b) fruit (×3). 3 *Zebrina pendula* leafy stem and solitary flower (×⅔). 4 *Tradescantia sillamontana* (a) leafy shoot with inflorescence subtended by boat-shaped, leafy bracts (×⅔) ; (b) flower with six stamens (×2) ; (c) cross section of trilocular ovary (×10). 5 *Rhoeo spathacea* shoot showing rosette of bromeliad-like leaves and inflorescence with boat-shaped bracts (×½). 6 *Tradescantia navicularis* juvenile plant (left) and adult shoot (right) (×⅔).

superior fused gynoecium and endospermic seeds with an embryostega. The Commelinaceae is probably derived from the Alismataceae and Butomaceae but shows evolutionary advance in having fused carpels.

Economic uses. The family has no agricultural importance. However, the genera *Commelina* (about 180 species), *Tradescantia* (about 35 species), *Zebrina* (about four species), *Cyanotis* (about five species), *Dichorisandra* (about 30 species) and *Rhoeo* (one species), are well known as house pot plants or as garden ornamentals. Most species of *Tradescantia* are sold under the popular names tradescantia, wandering Jew or wandering sailor and *Tradescantia virginiana* is known as the spiderwort.

An extract of leaves and stems of the tropical African perennial herb *Aneilema beninense* is used as a laxative, while the leaf sap of *Floscopa scandens* is used in tropical Asia to treat inflammation of the eyes. The young shoots and leaves of *T. virginiana* are edible and can be used in salads while the rhizomes of some species of *Commelina* are edible as are the leaves of *Commelina clavata*. Some species are weeds.   S.R.C.

ERIOCAULALES

ERIOCAULACEAE

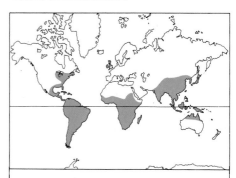

Number of genera: 13
Number of species: about 1,200
Distribution: mainly tropical and subtropical, centered in the New World.
Economic uses: limited use as "everlastings."

The Eriocaulaceae is a largish family of perennial or occasionally annual herbaceous plants often with grass-like leaves.

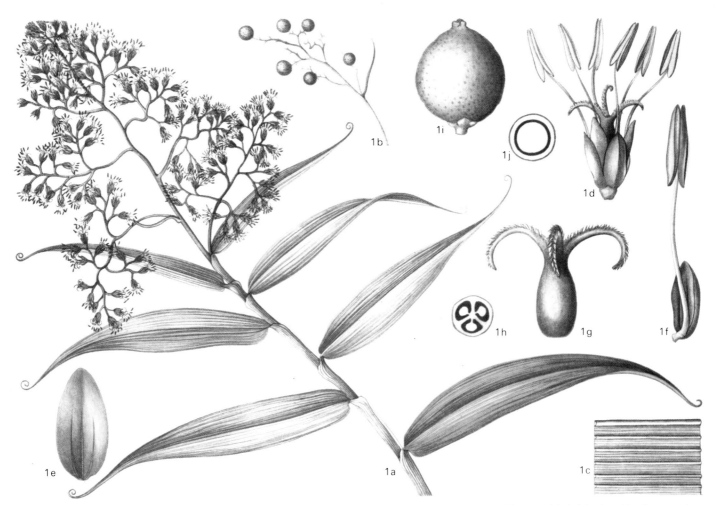

Flagellariaceae. 1 *Flagellaria guineensis* (a) shoot bearing a terminal branching racemose inflorescence and leaves with tightly sheathing bases and tips formed into a coiled tendril ($\times\frac{2}{3}$); (b) tip of shoot bearing fruit ($\times\frac{2}{3}$); (c) lower surface of leaf showing parallel veins ($\times 2$); (d) bisexual flower ($\times 3\frac{1}{3}$); (e) perianth segment ($\times 7\frac{1}{2}$); (f) stamen attached to perianth segment ($\times 5$); (g) gynoecium with broad style and three hairy stigmatic surfaces ($\times 5$); (h) cross section of ovary ($\times 5$); (i) fleshy indehiscent fruit ($\times 2\frac{2}{3}$); (j) cross section of fruit ($\times 1\frac{1}{3}$).

Distribution. The family is found throughout the tropics and subtropics, and a few species grow in temperate regions. The majority are found in the New World. Most species are found in swampy places or seasonally inundated regions, some are truly aquatic and others grow in dry areas.

Diagnostic features. The stems are corm-like or elongate. The leaves are in basal rosettes or growing from the stem; they are usually linear and somewhat grass-like. The flowers are regular, unisexual and borne in dense heads subtended by an involucre of bracts. The heads are solitary or in umbels. The peduncles usually extend beyond the leaves, which may sheath them at the base. Within each head the male and female flowers are mixed or the male flowers are in the center surrounded by female flowers; occasionally the male and female flowers are on separate plants. The perianth is in two series but not clearly differentiated into sepals and petals. The segments of the outer perianth are two or three in number and free, united or partly united; the inner series has two or three united or partly united segments or is lacking. The stamens are as many or twice as many as the outer perianth segments and inserted on the inner perianth segments

when these are present. The pollen grains are spiraperturate. The ovary is superior, with two or three fused carpels and two or three locules and a single terminal style bearing two or three elongate stigmas. There is a solitary, orthotropous, pendulous ovule in each locule. The fruit is a membranous, loculicidally dehiscent capsule. The seeds contain copious floury endosperm and a small embryo.

Classification. The family is relatively uniform in habit and the genera are distinguished on almost microscopic characters of the flowers. The largest genera are *Eriocaulon* (400 species), *Paepalanthus* (485 species), *Sygonanthus* (195 species) and *Leiothrix* (65 species).

The family has no near relatives and occupies a somewhat isolated position in the monocotyledons. It is usually placed near Xyridaceae and Rapateaceae as they also have heads of flowers, but these families show affinities with the Commelinaceae.

Economic uses. There are no reported economic uses for the family apart from their widespread sale when dried and stained as ornamental "everlastings." Some species of *Eriocaulon* are found as weeds in ricefields, but are not troublesome.　　C.D.C.

RESTIONALES

FLAGELLARIACEAE

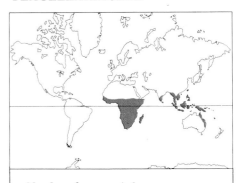

Number of genera: 1–3
Number of species: 3–7
Distribution: tropical and subtropical.
Economic uses: the stems of one species used in basket-making.

The Flagellariaceae is a small family of tropical herbs, often climbers.

Distribution. The family is tropical and subtropical from Africa, through Sri Lanka and Malaysia to the Pacific.

Diagnostic features. The erect or climbing stems are divided or undivided and arise from a sympodial creeping or floating rhizome. The leaves are long, sometimes ending in a tendril, and have at the base a leaf sheath embracing the stem. In *Hanguana* the leaves have petioles and are mostly radical.

The flowers are regular, bisexual or unisexual, and arranged in terminal branching racemes. The perianth is composed of six free or slightly fused segments in two whorls of three. They may be petaloid as in *Flagellaria* and *Hanguana* or scale-like as in *Joinvillea*. There are two whorls each of three stamens with free filaments, which may be attached to the base of the perianth segments. The ovary is superior, of three fused carpels and three locules, with a single ovule in each locule, attached to the central axis. The ovary is surmounted by a single style which terminates in three stigmatic lobes. The fruit is fleshy or drupe-like, containing a seed with a small embryo surrounded by copious endosperm.

Classification. Each of the three genera has distinctive characteristics which may be sufficiently disparate to suggest that this family is not a natural grouping.

Flagellaria, with three species native to tropical Africa, Indomalaysia, Australia and the Pacific, is a genus of climbers with dichotomously branching stems, solid internodes, leaves with closed sheathing bases and tips modified as tendrils. There is no covering of hairs or bristles, and no silica present in the leaf, but there are secretory cells. The flowers are bisexual and the perianth segments are free and petaloid.

Hanguana is a genus native to Sri Lanka, Indochina and Malaysia, comprising one or two species of robust, erect-stemmed herbs, with petiolate leaves and unisexual flowers (male and female on separate plants), the male possessing a rudimentary ovary and the female six sterile stamens. The perianth segments are greenish or yellow and slightly fused at the base.

Joinvillea is another genus of two species native to Malaysia and the Pacific. They are erect herbs but the stems are unbranched, the internodes hollow, and the leaves are long and narrow, with open sheathing bases. They are covered with a dense mat of branched hairs or bristles and contain abundant silica but no secretory cells. The flowers are bisexual and the six, free perianth segments are scale-like or bract-like.

Some botanists claim that these differences as well as others (eg the nature of the pollen) are sufficient to establish a separate family for each genus. Under this scheme of classification *Flagellaria* is the sole genus of the Flagellariaceae; *Hanguana* the sole genus of the Hanguanaceae, and *Joinvillea* the sole genus of the Joinvilleaceae.

Flagellaria has some features of anatomy and pollen that indicate a relationship with the Gramineae. *Hanguana* has some features which suggest relationships with *Lomandra* (Xanthorrhoeaceae) and possibly with the Palmae. All three genera may also have affinities with the Commelinaceae and Mayacaceae, with which they share such features as a biseriate perianth, usually six stamens and a superior ovary with a single style.

Economic uses. *Flagellaria indica* is the only species known to be used by Man. Its tough stems are used in Thailand and Malaysia for basket-making.   S.R.C.

CENTROLEPIDACEAE

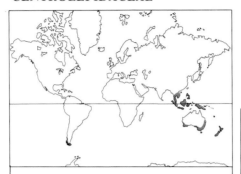

Number of genera: 5
Number of species: about 30
Distribution: Australia and New Zealand to SE Asia, and southern S America.
Economic uses: none.

The Centrolepidaceae is a family of small grass-like, rush-like or even moss-like annual or perennial herbs.

Distribution. The family is mainly found in Australia and New Zealand but extends to Southeast Asia and southernmost South America. It has obvious Antarctic affinities, with its major development in the Australian-Neozealandic region, from which it had radiated northwards and eastwards.

Diagnostic features. The plants are tufted or cushion-like herbs with linear, bristle-like leaves in dense basal rosettes in annuals, and imbricate and crowded along stems in perennials. The structure of the inflorescence and flower has been much discussed. The "flowers" of *Centrolepis* and *Gaimardia*, once thought to be bisexual, are now considered to be reduced inflorescences or "pseudanthia," cymose structures consisting of one (sometimes two) male flowers and two to many female flowers, all flowers being reduced to either one stamen or one carpel. The inflorescence is terminal and spike-like, with one to several pseudanthia within each of two or more glume-like floral bracts. Each pseudanthium may have none to two male flowers and none to many female flowers. The flowers are often fused and sometimes have thin, translucent subtending bractlets; perianth segments are absent. The male flowers have a single stamen with a thread-like filament and a unilocular (rarely bilocular), versatile anther with longitudinal de-

hiscence. The female flowers have a unilocular ovary, with one pendulous, orthotropous ovule, and one style (rarely three to ten, sometimes fused at the base). The fruit has a membranous pericarp, dehiscing by a longitudinal slit (or rarely indehiscent as in *Hydatella*). There is one seed per locule or carpel, with copious endosperm.

Classification. The family is usually divided into two tribes: TRITHURIEAE and CENTROLEPIDEAE. The Trithurieae with two-celled anthers comprise the genera *Trithuria* and *Hydatella*. The Centrolepideae with one-celled anthers comprise the genera *Brizula*, *Centrolepis* and *Gaimardia*.

The Centrolepidaceae is most closely related to the Restionaceae.

Economic uses. None are known.

                              D.M.M.

RESTIONACEAE

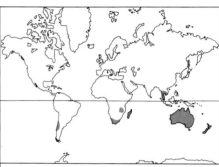

Number of genera: about 30
Number of species: about 320
Distribution: mainly S Hemisphere, with centers in S Africa, Australia, Tasmania and New Zealand.
Economic uses: limited uses for thatching and broom-making.

The Restionaceae is a small family of rush-like herbs with small, inconspicuous flowers.

Distribution. Except for one species in northern Vietnam, all are found in the Southern Hemisphere. The main concentrations of species are in South Africa (in the coastal or subcoastal lowland and mountain areas) and Australia, Tasmania and New Zealand. Others occur in Malawi, the Malay Peninsula, the Chatham Islands, Chile, Patagonia and Madagascar. There are no genera in common between Australasia and South Africa, but interesting links exist between species of *Leptocarpus* in Australasia, Malaysia and South America. This distribution is of significance in theories of continental drift.

The plants grow in a wide range of conditions, but favor seasonally wet habitats which dry out each year. Some species can tolerate very dry conditions, and others grow in standing water. It is of interest that whereas the aerial parts have obvious adaptations to drought, the roots frequently have cortical air cavities which are associated with wet soil conditions.

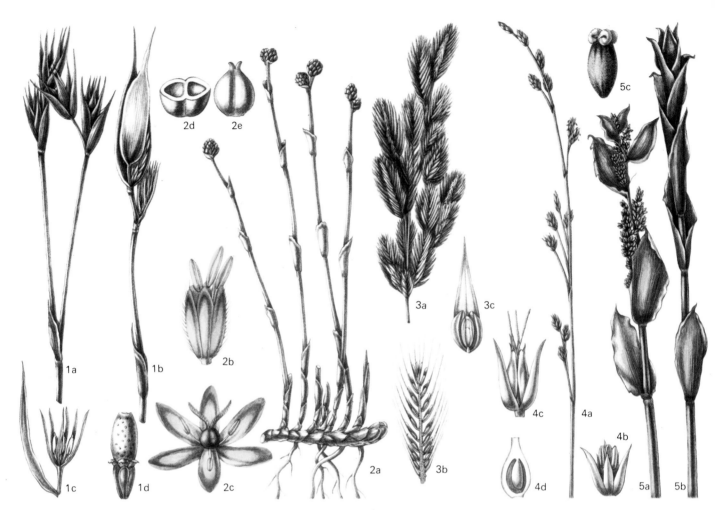

Restionaceae 1 *Willdenowia lucoeana* (a) male spikelets (×⅔) ; (b) female spikelets (×⅔) ; (c) male flower with sheath-like spathe (×2) ; (d) fruit (×2).
2 *Restio monocephalus* (a) habit (×⅔) ; (b) male flower with three stamens (×4) ; (c) female flower with two styles and three staminodes (×4) ; (d) cross section of fruit (×6) ; (e) fruit entire (×4). 3 *Thamnochortus insignis* (a) female spikelets (×⅔) ; (b) vertical section of female spikelet (×1½) ; (c) female flower (×3). 4 *Leptocarpus simplex* (a) shoot with male spikelets (×⅔) ; (b) male flower (×4) ; (c) female flower (×4) ; (d) vertical section of ovary (×4). 5 *Elegia juncea* (a) shoot with male spikelets (×⅔) ; (b) shoot with hidden female spikelets (×⅔) ; (c) fruit (×6).

Diagnostic features. Species range in height from about 4in (10cm) to 6.5ft (2m). Most have aerial parts composed of several- to many-noded tough, wiry shoots which may be fertile or sterile. The shoots are usually simple or slightly branched, but some species are characteristically much branched. Functional leaf blades are rarely developed but a small, dry blade may be present; usually only a sheathing leaf base which is split to the base can be seen at each node. Leaf bases, sometimes deciduous, may be prominent and well developed although non-photosynthetic. Very few species have ligules. The shoots are modified to carry out photosynthesis. They bear abundant stomata and can have from one to four layers of palisade-like cells. In cross-section the stems may be circular, semi-circular, more or less square or variously ribbed. They are solid or hollow. The rhizomes are creeping or tufted, below 0.4in (1cm) or up to 0.8in (2cm) in diameter. In most species they are closely covered with dry brown scales. The roots are fleshy or wiry.

Flowers are small, regular and unisexual, with male and female on separate plants (very rarely on the same plant); they are usually arranged in spikelets in loose inflorescences. The spikelets are one- to many-flowered and are commonly subtended by a sheath-like spathe. The perianth is composed of three to six thin, dry segments in two series. In a few species, no perianth is developed. Opposite the inner three perianth segments are three stamens in the male flowers; a rudimentary ovary may be also present. The female flowers may have a variable number of staminodes. The ovary is superior, consisting of one to three carpels and one to three locules, each containing a single pendulous, orthotropous ovule, attached to the apex. There are one to three styles, free or variously connate.

The fruits are dry and nut-like or occur as three-sided capsules. The seeds have a small embryo and abundant endosperm.

Classification. The family is regarded as being taxonomically difficult. There is often a high degree of similarity between male plants of the same genus, making it hard to match male and female plants of the same species using only characters of floral and gross morphology. The varied anatomy of the stems has been found to be of diagnostic and taxonomic significance and can be used as a guide to generic and even specific identity in some instances.

There are probably more than the 30 genera currently recognized. The principal genera include *Restio*, *Leptocarpus*, *Elegia*, *Chondropetalum*, *Thamnochortus* and *Willdenowia*. There are several monospecific genera. *Anarthria* and *Ecdeiocolea* are now given individual family status as the Anarthriaceae and Ecdeiocoleaceae respectively.

The Restionaceae appears to be closely related to the Centrolepidaceae and to the Juncaceae and Thurniaceae. Although it is difficult to compare a more or less "leafless" family such as the Restionaceae with other leafy ones, this association is supported by a range of characters such as anatomy and seed structure. Recent treatments incline to regard the Restionaceae as more closely related to the Centrolepidaceae than to Juncaceae.

Economic uses. Matting, thatching and brooms are variously provided by a few species of this family.   D.C.

POALES

GRAMINEAE
The Grass Family

The grasses or Gramineae (Poaceae is a permitted alternative name) comprise some 9,000 species grouped into about 650 genera. Although not the largest, the family is ecologically the most dominant and economically by far the most important in the world. It provides all the cereal crops (including rice), most of the world's sugar and grazing for domestic and wild animals, as well as bamboos, canes and reeds. The grasses also make a major contribution to the world's landscape (see pages 855ff).

Distribution. The family is cosmopolitan, ranging from the polar circle to the equator, and from mountain summits to the sea itself; it has been estimated that it is the principal component in some 20% of the earth's cover of vegetation. Few ecological formations lack grasses and many, such as steppe, prairie and savanna, are dominated by them. The great grasslands occupy a climatic zone between forest and desert, but are difficult to equate with any simple climatic parameter owing to the extent to which their distribution has been influenced by other plants and by animals. Indeed the spread of the grasses is a story of reciprocal adaptation, first with the herbivorous mammals and latterly with Man. (See p.862; 901.)

Diagnostic features. In a typical grass the root system is fibrous and often supplemented by adventitious roots from the lower nodes of the stem. Branching ("tillering") occurs mainly at ground level to form a rosette or tussock, often extended laterally by underground rhizomes or surface stolons to form a close sward. The upright stems are cylindrical, usually hollow but sometimes pithy, and mostly herbaceous although sometimes more or less cane-like or even woody. The leaves are borne in two rows at intervals along the stem, their point of origin being termed a node, and they are composed of two parts, sheath and blade. The sheath, a distinctive feature of grass morphology, tightly invests the stem and gives mechanical support to the soft meristematic zone situated just above each node. Differential growth at this meristem enables the stem to bend upright again after being flattened (lodging) by rain or trampling. At its upper end, the sheath passes into a parallel-veined blade, which also has a meristematic zone at its base, permitting the blade to continue growth despite the removal of its distal parts by grazing or cutting. The blade is typically long and narrow, but may be lanceolate to ovate in tropical shade-loving species; in a few genera it is deciduous from the sheath and occasionally it is narrowed at the base into a false petiole (the sheath being considered homologous with a true petiole). In size, leaves can vary from the bladeless

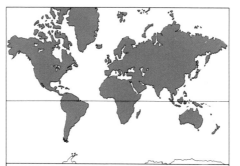

Number of genera: about 650
Number of species: about 9,000
Distribution: cosmopolitan.
Economic uses: cereal crops (including wheat, rice, maize, oats, barley, millet, sorghum), fodder for animals, sugar cane, bamboos and canes, lawns and some decorative ornamentals.

sheaths of the Australian *Spartochloa scirpoidea*, to the enormous blades up to 16ft (5m) long of the South American bamboo *Neurolepis nobilis*. At the junction of sheath and blade is a short membranous or ciliate rim (ligule), whose function is uncertain but may be to prevent rain entering the sheath. The combination of basal tillering and meristems at the node and base of the leaf blade enables the grasses to tolerate a degree of burning, trampling or grazing which effectively eliminates most competing families and which must contribute largely to the success of the family.

The inflorescence is a specialized leafless branch system, which usually surmounts the stem. Its basic units are termed spikelets, analogous to the flowers of petaloid plants. They are arranged in various ways, ranging from a single spike or raceme (in the latter case the pedicel is usually so short that the distinction is not very important), through an intermediate stage of several spikes arranged digitately or along an axis, to a many-branched panicle, this sometimes so condensed that it appears spike-like. The inflorescence develops inside the uppermost leaf-sheath, emerging only when almost mature. Extremes of size range from the spectacular 6.5ft (2m) plume of *Gynerium sagittatum*, down to the solitary single-flowered spikelet of *Aciachne pulvinata*.

An understanding of spikelet structure is essential for the identification of grasses. Visible from the outside are two opposite rows of scales arranged alternately along an axis (rhachilla). The two lowest scales (glumes) are empty, but the remainder (lemmas) each form part of a floret, whose floral parts are enclosed by the lemma on the outside and a delicate membranous scale (palea) on the inside. Glumes or lemmas are often produced into one or more, long, stiff bristles termed awns. The floral parts consist of two (rarely none or three) tiny scales called lodicules, three (rarely one to six or

more) stamens, and two (rarely one or three) feathery stigmas surmounting the ovary, which is superior and has a single locule containing one ovule, usually adnate to the adaxial side of the carpel. In origin, the spikelet can be related to a branch system in which the glumes and lemmas represent modified leaf-sheaths and the palea a prophyll (a special bract replacing the first leaf on the inner side of an axillary branch). The lodicules are taken to represent vestigial perianth members, there being intermediates between lodicules and stamens in a few bamboos (eg *Ochlandra*); their function is uncertain, but their turgor may help to open the floret. The basic pattern of two glumes and several florets is remarkably uniform through the family, apart from a few exceptions among the bambusoid grasses. However, an extraordinary number of variations has been developed from this simple basic theme by changes in the size, shape, ornamentation or sex of the parts or by reduction in their number.

Bisexual spikelets are the rule, although some of their florets are often unisexual or barren; occasionally male and female spikelets are borne on the same plant, rarely on separate plants. The florets open for only a few hours to permit the exposure of the sexual organs to wind-pollination, cross-pollination usually being ensured by protandry. The pollen itself is viable for less than a day, the shortest-lived of all angiosperm pollens. It is of a distinctive type, monoporate operculate, with a very finely granular surface.

Variants of normal flowering behavior are sometimes encountered. Apomixis (development of the ovule without fusion with a male gamete) occurs frequently in the family, though always interspersed with spells of sexuality. Cleistogamy (self-pollination within the closed floret) is not uncommon and may be associated with special spikelets hidden in the axils of the leaf sheath or even beneath the soil surface. Proliferation (the modification of spikelets into little leafy shoots) is commonly the result of hormone imbalance brought about by short days at the end of the season in genetically predisposed races, but in some mountain or arctic species the transformation of spikelets into bulbils has become a regular means of propagation. Somewhat similar abnormal growth effects are sometimes produced by hormone weedkillers. Vivipary (the germination of the seed while still attached to the parent) has been recorded in *Melocanna*.

Cytogenetically the grasses engage in a diversity of behavior which raises many problems for those attempting to divide them into discrete species. Some 80% of them have a polyploid chromosome number, and the occurrence of polyhaploidy (halving the chromosome number) has also been demonstrated; apomictic swarms are not unusual; and over 2,000 hybrids have been recorded, 200 of them fertile. In certain tribes a tendency to wide crossing makes it difficult to establish satisfactory generic boundaries (but the cross between *Saccharum* and *Bambusa*, often quoted as an example, is bogus). Nor should the role of purely vegetative clones in the life history of many perennial species be ignored. It has been estimated that a single plant of *Festuca rubra*, which spreads by rhizomes, may be over 800ft (some 250m) in diameter and up to 400 years old, and that a large tussock of *F. ovina* 26ft (8m) across could be, 1,000 years old.

The fruit is a caryopsis, although some bamboos have a rather fleshy pericarp (amounting to a berry several centimeters long in *Melocanna*) and a few genera (notably *Sporobolus*) have a loose seed within a free pericarp. Nearly always, however, the disseminule (including the grass "seed" of commerce) incorporates part of the inflorescence, ranging from an adherent palea to the complete inflorescence functioning as a tumbleweed. Dispersal is aided by wind-borne plumes of various kinds, by a great variety of hooks and barbs, occasionally by glue, and sometimes by a dark coloration inviting consumption by birds; *Streptogyna* and *Streptochaeta* are notable for their elegant hair-traps. Awns often play a part in dispersal, but in many species a more important function seems to be their ability to tuck the fruit beneath the soil surface by hygroscopic movements. The embryo is peculiar with no exact homologue among the angiosperms. Its most distinctive feature is the transformation of the cotyledon into a haustorial organ (scutellum) attached to the starchy (rarely liquid) endosperm. In many species the fruit is viable for five years or so; while a few exceed 30 years.

Classification. Grasses are rather uniform in their vegetative parts, so that recognition has relied heavily upon their spikelet structure. The older classifications were, in effect, arrangements of spikelet types in a logical sequence of increasing complexity. However, it has gradually emerged that a more natural grouping can be achieved with the aid of such features as internal leaf anatomy, photosynthetic pathway, basic chromosome number and embryo structure. The laborious task of cataloguing these cryptic characters is still incomplete and the significance of differences is not always easy to assess. Consequently grass classification is still in a state of flux and there is no wholly satisfactory overall account available. Nevertheless the basic features of an improved classification are becoming clearer. There are six subfamilies and over 50 tribes, only the larger or more interesting of which are listed below. Quite unrelated grasses may look very similar to the naked eye and even an expert can be misled unless the spikelets are carefully examined with the aid of a lens.

SUBFAMILY BAMBUSOIDEAE

A group of tribes with certain features of the internal leaf anatomy in common, the most distinctive being known technically as arm cells and fusoid cells. Many genera have unusual features, these being of two types: those forming links with the main stream of monocotyledon morphology, and those standing in isolation. The former are interpreted as primitive, and the latter as relics of discontinued evolutionary trends, together suggesting an ancestral role for the subfamily.

BAMBUSEAE. A few herbs, but mostly shrub or tree-like bamboos up to 130ft (40m) high. A number of genera display apparently primitive features. Thus some have three lodicules, six stamens and three stigmas, recalling the usual three-part monocotyledon type of flower; the number of glumes may be indefinite, some of them furnished with axillary buds which develop into spikelets, these also having buds in the lower axils, and so on; and the leaf- and spikelet-bearing branch systems may be imperfectly separated. Against this must be set the highly developed woody stem, and considerable variation in spikelet structure, including types with single florets or with sexual dimorphism between the florets. Thus they are "primitive" only in a rather restricted sense. A curious aspect of their biology is that many species flower only periodically, the interval being 10–120 years according to species, with surprisingly exact synchronization throughout the geographical range. Mainly tropical forest plants, reaching into warm temperate regions. Chief genera: *Arundinaria, Bambusa, Chusquea, Dendrocalamus, Phyllostachys, Sasa.*

STREPTOCHAETEAE. The only genus has single-flowered spikelets, and is remarkable for the three enormous lodicules, almost 1in (up to 2cm) long, palea cleft to the base, and lemma with long coiled awn; a supposed homology with six perianth members has led some authorities to regard it as exceptionally primitive. It undoubtedly has primitive features (4–5 glumes, 6 stamens, 3 stigmas), but it also has a sophisticated dispersal mechanism. The spikelets dangle from the awns like fish-hooks, and the lodicules deflect animals' hairs into the palea, where they are gripped by the converging sides of the cleft. Rain forest of tropical South America. Only genus: *Streptochaeta.*

STREPTOGYNEAE. The only genus has several-flowered spikelets equipped with another ingenious fish-hook mechanism. The florets have long tangled stigmas, the hair-trap being formed by a springy curved rhachilla segment pressing against the back of the palea. Rain forest in tropical Africa and America. Only genus: *Streptogyna.*

OLYREAE. Little herbs carpeting the ground in deep shade, or rambling canes at the edge of clearings. In common with many forest-dwelling grasses the leaves are often broad, and scarcely recognizable as belonging to grasses. The single-flowered spikelets are unisexual, a phenomenon encountered here and there in the family, the sexes being mixed or in different parts of the inflorescence. A small tribe, mostly from South America. Chief genus: *Olyra.*

PHAREAE. Similar to Olyreae, but the veins of the leaf-blade slant obliquely from the midrib, instead of running parallel to it as in most other grasses. A small tribe of tropical rain forest. Chief genera: *Leptaspis, Pharus.*

PARIANEAE. The single genus is remarkable for the large number of stamens, commonly about 30, in each floret. It is insect-pollinated, though this appears to be a secondary adaptation. Rain forest of South America. Only genus: *Pariana.*

ORYZEAE. A small but important tribe with single-flowered spikelets whose glumes are almost completely suppressed, though in *Oryza* two sterile lemmas simulate glumes. Tropical and warm temperate regions, mainly in swamps; rice is widely cultivated. Chief genera: *Oryza, Zizania.*

SUBFAMILY CENTOSTECOIDEAE

An enigmatic group with similarities to both Bambusoideae and Panicoideae; probably nearer the former, but occupying an isolated position.

CENTOSTECEAE. Broad-leaved herbs with panicles of single- to several-flowered spikelets. *Lophatherum* is unusual in possessing root tubers. A small tribe of worldwide distribution, mainly in rain forest. Chief genera: *Centosteca, Lophatherum, Orthoclada.*

SUBFAMILY ARUNDINOIDEAE

An unspecialized subfamily, defined more by the absence of distinctive features than by their presence. For this reason it is commonly regarded as close to the ancestral line from which the first non-bambusoid grasses have been derived.

DANTHONIEAE. Panicles of spikelets with 2–10 flowers; lemma usually bilobed, with an awn from between the lobes; ligule a line of hairs. Subtropics and warm temperate regions, particularly in the Southern Hemisphere; a few, such as moor grass (*Molinia*), in cool temperate regions. Chief genera: *Chionochloa, Danthonia, Molinia, Pentaschistis.*

ARUNDINEAE. Robust grasses with handsome panicles of plumose spikelets. In other respects its genera are not particularly close,

Gramineae. 1 *Arundinaria japonica* (a) tip of shoot showing leaves and inflorescence (×⅔). 2 *Phleum pratense* inflorescence (×⅔). 3 *Stipa capillata* fruit—a caryopsis crowned by a long feathery awn (×⅔). 4 *Aristida kerstingii* fruit with a three-branched awn (×⅔). 5 *Tristachya decora* inflorescence (×⅔). 6 *Avena sativa* (a) inflorescence (×⅔); (b) fruit (×6). 7 *Lolium perenne* habit showing adventitious roots, leaves with sheathing bases and inflorescence (×⅔) 8 *Poa annua* part of leaf showing (from the bottom) the sheathing base expanding into the blade with a ligule inserted where the blade and base meet (×6).

and their traditional association in the same tribe is open to question. Subtropics to cool temperate regions; includes reed grass (*Phragmites*) of marshes throughout the world, and pampas grass from South America (*Cortaderia selloana*) which can be seen as the centerpiece of many a temperate garden. Chief genera: *Arundo, Cortaderia, Phragmites.*

LYGEAE. Spikelets two-flowered, the glumes suppressed; the two lemmas are fused along their margins to form a rigid tube, divided longitudinally by the two paleas which are also fused together. A weird tribe from the Mediterranean; its only species is one of the esparto grasses. Only genus: *Lygeum.*

MICRAIREAE. The only genus is a moss-like plant, unique among the family for its spiral arrangement of the leaves. Australia. Only genus: *Micraira.*

SUBFAMILY CHLORIDOIDEAE

Characterized by the "Kranz syndrome," an assemblage of anatomical characters associated with an extra loop in the photosynthetic pathway, apparently making it more efficient in high light intensities. The spikelets break up at maturity.

ERAGROSTIDEAE. Panicles or racemes with several-flowered spikelets and three-nerved lemmas. A large tropical tribe, with many pioneer species of bare ground and disturbed places; tef and finger millet are grown as cereals. Chief genera: *Dactyloctenium, Eleusine, Eragrostis, Leptochloa.*

CHLORIDEAE. Racemes of spikelets containing only one fertile floret, with or without extra sterile ones; perhaps rather arbitrarily separated from Eragrostideae. A large tribe, mainly of tropical and subtropical savannas. It includes Bermuda grass (*Cynodon dactylon*), the commonest tropical lawn species; grama (*Bouteloua*) and the dioecious buffalo grass (*Buchloe*) from the North American plains; and *Spartina* from intertidal mudflats on either side of the Atlantic. Chief genera: *Bouteloua, Chloris, Cynodon, Lepturus, Spartina.*

SPOROBOLEAE. Panicles of little single-flowered spikelets, but otherwise scarcely separable from Eragrostideae. Tropics and subtropics in open places. Chief genera: *Muhlenbergia, Sporobolus.*

ZOYSIEAE. Like Chlorideae, but with the spikelets falling entire at maturity and often of bizarre shape. Old World tropics. Chief genera: *Perotis, Tragus, Zoysia.*

ARISTIDEAE. Panicles of single-flowered needle-like spikelets, the lemma with a three-branched awn. Tropics, particularly in hot, dry places. Chief genus: *Aristida.*

SUBFAMILY PANICOIDEAE

The Kranz syndrome is usually present, though not always well marked. The spikelets are strictly two-flowered, the lower floret male or barren, the upper bisexual and usually different in appearance.

ARUNDINELLEAE. Relatively unspecialized, the spikelets disarticulating between the florets at maturity in the usual way. In many species the emergent panicle bears tiny juvenile spikelets, unlike most grasses whose spikelets are almost fully grown before emergence from the uppermost sheath. Tropical savannas, mainly in the Old World. Chief genera: *Arundinella, Loudetia.*

PANICEAE. Spikelets fall entire at maturity, the grain encapsulated by the hard, often bony, lemma and palea of the upper floret; inflorescence a panicle, or composed of racemes in various arrangements. In some genera (notably *Setaria* and *Pennisetum*) the spikelets are surrounded by an involucre of bristles, derived from modified panicle branches. A large and important pantropical tribe; includes the crops fundi, proso, foxtail and bulrush millets. Chief genera: *Axonopus, Brachiaria, Digitaria, Echinochloa, Panicum, Paspalum, Pennisetum, Setaria.*

ANDROPOGONEAE. Spikelets fall entire at maturity, protected by the tough glumes. They are borne on racemes in pairs, one member of each pair sessile, the other raised on a pedicel. Sometimes both members of a pair are alike, but usually they are quite different, the pediceled often sterile; the disseminule may then be a most complex organ in which the adjacent rachis internode, the pedicel and the modified pediceled spikelet all participate in the protection of the fertile sessile spikelet, sometimes supplemented by special barren spikelet pairs forming a kind of involucre at the base of the raceme. The racemes may be borne in a terminal panicle, but are commonly single or paired, in which case there is often copious axillary branching. The whole system of axillary inflorescences and subtending leaves, themselves highly modified, may then be raised to the top of the stem in a manner that simulates a panicle. A large and important pantropical tribe, often of great morphological complexity; includes the crops sorghum, maize, sugar cane and lemon grass. Chief genera: *Andropogon, Coix, Cymbopogon, Erianthus, Euchlaena, Hyparrhenia, Miscanthus, Saccharum, Sorghum, Themeda, Vetiveria, Zea.*

SUBFAMILY POOIDEAE

Differs from the other, primarily tropical, subfamilies in many cryptic characters concerning anatomy (notably the absence of micro-hairs on the leaf epidermis), cytology and physiology. The subfamily in fact constitutes a major evolutionary departure, though this is not apparent from the external morphology. Indeed much taxonomic research during the last two or three decades has been directed towards the gradual elimination of misplaced genera from other tribes.

POEAE. Several-flowered spikelets, mostly in panicles, with five- to seven-nerved lemmas longer than the glumes and with or without a straight awn from the tip (compare with the three-nerved lemmas of Eragrostideae). A large pantemperate tribe; includes rye grass (*Lolium perenne*), the foremost species of high-grade temperate pastures; *Festuca* used in fine lawns; and *Poa annua*, possibly the most ubiquitous of all grasses. Chief genera: *Briza, Cynosurus, Dactylis, Festuca, Lolium, Poa.* (*Glyceria* (Glycerieae) and *Melica* (Meliceae) belong to tribes which differ only in detail from Poeae.)

AVENEAE. Distinguished from Poeae by the long papery glumes enclosing the lemmas, which often have a kneed awn from the back; ligule membranous (compare with Danthonieae, formerly included in Aveneae). A large pantemperate tribe; includes the cereal oats. Chief genera: *Anthoxanthum, Avena, Deschampsia, Helictotrichon, Holcus, Phalaris.*

AGROSTIDEAE. A single-flowered variant of Aveneae, and included in that tribe by some authorities. A large pantemperate tribe; includes *Agrostis*, a typical genus of second-rate European pastures, as well as a number of other common hay and forage species. Chief genera: *Agrostis, Alopecurus, Ammophila, Lagurus, Milium, Phleum.*

BROMEAE. Outwardly resembling Poeae, but with the unusual starch grains of Triticeae, thus forming a link between the two tribes. Pantemperate. Chief genus. *Bromus.*

TRITICEAE. One- to several-flowered spikelets arranged in spikes. Further distinguished by the unusual round starch grains in the seed. A peculiarity of the tribe is a tendency to wide hybridization, making the delimitation of genera unusually difficult. A pantemperate tribe notable for its cereal genera wheat, barley and rye. Chief genera: *Aegilops, Agropyron, Elymus, Hordeum, Secale, Triticum.*

STIPEAE. Panicles of single-flowered, needle-like spikelets, often with conspicuous awns; leaves typically harsh and narrow. A small tribe whose largest genus, *Stipa*, is characteristic of dry steppes throughout the world. Chief genus: *Stipa.*

The relationship of grasses to other families is obscure. Their spikelets serve to distinguish them from all other families except the Cyperaceae, and their close superficial resemblance to this family is not maintained in matters of detail, probably indicating no more than parallel evolution from a rather remote common ancestry. The Cyperaceae may be distinguished by the presence of one or more of the following

Gramineae (continued). 9 *Andropogon fastigatus* inflorescences ($\times \frac{2}{3}$). 10 *Imperata cylindrica* inflorescence ($\times \frac{2}{3}$). 11 *Cynodon dactylon* habit showing creeping stem bearing adventitious roots and branching (tillering) at ground level ($\times \frac{2}{3}$). 12 *Brachiaria brizantha* inflorescence ($\times \frac{2}{3}$). 13 *Bromus commutatus* (a) exploded view of a floret showing two scales (the awned lemma and hairy palea) and flower with three stamens and two feathery styles ($\times 4$); (b) spikelet showing lower scales without awns (glumes) and upper scales with awns (lemmas). 14 *Olyra ciliatifolia* leaves with parallel veins and inflorescence ($\times \frac{2}{3}$).

9   10   11   12   13a   13b   14

features: solid triangular stems; leaves without ligules; umbellate inflorescences subtended by leaf-like bracts; spirally arranged spikelet scales.

Some evidence of derivation from a general commelinaceous type is found in the Bambusoideae, most authorities tentatively suggesting the Flagellariaceae as a possible living relative. The tenuous link between grasses and other monocotyledons is thus strongest among inhabitants of the tropical forest zone, pointing to the forest environment as the cradle of the grasses, but leaving their early adoption of wind-borne pollination unexplained. The first grasses to spread from the forest fringes into the dry savanna were probably akin to the present-day Arundinoideae. From them eventually diverged the two major tropical groups, Chloridoideae and Panicoideae; They were also, it is assumed, akin to the Pooideae, which adapted to cool climates and invaded the temperate zone.

The time-scale for the evolution of the family is difficult to establish, there being little help from fossil evidence. This amounts to scarcely more than grass-type pollen at the end of the Cretaceous; florets of an extant genus, *Stipa*, in the Oligocene; and herbivorous mammals with grass-eating teeth in the Miocene, indicating that by this time grassland had become an ecological formation. Geographical distribution casts some light on the subject: whereas the major tribes occupy worldwide climatic belts, their constituent genera tend to be confined to single continents. The implication is that the tribes were in existence before the continents drifted beyond the reach of seed dispersal at the end of the Cretaceous (the timing of this event is itself contentious), generic evolution then continuing upon the separate continents.

Economic uses. The adoption of the grasses as a principal source of food was a milestone in human development, many, if not most, of the great civilizations being founded on the cultivation of grass crops. Opportunistic gathering ("ramassage") of wild grain has always been a common practice among primitive people, but domestication entailed the selection of strains whose inflorescence does not shatter to disperse the seed before it can be harvested. This first happened 8,000–10,000 years ago in southwestern Asia and the Middle East, where wild species of *Triticum* and *Hordeum* yielded the cereals wheat and barley. With the spread of agriculture through temperate Europe and Asia, various grasses adapted to life as arable weeds, some of which were themselves domesticated as oats (*Avena sativa*) and rye (*Secale cereale*). Elsewhere archeological evidence is more sketchy, but domestication seems to have occurred somewhat later. Rice (*Oryza sativa*) became the principal cereal of tropical Asia, supported by foxtail millet (*Setaria italica*) and proso (*Panicum mili-*

aceum). In Africa the main indigenous cereals are sorghum (*Sorghum bicolor*) and bulrush or pearl millet (*Pennisetum glaucum*), supplemented by a number of rather local minor grains, including finger millet (*Eleusine coracana*), fundi (*Digitaria exilis*), tef (*Eragrostis tef*) and an independently domesticated species of rice (*Oryza glaberrima*). Maize (*Zea mays*) is the indigenous American cereal. Although not a cereal, sugar cane (*Saccharum officinarum*), from Southeast Asia, may be mentioned here.

The second facet of Man's dependence on the grasses springs from the domestication of animals, which was roughly contemporaneous with the beginnings of agriculture. Until recent times livestock rearing was based upon the exploitation of natural grasslands, although the preservation of fodder as hay had been introduced by the Roman era. Sown pastures, based on rye grass, date from the late 12th century in north Italy and from the late 16th century in northern Europe. (See p.938.)

Bamboos provide an ideal building material in many parts of the world, and grass is also employed for building construction in the form of thatch and matting. To the engineer grasses are invaluable for stabilizing sand dunes, road verges and other raw soil surfaces. Many species have been used for papermaking, the best known being esparto, a name variously applied to *Stipa tenacissima*, *Ampelodesma tenax* and *Lygeum spartum*.

An aromatic oil is distilled from the leaves of lemon grass (several species of *Cymbopogon*), imparting a citronella scent to soaps and other perfumery. Among a host of minor uses may be mentioned necklace beads (*Coix* involucres), brush bristles (*Sorghum* inflorescence branches), pipe bowls (*Zea* cobs), edible bamboo shoots, clarinet reeds (*Arundo donax* stems), fishing rods (bamboo species) and corn dollies or various garishly dyed inflorescences sold as house decorations. In the form of lawns grasses have an honored place in horticulture, though few of them have been admitted voluntarily to the herbaceous border. A well-known exception is the variegated form of *Phalaris arundinacea*, often called gardener's garters.

The obnoxious properties of grasses lie mainly in their success as weeds of cultivation; those whose spikelets are equipped with pungent spikes or barbs may also become a serious nuisance to domestic animals when present in quantity. Some tropical forage species are known to develop a lethal content of hydrocyanic acid under conditions associated with the partial wilting of lush growth, but still largely unpredictable. Poisonous properties may also arise from fungal infections, St Anthony's fire, an affliction caused by eating cereals infected by ergot (*Claviceps*, especially *C. purpurea*), being the most notorious. W.D.C.

JUNCALES

JUNCACEAE
Rushes

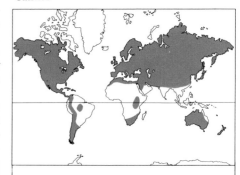

Number of genera: 9
Number of species: about 400
Distribution: worldwide, but chiefly cold temperate or montane regions, in damp habitats.
Economic uses: stems used in basketwork, mat-making and chair bottoms, with some waterside ornamentals.

The Juncaceae is a smallish family of tufted perennial or annual herbs (rushes) and, rarely, woody shrubs (*Prionium*).

Distribution. The family occurs worldwide but chiefly in cold temperate or montane regions, in wet or damp habitats (see p.875ff.)

Diagnostic features. The perennial species have erect or horizontal rhizomes. The stems are erect, cylindrical and normally only leafy at the base. The leaves are cylindrical or flat and grass-like, sheathing at the base or reduced entirely to sheaths and mostly arranged in basal tufts when present. The flowers are regular, bisexual or unisexual (with male and female on the same or on separate plants), wind-pollinated and consequently small and insignificant, sometimes solitary but more often in open panicles, corymbs or clustered heads. The perianth segments consist of two whorls of three (or rarely one whorl of three) scales which are leathery or thin and papery, sometimes with a dried-up appearance at the tips and edges. They are dull in color, often green, brown or black but sometimes also white or yellowish. There are six or three stamens usually opposite the perianth segments. The ovary is superior, of three fused carpels comprising one or three locules, with few to numerous ovules on axile or parietal placentas. There may be one style or three, but there are always three stigmas. The fruit is a dry capsule which dehisces loculicidally, with one to many small globose, angled or compressed seeds which have starchy endosperm and a straight embryo.

Classification. The nine genera include the antarctic rhizomatous perennials *Rostkovia* (monoecious, perianth segments equal in length, obovoid seeds) and *Marsip-*

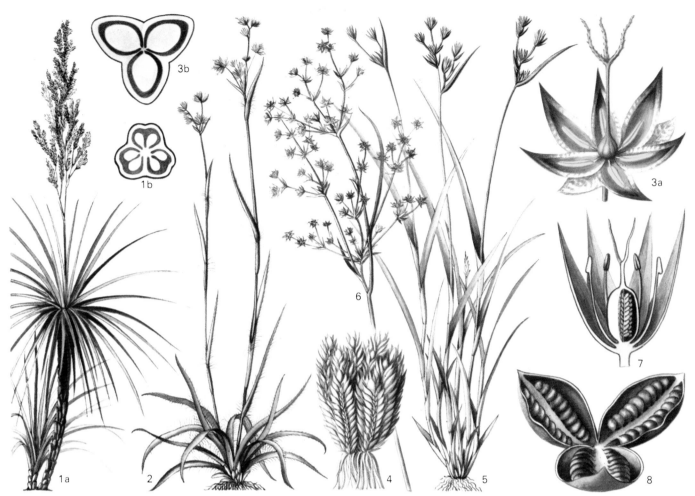

Juncaceae. 1 *Prionium serratum* (a) a woody shrub ($\times\frac{1}{15}$); (b) cross section of trilocular ovary ($\times$20). 2 *Luzula nodulosa* an herbaceous perennial with sheathing leaf bases ($\times\frac{1}{4}$). 3. *L. spadicea* (a) flower ($\times$20); (b) cross section of trilocular ovary ($\times$100). 4 *Distichia muscoides* a low-growing cushion plant with leaves in two rows and terminal capsules ($\times\frac{2}{3}$). 5 *Juncus bufonius* an herbaceous perennial with linear erect leaves with loosely sheathing bases and flowers in dense cymose heads subtended by leaf-like bracts ($\times\frac{2}{3}$). 6 *J. acutiflorus* inflorescence ($\times\frac{2}{3}$). 7 *J. bulbosus* half flower ($\times$14). 8 *J. capitatus* dehiscing capsule consisting of three valves ($\times$18).

pospermum (similar, but with shorter inner perianth segments, and pointed, spindle-shaped seeds). The Andean rhizomatous perennials of *Andesia* are thick cushion plants with equal perianth segments and ovoid seeds. Other South American groups include the three closely related dioecious genera from the Andes: *Oxychloe* (irregular leaves with spreading blades) and the regular-leaved, cushion plants of *Distichia* and *Voladeria* from Ecuador. Perhaps the most unusual genus of the family is *Prionium*, a group of subarborescent shrubs from South Africa with a terminal tuft of toothed leaves, closed leaf sheaths and flowers in large panicles. *Juncus* is a cosmopolitan genus of herbaceous rushes characterized by their entire leaves with open leaf sheaths and small inflorescences of bisexual flowers producing capsules with many seeds. *Luzula*, another fairly widespread genus, is most common in the Northern Hemisphere, very similar in many ways to *Juncus* but differing in its closed leaf sheaths, hairy leaf blades and three-seeded capsules.

The Juncaceae is currently considered to be related either to the Liliaceae through the putative primitive genus of the family,

Prionium, or to the Restionaceae, which it generally resembles in many more respects. The Juncaceae and Restionaceae are both florally reduced families, a feature they have in common with the Cyperaceae and Gramineae; all four are most probably individually derived evolutionary lines from a common stock resembling the modern Commelinales order.

Economic uses. The family is not generally of much commercial value. However, among the well-known products are juncio, used in binding, derived from the sea rush, *Juncus maritimus*; palmite, a strong fiber made from the serrate leaves of the palmiet, *Prionium serratum* (*P. palmitum*); and the split rushes used in basket making and chair-bottom manufacture, taken from the stems of the soft rush, *J. effusus*, and the heath rush, *J. squarrosus*. C.J.H.

THURNIACEAE

The Thurniaceae is a small family of perennial sedge-like herbs endemic to Guyana and certain parts of the Amazon valley.

The leaves are elongated and leathery, with sheathing bases and leaf margins either

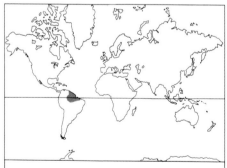

Number of genera: 1
Number of species: 3
Distribution: Guyana and parts of Amazon valley.
Economic uses: none.

serrulate, as in *Thurnia sphaerocephala* and *T. polycephala*, or entire, as in *T. jenmanii*. The stems are three- or four-angled and bear one or several heads of flowers subtended by several basal, leafy bracts. The flowers are small, irregular, pendulous and bisexual, with six persistent narrow perianth segments arranged irregularly below the ovary. The six stamens extend far beyond the perianth parts. The ovary of three fused carpels has

Cyperaceae. 1 *Carex decurtata* (a) entire plant showing habit ($\times\frac{2}{3}$); (b) spikelet containing both male and female flowers ($\times 3$); female flower (c) entire showing three-branched stigma ($\times 6$) and (d) opened out to show the superior ovary ($\times 8$); (e) male flower with three stamens ($\times 6$). 2 *Cladium tetraquetrum* (a) habit showing sheathing leaf bases ($\times\frac{2}{3}$); (b) inflorescence ($\times 6$); (c) spikelet ($\times 6$); (d) flower and subtending bract (glume) ($\times 6$). 3 *Cyperus compressus* (a) habit ($\times\frac{2}{3}$); (b) flower showing trifid style ($\times 18$); (c) spikelet of bisexual flowers ($\times 3$); (d) flower with three stamens and a superior, lobed ovary crowned by three styles ($\times 12$).

three locules each with one to numerous axile ovules. There are three filiform stigmas. The fruit is a three-angled capsule. The seeds contain endosperm. The family is most closely related to the Juncaceae and has at times been included within it, but anatomical evidence (such as the presence of silica bodies in the leaf epidermis) clearly indicates that the Thurniaceae should be maintained as a distinct family. Indeed, some authorities believe that such anatomical features as the curious inverted vascular bundles observed in the leaves of *T. sphaerocephala* and *T. jenmanii* indicate that the family has no close affinities with the Juncaceae. No economic uses are known.   S.A.H.

CYPERALES

CYPERACEAE
Reeds and Sedges
The Cyperaceae is a large family of mainly perennial, and a few annual, grass-like herbs.
Distribution. The family is distributed in all parts of the world but more especially in damp, wet or marshy regions of the temperate and subarctic zones. The genus *Carex*

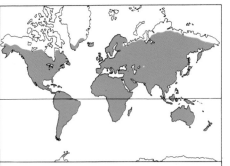

Number of genera: about 90
Number of species: about 4,000
Distribution: cosmopolitan, especially damp temperate and subarctic habitats.
Economic uses: stems and leaves used in mat-, hat-, basket- and paper-making and as fodder for animals; some edible tubers (tigernut, Chinese water chestnut), locally-used medicines and several pot plants and water garden ornamentals.

(true sedges), in particular, is of considerable ecological importance.
Diagnostic features. The plants have a creeping underground rhizome from which

arise solid aerial stems (culms) which are often three-angled in cross-section, generally unbranched below the inflorescence and often leafless. The leaves, usually arranged in a tuft around the base of the stem, are normally disposed in three ranks; they have a grass-like blade, a closed (or rarely open) sheath around the stem, and usually no ligule.

The small, inconspicuous flowers are bisexual or unisexual (with male and female usually on the same plant), and arranged in spikelets. Each flower is in the axil of a glume (bract). The perianth is represented by scales, bristles or hairs and in some species is entirely absent. There are one to six stamens, but usually three; the filaments are free. The ovary is superior, of two or three fused carpels forming a single locule with a single ovule inserted at the base. The style is divided into two or three teeth or branches and is sometimes persistent on the ripe fruit, which is an achene. The seed contains a small embryo surrounded by copious mealy or fleshy endosperm.

Classification. The two major systems for classifying the genera of this family have depended on an initial division into either three subfamilies or seven tribes. In the former system (after Engler) the subfamilies are SCIRPOIDEAE (including *Cyperus*, *Eriophorum*, *Scirpus*, *Eleocharis*); RHYNCHOSPOROIDEAE (including *Rhynchospora*, *Scirpodendron*, *Cladium* and *Scleria*); and CARICOIDEAE (including *Carex* and *Uncinia*). Both this system and the other (after Hutchinson) are based primarily on features of the inflorescence, flowers and fruit. For example, *Cyperus* and *Scirpus* have several- to many-flowered spikelets while those of *Rynchospora* and *Cladium* are mostly one- or two-flowered. All these genera have bisexual flowers while those of *Scleria* and *Carex* are unisexual.

The Cyperaceae is perhaps closest to the grasses (Gramineae), but the relationship is not close despite the superficial similarities in habit and appearance. The sedges are generally distinguished by the often solid and three-angled stems, the generally closed leaf sheath and the absence of a ligule. Another distinctive feature is that each individual flower is usually subtended by a single glume.

Economic uses. The family contains a large number of useful species which are employed for a variety of purposes. *Cyperus* includes the papyrus or paper reed (*Cyperus papyrus*), whose stems provide the papyrus paper much used in ancient times. The stems of a number of other *Cyperus* species, such as *C. malacopsis* and *C. tegetiformis* (Chinese mat grass), are used for mat-making while a few species (eg *C. esculentus*, the chufa, tigernut, earth almond or rush nut) have edible storage organs. Some species, such as *C. longus* (galingale) and *C. articulatus*, have sweet-scented rhizomes and/or roots which can be used in perfumery.

Carex includes *Carex atherodes* which is used as a hay grass in the United States of America. The stems and leaves of *C. brizoides* are used as a packing material in some central European countries. Both *C. paniculata* and *C. riparia* are used in stables in place of straw, and *C. dispalatha* is cultivated in Japan for its leaves, which are used to make hats.

Stems of *Cladium mariscus* are used for thatching houses in Europe and parts of North Africa. The stems of the tropical and subtropical American *C. effusum* (saw grass) are a source of cheap paper. The stems of the Pacific species *Eleocharis austro-caledonica* are used for basket-making while *E. tuberosa* (matai, Chinese water chestnut) is cultivated in China and Japan for its edible tubers. The stems and leaves of *Lepironia mucronata* are used for packing and for basket work. *Mariscus umbellatus* has edible rhizomes, while *M. sieberianus* is used as a vermifuge in Sumatra.

Scirpus contains a large number of useful species, some of which have medicinal uses; the roots of *Scirpus grossus* and *S. articulatus* are used in Hindu medicine as a curative for

diarrhoea and as a purgative respectively. The tubers of *S. tuberosus* are eaten as a vegetable in Japan and China. The stems of *S. totara* (tropical South America) are used for making canoes and rafts and those of *S. lacustris*, the bulrush of North and Central America, in basketwork, mats and chair seats.

Some species of *Carex*, *Cyperus*, *Leiophyllum* and *Scirpus* are cultivated as pot plants and water garden ornamentals.　　S.R.C.

TYPHALES

TYPHACEAE
Reedmace Bulrush and Cattails

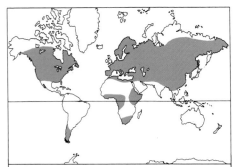

Number of genera: 1
Number of species: about 15
Distribution: almost cosmopolitan in freshwater habitats.
Economic uses: leaves used for basketwork, especially from the reedmace bulrush (*Typha latifolia*).

The Typhaceae is a small family of gregarious aquatic herbs consisting of the single genus *Typha* with about 15 species, which includes the reedmace bulrush and cattails.

Distribution. The Typhaceae occur in habitats of shallow freshwater such as reed swamps, lakes, rivers and ponds in many temperate and tropical localities. (See also pp. 880–885).

Diagnostic features. Most species are very tall plants, growing to 6ft (2m) or more, with long simple stems that are usually submerged at the base. The leaves arise mostly from the subterranean part of the stem and invariably consist of linear, aerial, elongated blades which are rather thick and spongy. The flowers are unisexual and pollinated by the wind; they are characteristically crowded into a long, dense, club-shaped terminal spadix, with the female flowers occurring in the lower half of the inflorescence and the males arranged above them. The two sexes are either indistinguishable and contiguous forming a single "club," or quite separate with an articulate segment of the stem between them to form a double club. The perianth segments are somewhat indeterminate in terms of petals or sepals and uniformly consist of numerous slender threads or elongated spoon-shaped scales

mixed with ovaries or stamens. The stamens have two to five slender, free or fused filaments with linear anthers attached at the base. The crowded female florets each consist of an ovary with a single locule, tapered at the apex into a narrow ribbon-shaped stigma. The fruits are achenes with a long stipe covered in hairs which aid dispersal by the wind. The seeds have mealy endosperm and a long, narrow embryo.

Classification. The Typhaceae together with the Sparganiaceae form a very distinct order, but the wider relationships of these two families are somewhat obscure; they probably represent an independent evolutionary line from an ancestor somewhat resembling the Commelinaceae of today.

Economic uses. The leaves of the reedmace bulrush (*Typha latifolia*) are used as a weaving material for chair bottoms, mats and baskets, and the plant is also cultivated for the ornamental value of its large brown cylindrical fruiting spears.　　C.J.H.

SPARGANIACEAE
Bur-reeds

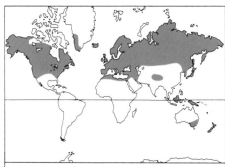

Number of genera: 1
Number of species: about 15
Distribution: mainly temperate zone of the N Hemisphere and in the Arctic, in aquatic and marshy habitats.
Economic uses: food and cover for waterfowl.

The Sparganiaceae is a family of perennial aquatic or amphibious herbs, with a single genus *Sparganium* (bur-reeds), which provides cover and food for numerous aquatic organisms, especially waterfowl.

Distribution. Most species are found in the temperate and Arctic regions of the Northern Hemisphere, growing gregariously in water or in marshes. One or two species occur in Southeast Asia and Australasia.

Diagnostic features. The stems are corm-like with elongate rhizomes. The leaves are linear and arranged in two vertical rows with sheathing leaf bases. The juvenile leaves are thin, strap-shaped and submerged while the mature leaves are floating or erect and emergent. The flowers are unisexual and crowded into separate globose heads; the female heads are towards the base in each inflorescence. The perianth has from three to six elongate scales. The male flower has from one to eight stamens. The female flower has one, occasionally two, or rarely three, superior, united carpels comprising one to three locules with one pendulous ovule in each. Whatever the number of carpels, the style is single and persists as a beak in fruit. The fruit is a drupe with a dry, spongy exocarp and a hard endocarp. The seed has mealy endosperm and a central embryo.

Classification. Recent anatomical and embryological work has shown that the Sparganiaceae is closely allied to the Typhaceae, although the affinities of these two families with the rest of the monocotyledons are disputed. There is also some evidence to suggest a relationship to the group known as the Helobiae, which includes the orders Alismatales, Hydrocharitales and Najadales, and it is interesting to note that the Sparganiaceae shares some parasitic fungi with the Araceae. Fossil remains of *Sparganium* indicate that the earlier species were larger and structurally more complex than those of today.

Economic uses. *Sparganium* stands provide sheltered nesting and roosting places for wildfowl and in late autumn the fruits form an important part of their diet.

C.D.C.

BROMELIALES

BROMELIACEAE
The Pineapple Family

Number of genera: about 50
Number of species: about 2,000
Distribution: centered in tropical and warm temperate America.
Economic uses: fruits (pineapple), fibers (Spanish moss, pineapple, caroa) and several ornamentals (eg *Billbergia, Cryptanthus, Pitcairnia*).

The Bromeliaceae is a large and distinctive family, including the pineapple, Spanish moss (*Tillandsia*), and various greenhouse ornamentals and house plants.

Distribution. The family is tropical or warm temperate, native to the New World with the exception of one species, *Pitcairnia feliciana*, which occurs in West Africa. The family extends from the southern United States of America south to central Argentina and Chile. One species, *Tillandsia usneoides*, has

a distribution as wide as that of the entire family. The family as a whole is adapted to xerophytic conditions and many genera have become epiphytes.

Diagnostic features. Most bromeliads are short-stemmed herbaceous plants with basal rosettes of stiff, often spiny, leaves which frequently have colored bases. A few are subshrubs, and some species of the Andean genus *Puya* reach a height of 10ft (3m) and have a similar habit to the giant lobelias of the mountains of tropical Africa. The least specialized members of the family (eg *Pitcairnia, Puya*) are terrestrial plants with fully developed root systems. They have unexpanded leaf bases and leaf hairs which serve only to reduce transpiration. Tank-root types (eg pineapple) have few true roots but the overlapping leaf bases act as reservoirs for water and humus, which are utilized by adventitious roots growing up between the leaf bases. More specialized tank types, which include the majority of genera, have still larger leaf-base tanks, and absorption from the tanks is carried out mainly by specialized leaf hairs (trichomes), not by the roots. The tanks may hold up to 1.3 gallons (about 5 liters) of water and contain a considerable flora and fauna, including species of *Utricularia* (bladderwort), tree frogs and various insects. The most specialized genera (eg *Tillandsia*) are entirely epiphytic, have roots only as young seedlings, lack leaf-base tanks and absorb water from the atmosphere by means of multicellular scale-like trichomes. These expand when wetted, so water is drawn into the dead cells of the scale and thence osmotically through the living cells of the stalk of the trichome into the leaf. The scales collapse when dry, permitting gas exchange through the stomata but reducing water loss from the surface of the plant. The plants can thus survive in very dry habitats, but not in very humid habitats such as rain forests.

The inflorescence is terminal, produced out of the center of the tank in tank types, and may be a spike, raceme or panicle. Many bromeliads die after flowering, including some of the genera cultivated for their inflorescence, but these produce suckers and can be readily propagated. The flowers are bisexual (rarely unisexual), regular (somewhat irregular in *Pitcairnia*) and borne in the axils of bracts, which are often brightly colored. The perianth is usually clearly differentiated into greenish calyx and showy petaloid corolla, each with three segments. The six stamens are often attached to the base of the perianth. The ovary, of three fused carpels, may be superior or inferior and contains three locules, each with numerous ovules on axile placentas. Three stigmas are borne on a slender style. The fruit is a berry or capsule. In the pineapple (*Ananas*) and the related *Pseudananas*, the individual fruits fuse and the inflorescence swells to form a multiple fruit. The seeds

contain a small embryo and a mealy endosperm. In several genera the seeds have wings or long feathery or tailed appendages, presumably to assist in dispersal.

In most genera the showy inflorescences and the nectaries on the septa of the ovaries are adaptations to pollination by insects or birds. The flowers are protandrous: when the anthers open, the stigmas are spirally twisted into a head and their receptive surfaces are exposed later. This favors cross-pollination. A few genera (eg *Navia*) appear to be wind-pollinated. Versatile, freely moving anthers are characteristic of the family.

Classification. The Bromeliaceae is divided into three subfamilies:

PITCAIRNIOIDEAE. About 13 genera and one-third of the species, containing mainly terrestrial xerophytes; the ovary is superior, the fruit is a capsule, and the seeds are winged or tailed; chief genera *Pitcairnia, Puya, Dyckia*.

BROMELIOIDEAE. About 30 genera, including both terrestrial and epiphytic forms; the ovary is inferior, the fruit is a berry and the seeds have neither wings nor appendages; chief genera *Bromelia, Ananas, Billbergia, Aechmea*.

TILLANDSIOIDEAE. About 6 to 12 genera, all of which are entirely epiphytic; the ovary is superior, the fruit is a capsule and the seeds have feathery appendages formed by the splitting of the elongated outer integument and part of the funicle; chief genera *Tillandsia, Vriesea*.

The family is not closely related to any of the other families of monocotyledons, but shows some affinities with the Commelinaceae and the Zingiberaceae.

Economic uses. The pineapple (*Ananas comosus*) is an important edible fruit of the tropics and subtropics. Annual world production exceeds $3\frac{1}{2}$ million tons, and about two-thirds of this is consumed in the areas of production. Most commercially grown pineapples are canned or made into juice, which is a good source of vitamins A and B.

Various species produce fibers used locally for making cloth and cordage, notably the pineapple in the Philippines, pita (*Aechmea magdalenae*) in Colombia and caroa (*Neoglaziovia variegata*) in Brazil.

Bromeliaceae. 1 *Aechmea nudicaulis* var *nudicaulis* inflorescence and leaf ($\times\frac{2}{3}$). 2 *Pitcairnia integrifolia* (a) leaf ($\times\frac{2}{3}$); (b) inflorescence ($\times\frac{2}{3}$); (c) vertical section of ovary showing numerous ovules on axile placentas ($\times 4$). 3 *Billbergia pyramidalis* (a) leaf with spiny margins and inflorescence with large red bracts ($\times\frac{2}{3}$); (b) half flower with an inferior ovary crowned by a single style with a lobed stigma and stamens inserted at the corolla base ($\times 1\frac{1}{3}$); (c) cross section of the trilocular ovary showing axile placentas ($\times 4$). 4 *Vriesia carinata* habit ($\times\frac{2}{3}$). 5 *Ananas comosus* (the pineapple) a multiple fruit (produced from the entire inflorescence) and "crown" of leaves produced by continued growth of the axis ($\times\frac{1}{3}$).

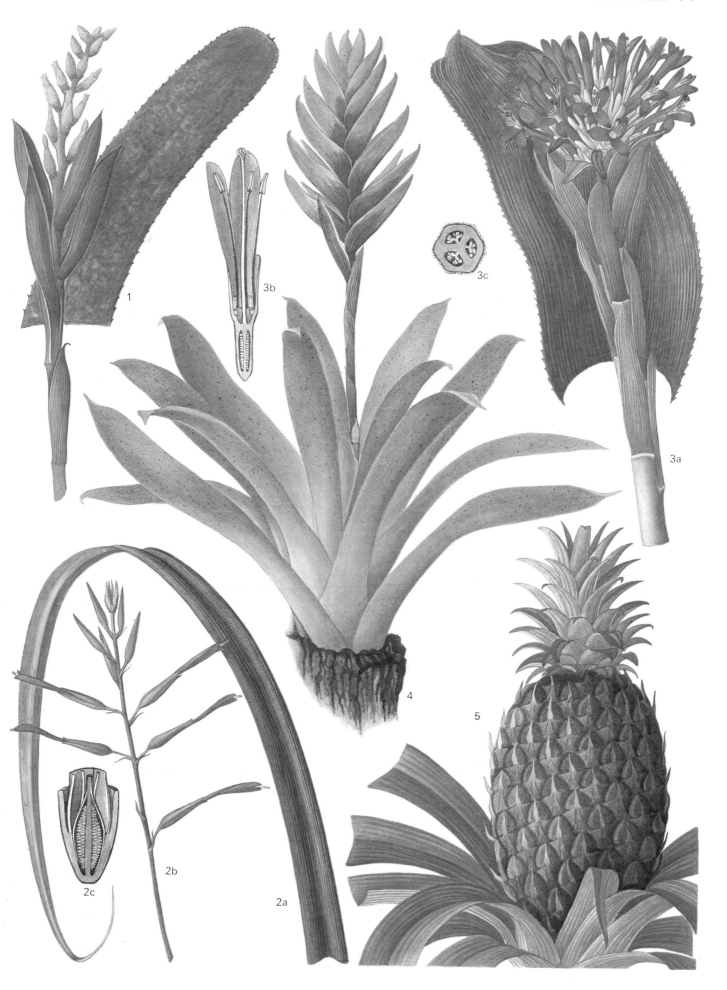

1

3b

3c

2b

2c

2a

3a

4

5

Pineapple leaf fibers have also been used experimentally to produce paper. Pineapple stems and fruits are a possible commercial source of a proteolytic enzyme, bromelain. Spanish moss (*Tillandsia usneoides*) is used as a substitute for horsehair in upholstery. Various genera are grown as ornamentals, in the open in frost-free regions, under glass or as house plants in temperate regions. The foliage alone may be attractive, as in variegated forms of the pineapple, the striped leaves of certain species of *Billbergia*, *Cryptanthus* and *Guzmania*, and the dense rosettes of *Dyckia*, *Nidularium* and *Aregelia*. Other genera also produce showy inflorescences, for example *Pitcairnia*, *Billbergia*, *Aechmea* and *Vriesea*. *Bromelia* and *Neoregelia* are also cultivated.

In parts of the dry tropics, the water retained in the leaf-base tanks of certain native bromeliads may serve as a breeding ground for malaria-carrying anopheline mosquitos. While stretches of open water can easily be sprayed for mosquito control, the tanks of epiphytic and terrestrial bromeliads cannot, and presence of bromeliads has been hampering elimination of malaria in some parts of the tropics.   B.P.

ZINGIBERALES

MUSACEAE
Bananas and Manila Hemp

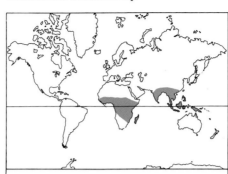

Number of genera: 2
Number of species: about 40
Distribution: chiefly wet tropical lowlands from W Africa to the Pacific.
Economic uses: major food crop (banana) and cordage fibers (abaca, Manila hemp).

The Musaceae is a small family mainly of gigantic, tender, evergreen, perennial herbs, the most important cultivated member being the banana.

Distribution. The Musaceae is an Old World family spread from West Africa to the Pacific (southern Japan to Queensland). *Musa* is Asian, with greatest diversity in the area Burma–New Guinea, and most species live in the wet tropical lowlands, with outliers in cooler hilly country from southern Japan to the Himalayas; they are essentially jungle weeds of disturbed habitats. A very few outlying occurrences of *Musa* species in the central Pacific and coastal East Africa (Pemba) may well be introduced by Man. The genus *Ensete* is predominantly African but with some representations in Asia as far as Southeast Asia and southern China.

Diagnostic features. All species are laticiferous herbs, large to gigantic in size, with pseudostems formed from the leaf sheaths. *Musa* is rhizomatous-stooling and perennial; *Ensete* is unbranched and monocarpic. The leaves are very large, sheathing and spirally arranged; they are oval and have a thick midrib with parallel veins running from it to the margin.

The inflorescences are heavily bracteate and terminal, derived from the growing

Musaceae. 1 *Musa rubra* (a) spike with female flowers below and upper male flowers subtended by large bracts ($\times\frac{2}{3}$); (b) female flower ($\times 1$); (c) male flower ($\times 1$); (d) fruit—a fleshy berry ($\times\frac{2}{3}$); (e) toothed apex to upper perianth ($\times 1$); (f) single lower perianth segment ($\times 1$). 2 *Ensete edule* (a) large herb (up to 10m high) with "stem" formed of sheathing leaf bases; (b) bract subtending numerous flowers ($\times\frac{1}{6}$); (c) male flower ($\times\frac{2}{3}$); (d) bisexual flower ($\times\frac{2}{3}$); (e) cross section of ovary ($\times 1$); (f) seed with window cut out to show embryo ($\times 1$). Strelitziaceae. 3 *Strelitzia reginae* (a) inflorescence—a cincinnus in the axil of a boat-shaped bract in which the flowers unfold in succession ($\times\frac{1}{2}$); (b) half flower ($\times\frac{1}{2}$).

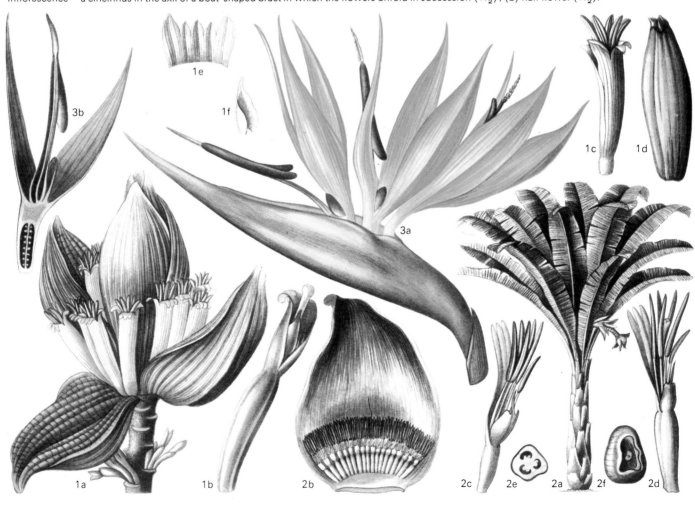

points of the basal corms. The flowers are irregular and usually unisexual, with females in basal clusters and males terminal on the same plant. There are two whorls of three petal-like perianth segments, and five stamens plus a small staminode. The pollen is sticky and pollination is commonly by bats. The ovary is inferior, of three fused carpels and three locules, each containing numerous ovules on an axile placenta. The style is filiform and the stigma lobed. The fruit is a fleshy berry containing numerous stony seeds, and the fruits finally form compact infructescences ("bunches"). The seed has copious endosperm and a straight embryo.

Classification. The two genera are *Musa* (30–40 species) and *Ensete* (about six species). The family is placed in the Zingiberales, which includes the Strelitziaceae, Lowiaceae, Zingiberaceae, Marantaceae and Cannaceae. These families are certainly its nearest relatives but no close relationships can be detected. The genus *Heliconia* used to be included in the Musaceae, but is here placed in the Strelitziaceae.

Economic uses. The family provides a major food crop, the banana. Cultivated bananas evolved in Southeast Asia from two wild species, *Musa acuminata* and *M. balbisiana.* The plants are grown from suckers and banana varieties are therefore clones. The fruits develop without forming seeds and become filled with the characteristic sweet-acid-aromatic parenchymatous pulp that is eaten. Bananas are of enormous importance as food (locally staple) in the tropics and an important item in international trade.

Abaca or Manila hemp, a declining product of the Philippines used to make ropes and cordage, derives from *M. textilis.* *Ensete ventricosa* (*Musa ensete,* the inset, or Abyssinian banana) is cultivated for its fiber and for food: the stem pulp and young shoots are eaten cooked. Like some dwarf cultivars of *Musa* (eg *M. acuminata* 'Dwarf Cavendish'), it is an occasional greenhouse plant in temperate countries. N.W.S.

STRELITZIACEAE
Bird of Paradise Flower
The Strelitziaceae is a small and economically unimportant, but varied, attractive and interesting group of tropical banana-like herbs and trees.

Distribution. The four genera have a disjunct distribution in the tropics: *Ravenala* (one species, Madagascar), *Phenakospermum* (one species, Guiana), *Strelitzia* (four species, South Africa) and *Heliconia* (about 50 species, tropical America).

Diagnostic features. *Heliconia* is herbaceous, but the other three genera tend to woodiness and indeed *Ravenala madagascariensis* can grow into a large tree. The stems are formed by the sheathing leaf bases. The leaves are alternate, in two ranks, medium to very large, with long petioles. They have a thick midrib and numerous pinnately parallel

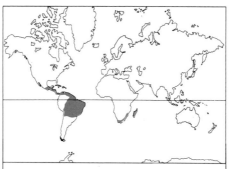

Number of genera: 4
Number of species: about 55
Distribution: tropical America, S Africa, Madagascar.
Economic uses: ornamentals, eg bird of paradise flower (*Strelitzia*), traveller's palm (*Ravenala*).

veins extending to the margin. The flowers are irregular, bisexual and borne in terminal or lateral long-stalked cincinni which are enclosed in a large boat-shaped bract. The perianth consists of two whorls each of three segments, the outer whorl more or less equal and the inner whorl comprising two unequal lateral segments and the third elongated and arrow-shaped, folding around the style. There are five (rarely six) stamens with long, rigid filaments crowned by linear anthers with two locules. The ovary is inferior, comprising three fused carpels, with three locules, each with one to many ovules on axile placentas. The style is filiform with a three-lobed stigma. The fruit is a woody capsule dehiscing loculicidally by three valves, or a fleshy schizocarp. The seeds contain a straight embryo in endosperm and may or may not have an aril.

Classification. *Strelitzia, Ravenala* and *Phenakospermum* have perianth segments free, the ovary contains numerous ovules and the fruit is a capsule. In *Strelitzia* the flowers are very irregular and the seeds have an aril. In *Ravenala* and *Phenakospermum* the flowers are only slightly irregular; in the former there are six stamens and the seeds have an aril and the latter has five stamens and the seeds have no aril. *Heliconia* has only a single basal ovule in each locule, the fruit is a schizocarp splitting into three one-seeded parts, and the seeds are without an aril. *Phenakospermum* was once included within *Ravenala,* but is now considered taxonomically distinct as well as very disjunct in distribution. *Heliconia* may be either separated into its own family, the Heliconiaceae, or included in the Musaceae.

The Strelitziaceae is most nearly allied to the Musaceae and Lowiaceae, differing from the former in having leaves and bracts in two ranks, bisexual flowers and fruit not a berry. (Lowiaceae does not have an entry in this book, but comprises just one genus, *Orchidantha* (*Lowia*), with two species native to Malaysia and Borneo. They are more or less stemless rain forest herbs, the main

features dissimilar to those of the Musaceae and Strelitziaceae being bisexual flowers with a long hypanthium, much surpassing the ovary, and leaves with conspicuous transverse minor veins.)

Economic uses. All genera are more or less ornamental. *Ravenala* (traveller's tree) is a stately tree widely grown in the tropics. *Strelitzia* species (bird of paradise flower) are also common there and in temperate glasshouses. *Heliconia,* with a more or less banana-like habit and ecology, was little cultivated 30 years ago but now, very justifiably, appears ever more prominently in tropical gardens. N.W.S.

ZINGIBERACEAE
Ginger, Cardamom and Turmeric

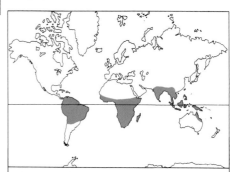

Number of genera: 49
Number of species: about 1,300
Distribution: tropical, chiefly Indomalaysia.
Economic uses: spices (eg ginger, cardamom, turmeric), perfumes, medicines, dyes and tropical and greenhouse ornamentals (eg *Hedychium, Costus*).

The Zingiberaceae is a distinctive family of perennial aromatic forest plants which yield spices (including ginger), dyes, perfumes, medicines, and a number of ornamental species cultivated for their showy flowers.

Distribution. The family is tropical, occurring chiefly in Indomalaysia.

Diagnostic features. All species have branched, underground, fleshy rhizomes and frequently possess tuberous roots. The aerial stems, when present, are invariably short, usually leafless, but sometimes quite leafy. The leaves emerge from the rhizomes as two distinct ranks and toward the base they consist of open or closed sheaths. The blades are fairly large with numerous, closely parallel, pinnate nerves diverging obliquely from the midrib. A distinctive long ligule is to be found at the junction of the sheath and blade. The inflorescence usually occurs as a dense head or cyme but can also be a raceme or consist of a solitary flower. The flowers are irregular and bisexual and their structure is unique and very complicated, the most distinctive part being a conspicuous two- or three-lobed lip (labellum) produced by the fusion of two staminodes. There is only one fertile stamen, corresponding to one of the

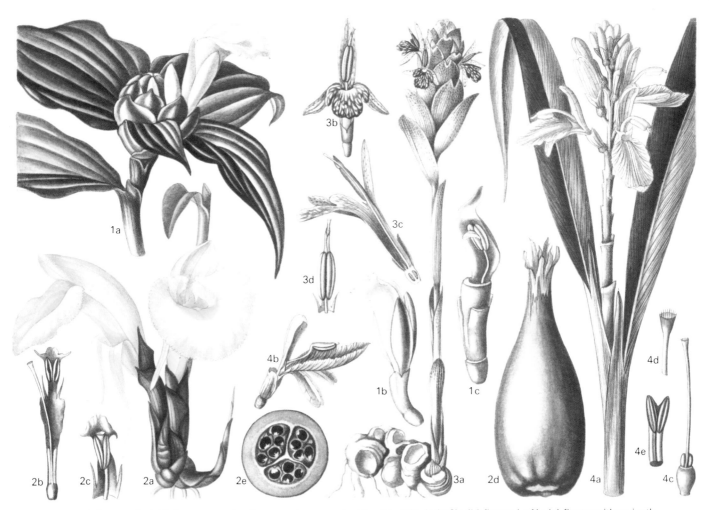

Zingiberaceae. 1 *Costus afer* (a) inflorescence showing upper leaves each with a basal ligule ($\times\frac{2}{3}$); (b) flower ($\times1$); (c) flower with perianth removed showing staminode, fertile stamen and hood-like stigma ($\times\frac{1}{2}$). 2 *Aframomum melegueta* var *minor* (a) habit ($\times\frac{2}{3}$); (b) ovary, style, stigma and petaloid fertile stamen with two anthers ($\times\frac{2}{3}$); (c) stigma cupped between anthers ($\times1$); (d) fruit ($\times\frac{2}{3}$); (e) cross section of fruit ($\times\frac{2}{3}$). 3 *Zingiber officinale* (ginger) (a) habit ($\times\frac{1}{2}$); (b) flower ($\times1$); (c) half flower ($\times1$); (d) anthers with extended connective folded around the style ($\times10$). 4 *Alpinia officinarium* (a) upper leaves and inflorescence ($\times\frac{2}{3}$); (b) flower ($\times1$); (c) gynoecium ($\times1\frac{1}{3}$); (d) stigma ($\times4$); (e) anthers ($\times1\frac{1}{3}$).

members of the inner whorl of stamens; the other two members may be present as staminodes flanking it on each side, or may be absent altogether. One "stamen" of the outer whorl is absent altogether and the other two staminodes form the labellum. The flower is enclosed by three outer perianth segments fused into a tubular calyx, and three inner segments which are petal-like, often showy and more or less united, with the posterior segment often enlarged; the whole is subtended by a bract which is often sheathing. The style is quite reduced and often so thin that it cannot support itself. It is fused to a groove along the length of the anther and only the stigma protrudes above it. The ovary is inferior, of three fused carpels with either three (occasionally two) locules with axile placentas or one locule with parietal (rarely basal) placentas. There are usually numerous ovules in each locule. The fruit is a brightly colored and sometimes very fleshy capsule. The seeds are large, rounded or angled, with copious endosperm: many are wrapped in a distinctive red aril.

Classification. The chief genera are *Zingiber* (80–90 species), *Costus* (150 species), *Alpinia* (250 species), *Curcuma* (70 species), *Kaemp-feria* (55 species), *Hedychium* (50 species).

Together with the Musaceae, the Cannaceae, the Strelitziaceae and the Marantaceae, the Zingiberaceae forms an isolated order, the Zingiberales, which belongs to the superorder Commelinidae. The genera *Costus*, *Dimerocostus*, *Monocostus* and *Tapeinochilos* are separated by some authorities into the family Costaceae.

Economic uses. A large number of the principal genera have beautiful flowers and many of them are cultivated in the tropics, and as hothouse ornamentals in temperate countries. Particularly striking examples include various species of *Hedychium* (ginger lily), *Kaempferia*, *Costus* and *Roscoea*.

Many Zingiberaceae are rich in volatile oils and are widely used as condiments, herbs, dyes and medicinal plants. Perhaps the best known is ginger (*Zingiber officinale*). Other important products include the abir, a perfumed powder obtained from the rhizome of *Hedychium spicatum*; East Indian arrowroot, derived from the tubers of *Curcuma angustifolia*; *C. longa* (*C. domestica*), which yields turmeric, one of the main coloring and aromatic ingredients of curry powder and also used as a yellow dye;

zedoary, a spice, tonic and perfume made from the rhizomes of *C. zedoaria*; *Alpinia officinale* of Hainan and *A. galanga* of the Moluccas, which yield the medicinal and flavoring rhizome galangal; and *Elettaria cardomomum* from Indonesia, which yields the eastern spice cardomom. Several useful products are also derived from different species of *Aframomum*, including the spice Melegueta pepper (*Aframomum melegueta*).

C.J.H.

CANNACEAE
Queensland Arrowroot

The Cannaceae is a family containing a single genus, *Canna*, comprising large perennial herbs with spectacular flowers. *Canna edulis* yields purple or Queensland arrowroot, and several species are grown as greenhouse and tropical garden ornamentals.

Distribution. The family is tropical and subtropical, native to the West Indies and Central America.

Diagnostic features. The plants have a swollen underground tuberous rhizome, from which arise aerial stems bearing large, broad, pinnately veined leaves with a distinct

Cannaceae. 1 *Canna indifolia* tip of inflorescence ($\times\frac{2}{3}$). 2 *Canna glauca* (a) base of plant showing swollen rhizome and sheathing leaf bases ($\times\frac{2}{3}$); (b) leaf ($\times\frac{2}{3}$); (c) inflorescence ($\times\frac{2}{3}$); (d) flower; shown from base upwards are: worty inferior ovary, two green sepals, two orange lanceolate petals, outer staminode whorl of two broad wings plus curved labellum, inner staminode whorl of wing-like staminode plus slightly coiled staminode with coiled half-anther attached and central petaloid style with hairy stigmatic surface ($\times 1$). 3 *Canna generalis* (a) half section of flower base ($\times 1$); (b) cross section of ovary ($\times 2$); (c) worty fruits ($\times\frac{2}{3}$); (d) cross section of fruit ($\times\frac{2}{3}$).

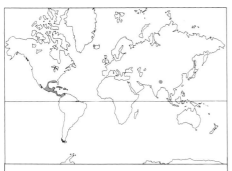

Number of genera: 1
Number of species: 30–55
Distribution: tropical and subtropical in Central America and the W Indies.
Economic uses: purple or Queensland arrowroot grown commercially and numerous greenhouse and tropical garden ornamentals (cannas).

midrib. The petiole sheathes the stem, but there is no ligule.

The flowers are large, conspicuous, bisexual and borne in racemose inflorescences, each flower being subtended by a bract. The perianth comprises three free, imbricate sepals which are usually green, and three petals which are similar, but narrower and fused at the base, with one of them usually smaller than the others. The petals are united to the fused staminal column, which is composed of four to six, mainly sterile, petal-like and brightly colored stamens, which form the most showy part of the flower. Essentially, the stamens form two series or whorls of which the outermost is composed of three petaloid staminodes, the largest of these (the labellum) being reflexed and rolled back on itself. The inner series consists of one or two staminodes and a free petaloid fertile stamen with half an anther joined to it along one edge. The ovary is inferior, of three fused carpels, and has three locules each containing two rows of numerous ovules on axile placentas. The single petaloid style is usually longer than the staminal tube. The fruit is a warty capsule containing many small seeds with straight embryos and very hard endosperm.

Classification. The variable numbers of species accredited to *Canna* reflect the differences in interpretation by different botanists. Criteria of value in classifying the genus include shape of leaves and perianth parts, length of the staminal tube, and numbers and shape of the staminodes.

This family belongs to the same order as the families of the banana (Musaceae), ginger (Zingiberaceae) and arrowroot (Marantaceae), with which it shares such features as irregular flowers, reduction in the number of functional stamens, inferior ovary and seeds with endosperm. It differs from the closely related Zingiberaceae in not having ligules.

Economic uses. *Canna edulis* is a species of considerable economic importance as the rhizomatous tubers are the source of a starch known as purple or Queensland arrowroot. It is grown as a food crop in the Pacific and parts of Asia, and on a commercial scale in Australia. The starch is easily digested and therefore suitable for incorporation in invalid and infant diets. The rhizomes of some other species, such as *C. bidentata*, are sometimes used as emergency foods, while those of *C. gigantea* and *C. speciosa* yield extracts with medicinal properties. A number of the species (notably *C. indica*) have been developed as ornamental plants for heated greenhouses in temperate zones or in tropical gardens. S.R.C.

Marantaceae. 1 *Calathea villosa* (a) leaf showing basal sheath, petiole and blade ($\times\frac{2}{3}$); (b) inflorescence with flowers subtended by green bracts ($\times\frac{2}{3}$). 2 *C. concolor* (a) flower comprising fused sepals, three irregular petals, two petaloid staminodes and one petaloid stamen with fertile anther and a hooded style ($\times$ 1); (b) upper part of flower opened ($\times$ 1). 3 *Stromanthe sanguinea* (a) upper leaf and inflorescence ($\times\frac{2}{3}$); (b) flower ($\times$ 2); (c) flower opened out ($\times$ 3). 4 *Maranta arundinacea* (a) shoot with leaves and inflorescence ($\times\frac{2}{3}$); (b) tuber ($\times\frac{2}{3}$); (c) flower ($\times$ 1); (d) petaloid staminodes, dorsal view of fertile stamen and style ($\times$ 1$\frac{1}{3}$); (e) cross section of unilocular ovary ($\times$ 3); (f) fruit ($\times$ 2).

MARANTACEAE

Arrowroot

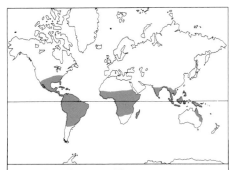

Number of genera: 30
Number of species: about 350
Distribution: mainly tropical, chiefly America.
Economic uses: true arrowroot (*Maranta arundinacea*), flowers and tubers of *Calathea* species eaten, leaves used for roofing and basketwork locally, and many greenhouse ornamentals (*Calathea* and *Maranta*).

The Marantaceae, a smallish tropical family of herbaceous perennials, includes several useful species, such as the West Indian arrowroot (*Maranta arundinacea*).

Distribution. Most of the 30 genera are native to tropical America; seven are native to Africa and six to Asia.

Diagnostic features. The plants usually have underground rhizomes or tubers. The leaves are arranged in two rows and the petioles have sheathing bases. The leaf blade is narrow or broad, with pinnate veins running closely parallel from the midrib. The petiole may be winged, and where it joins the blade it is generally swollen into a pulvinus – a mass of cells active during movements of the leaf in response to stimuli.

The inflorescence is a spike or panicle usually subtended and enclosed by spathe-like bracts. The flowers, which are not very conspicuous, are irregular and bisexual, usually with an outer series of three free sepals and an inner series of three distinctly petaloid segments, more or less united into a tube and irregularly three-lobed. The androecium is attached to the corolla and consists of only one fertile stamen (usually petaloid and with a single-celled anther), other stamens being absent or variously modified to form petaloid staminodes. The ovary, of three fused carpels, is inferior and

has either three locules or one (the other two aborting), each locule containing one basal, erect ovule. There is a single style. The fruit is either fleshy or a loculicidal capsule. The seeds have an aril and abundant endosperm surrounding a curved embryo.

Classification. The genera may be divided into two tribes, the PHRYNIEAE (ovary with three locules) and the MARANTEAE (ovary with one locule). The former includes such genera as *Calathea* (one staminode), *Marantochloa* (two staminodes and deciduous bracts) and *Phrynium* (two staminodes and persistent bracts), and the latter contains *Ischnosiphon* (persistent bracts), *Thalia* (one outer staminode) and *Maranta* (two conspicuous outer staminodes).

The Marantaceae is closely related to the Musaceae, Zingiberaceae, Cannaceae and Strelitziaceae, these families sharing sufficient vegetative and floral characters to be placed in the same order (Zingiberales). The Marantaceae is the most highly evolved family of this group by virtue of the extreme reduction in both stamens and carpels.

Economic uses. Economically the most important genus is *Maranta*. West Indian arrowroot or maranta starch is obtained by grinding and washing the rhizomes of *Maranta arundinacea*. The species is cultivated commercially in the West Indies and tropical America as the starch, being readily digestible, is useful in special diets. The tough and durable leaves of *Calathea dis-* *color* are used to make waterproof baskets and those of *C. lutea* are used for roofing houses in the Caribbean and Central America. The flowers of two Mexican species, *C. macrosepala* and *C. violacea*, are cooked and eaten as a vegetable. The so-called topi- tambu, or sweet corn root, is the edible tuber of the West Indian species *C. allouia*. Some species of *Calathea* and *Maranta* are cultivated in temperate zones as greenhouse ornamentals and houseplants for their attractive foliage.   S.R.C.

ARECIDAE

ARECALES

PALMAE
The Palm Family

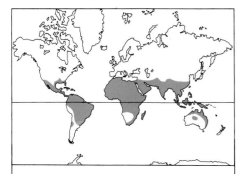

Number of genera: about 212
Number of species: about 2,780
Distribution: chiefly tropical, with some subtropical and a few temperate outliers.
Economic uses: most important products are coconuts, copra, dates, sago, palm oil, fibers (eg coir, raffia). Many are grown as ornamentals.

The Palmae (Arecaceae) is a natural and ancient group of plants. Amongst the monocotyledons only the Orchidaceae, Gramineae and Liliaceae have more genera and species, and in the moister tropics, which palms epitomize, only the orchids equal them in conspicuousness.

Distribution. Palms are mainly tropical and occur in all habitats from perhumid lowland rain forest to deserts and from mangrove swamps to high mountain thickets. There are a few subtropical and temperate outliers, including the European species *Chamaerops humilis* which attains latitude 44°N. All palms have a single apical bud and if that is killed by frost the stem dies. Few species have overcome this limitation. *Trachycarpus* reaches 8,000ft (2,400m) altitude at 32°N in the Himalayas, where the land is under snow from November to March, and *Serenoa* reaches 30°N in North America. The distribution of palms is strikingly disbalanced. Africa has 16 genera and 116 species. This contrasts with 29 genera and 132 species in the nearby but much smaller Indian Ocean islands (Mascarenes, Comoro islands and Madagascar). The New World has 64 genera and 857 species, mostly in South America. The eastern tropics are easily the richest,

with 97 genera and 1,385 species. The poverty of Africa (the whole continent has fewer palms than Singapore island) is believed to result from desiccation during the Pleistocene which greatly reduced the extent of moist habitats. It is noteworthy that nearly all palms are restricted to one of these four regions. Amongst species exceptions are the date palm (*Phoenix dactylifera*) and the coconut (*Cocos nucifera*), both widely cultivated, and two other species found in both Africa and the Indian Ocean islands. At the generic level, the raffia palms (*Raphia*) and oil palms (*Elaeis*) span the Atlantic and four genera are common to Africa and Asia (*Borassus*, *Calamus*, *Hyphaene* and *Phoenix*).
Diagnostic features. The life form of the palms is distinctive; it is characterized, for example, by the coconut, with its single unbranched trunk bearing a terminal tuft of feather-like leaves, with axillary inflorescences and a basal mass of slender, renewing roots. The family as a whole contains a great deal of diversity, but much less within the natural groups now recognized. The stem has no secondary thickening (the seedling builds up an inverted cone to the full width before growth commences and this width is then maintained) and is traversed by numerous small, separate vascular bundles, each with a hard fibrous sheath; these may be more or less evenly spaced (as in the coconut) or concentrated at the periphery (from which hard springy planks can then be made, though these trunks are as hard as steel to cut). The surface is often hoop-marked by leaf scars. Branching occurs very rarely and is in most cases truly dichotomous (*Hyphaene*, *Nypa*) which is a rare mode in flowering plants as a whole. The apical bud is usually well protected by leaf bases or spines, or the tissues may be poisonous. The vasculature, with major bundles in the stem center, is characteristic of monocotyledons, and is fundamentally different from the arrangement in dicotyledons.

Monocotyledon trees have several features in common: a few large leaves are formed one at a time at the stem tip, each with a broad sheathing base. The young, still-furled leaf stands in the crown center like a sword. The palm leaf, however, is more complex than that of other monocotyledons. The blade is plicate (folded like a fan) and the folds are either displayed more or less normally along both sides of an extended

rachis, as in the feather palms, or else arise crowded from a short central rib or costa, as in fan palms. A few species of both kinds have entire blades (eg *Licuala grandis*, *Verschaffeltia splendida*). The folds develop as the leaf grows in bud before it is unfurled and, as it expands from the bud, swellings (pulvini) develop which push the folded leaflets out to their mature position. The leaflets may contain one fold or several and be linear, fishtail-shaped, acute or praemorse (looking as if bitten off). Before final expansion of the leaf, superficial cells often divide to form hairs or scales which are often of great complexity and beauty. The loose surface layer so formed acts as a lubricant during the opening of the leaf. Large fan leaves are intermediate between the feather and fan types, and have a massive central costa (costapalmate). A more fundamental distinction, however, is between leaves that are V-folded (induplicate) and those that are Λ-folded (reduplicate). The former never possess an apical leaflet, the latter always have one – a distinction that arises early in development. Nearly all fan leaves are reduplicate. Leaves vary enormously in size; *Raphia fainifera* has the largest flowering plant leaf, sometimes over 65ft (20m) long.

Palm inflorescences are highly diverse, from huge panicles with many orders of branching (*Calamus*) or tree-like monopodia with some 250,000 flowers (talipot palm), down to simple spikes. They are usually lateral and borne in the crown or below it, but are occasionally terminal (*Corypha*, *Metroxylon*). Stems of the latter mode are monocarpic, storing up starch in the trunk and utilizing it in one gigantic burst of reproduction after which the whole plant dies. The caryotoid palms are intermediate. In most of them axillary inflorescences form from the stem tip downwards and the stem progressively dies.

The flowers may be bisexual or unisexual, the sexes then being borne either on the same plant (monoecious) or on separate plants (dioecious); some species have bisexual and unisexual flowers on the same plant (polygamous). Floral parts are normally in threes. There are three separate or connate sepals which may be imbricate, and three separate or connate petals which may be imbricate in female flowers and valvate in male flowers. The stamens are in two whorls each of three. The anthers have two locules and open by longitudinal slits. The ovary is

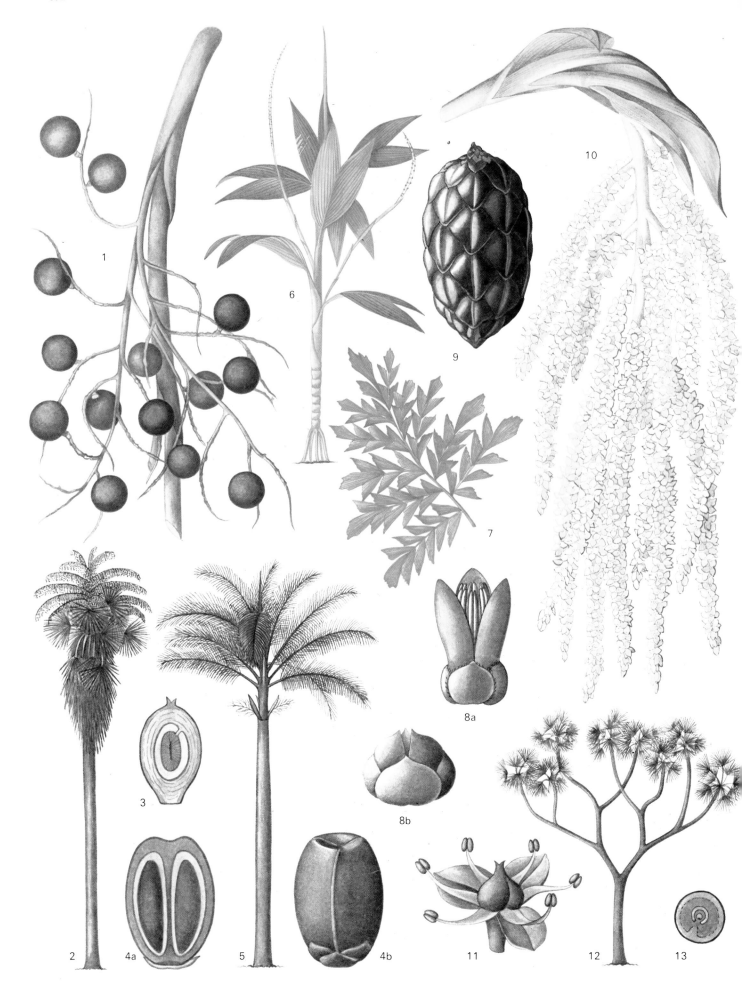

superior and comprises three carpels which are either free (apocarpous) or fused (syncarpous). In syncarpous ovaries there are either one or three locules. There are three (or sometimes one) erect or pendulous anatropous (rarely semi-anatropous or orthotropous) ovules in each locule. The ovary is vestigial or absent in male flowers. There are adaptations to pollination by wind (*Cocos*, *Elaeis*, *Phoenix*) or beetles (*Bactris*, *Johannesteijsmannia*) or other insects. Numerous stamens (eg *Phytelephas*) or other parts may represent modifications to permit insect feeding. The flowers commonly persist only one day or less. The pollen is monocolpate.

The fruits are mostly one-seeded berries or drupes with a vast range in size; *Lodoicea* (double coconut) has the world's largest seed. The fruit surface is most often smooth but may be warty or covered with beautiful, geometrically arranged scales. The mesocarp is fleshy, or dry and variously fibrous. The endocarp if distinct is mostly thin. Many fruits are brightly colored and virtually all are indehiscent. The storage tissue is endosperm which is oily or fatty rather than starchy; it is sometimes extremely hard in which case it is known as vegetable ivory and utilized for carvings or (formerly) for buttons. Germination is hypogeal (the basic mode in monocotyledons); often the cotyledon remains as a haustorium within the testa.

Classification. The palms, though conventionally considered to be a single family, could equally well be considered to be a group of families. Palms are difficult to work with, poorly collected, and intractable to the herbarium method. They have therefore been relatively neglected by taxonomists. They are supremely a group for the field botanist for whom they provide an exhilarating challenge.

Classic subdivisions of this great family do not closely reflect natural groups. Recently a revised subdivision into 15 natural groups belonging to five evolutionary lines has been proposed.

CORYPHOID LINE
The three groups of this line comprise all the

Palmae. 1 *Livistonia rotundifolia* part of branch bearing indehiscent fruit (×⅔). 2 *Corypha umbrauculifera* habit showing massive terminal inflorescence. 3 *Elaeis guineensis* vertical section of the fruit containing a single seed. 4 *Arenga westerhoutii* (a) vertical section of fruit with two seeds (×⅔); (b) fruit (×⅔). 5 *Roystonea regia* habit. 6 *Chamaedorea geonomiformis* a small reed-like palm shown here producing male inflorescences. 7 *Caryota mitis* bipinnate leaf (×⅔). 8 *Caryota cumingii* (a) male flower with three sepals, three petals and three stamens (×6); (b) female flower (×5). 9 *Raphia vinifera* scaly fruit a distinctive feature of the Lepidocaryoid line (×⅔). 10 *Chamaedorea fragrans* male inflorescence (×⅔). 11 *Corypha umbrauculifera* bisexual flower (×6). 12 *Hyphaene thebiaca* habit showing the dichotomous branching, an unusual feature in the palms. 13 *Phoenix* sp cross section of ovary with a single locule and ovule (×6).

genera with induplicate leaves (except the caryotoid line), all those with palmate leaves (except two of the lepidocaryoids), and 14 of the 15 apocarpous genera, many of which also have perfect flowers.

CORYPHOID PALMS. This includes those palms, indubitably the most primitive, with much-branched inflorescences of bisexual apocarpous flowers and the most primitive wood vessels (the *Trithrinax* alliance). This large group (32 genera, 300 species) shows very diverse inflorescence and flower structure and syncarpy as well as apocarpy. The chromosome complement is a uniform n = 18. Many genera have brightly colored fruits apparently adapted to dispersal by birds.

PHOENICOID PALMS. This comprises the single genus *Phoenix* which is clearly related to the coryphoids but has pinnate, induplicate leaves (in which it is unique) and is dioecious, and somewhat dimorphic. The flowers are probably wind-pollinated in specialized inflorescences. *Phoenix* occurs in Africa and Asia, mainly in dry habitats though several species occur in swamps including two in mangrove forest; one species occurs in Crete.

BORASSOID PALMS. This comprises six genera and 56 species of more specialized palms which seem clearly related and derived from a coryphoid stock. They are dioecious with stout inflorescences and dimorphic flowers often sunken in pits in the axis. Leaves are large and costapalmate. Chromosome number is n = 18, 17 or 14. Fruits are fibrous or corky. The group is restricted to the Old World. *Borassus* is the least specialized genus and ranges most widely, from Africa and Madagascar to India, New Guinea and possibly Queensland. Other genera include *Latania* and *Lodoicea*.

LEPIDOCARYOID LINE
This derives its name from the unique, highly distinctive scaly fruits. Nearly all climbing palms belong here, including rattan cane (*Calamus*), as well as *Raphia*, the fabulous *Pigafettia*, the sago palms (*Metroxylon*) and the important New World genera *Mauritia* and *Mauritiella* (the only palms with induplicate palmate leaves and which are therefore bifid at the apex). Nearly all are armed with spines on the trunk, leaf sheath, leaves and inflorescence. There is a wide diversity of inflorescence type but a uniform pattern of floral arrangement. The flowers are bisexual and the plants polygamous, monoecious or dioecious. The fruits commonly have a fleshy layer, sweet to devastatingly sour, probably an attractant for dispersing mammals and birds. Chromosome number is n = 14. This large line (22 genera, 664 species) is mainly confined between 25° north and south and to the wet tropics.

NYPOID LINE
This comprises a single monotypic genus, *Nypa*, an inhabitant of salt water. This is the only non-coryphoid genus with an apocarpous gynoecium. The carpels have a vascular

structure different from that of all other palms. Chromosome number is n = 17. *Nypa* is the oldest fossil palm with records back to the Cenomanian (100–110 million years) and is one of the seven oldest angiosperms known. The present range is Far Eastern but fossils extend to Europe and southern England (Eocene, London Clay), indicating a distribution along the former Tethys Sea, to West Africa and to America. *Nypa* is highly distinctive and has no close relatives but is possibly closer to the arecoid line than to any other.

CARYOTOID LINE
This line comprises three monoecious genera and 35 species. The leaves are morphologically induplicate in vernation but are anatomically reduplicate. Some are bipinnate (*Caryota*), others have pinnately nerved leaflets. The flowers are unisexual. In most species stems flower basipetally then die. The fruits are fleshy, and often contain irritant spicules but are nevertheless animal-dispersed. Chromosome number is n = 5.

ARECOID LINE
This line, comprising nine separate groups and with 146 genera and 1,684 species, contains 68% of all the known palm genera and 60% of the species.

PSEUDOPHOENIX. This single Caribbean genus of four species is the most primitive. *Pseudophoenix* has much-branched inflorescences, bisexual flowers and fruits with one to three seeds.

COCOSOID PALMS. This comprises 28 genera and 583 species and contains the well-known oil palm (*Elaeis guineensis*) and coconut (*Cocos*). Twenty-four of the genera are South American (and include a few climbers), two more are found in the West Indies, one is in South Africa and *Cocos* itself is best considered to be of Melanesian origin. Many of the less specialized species are adapted to cooler, drier, more seasonal climates. This group has previously been considered to be a separate line but is in fact very close to the arecoids. The most conspicuous difference is the bony endocarp with three pores. The single large inflorescence bract is distinctive but is a feature shared with other arecoids. The flowers are dimorphic, in triads, and the chromosome number is n = 15 or 16.

ARECOID PALMS. In the restricted sense this is a widely distributed and numerous group (88 genera, 760 species). It is highly advanced with a single inflorescence bract and strikingly dimorphic flowers borne in triads. Chromosome number is n = 16 or 18. These palms are mainly confined to humid rain forests within the tropics. Eighteen natural alliances can be recognized. America has 10 genera, Africa only one, the Indian Ocean islands 19 genera and the eastern tropics 58, of which the *Clinostigma* alliance has shown exceptionally prolific evolution at genus level.

The other groups of the Arecoid line are the CEROXYLOID (America, Indian Ocean),

CHAMAEDOROID (America, Indian Ocean), IRIARTOID (America), PODOCOCOID (Africa), GEONOMOID (America) and PHYTELE-PHANTOID (America).

Palms contain, amongst their great diversity, many primitive traits of the monocotyledons and must be considered as an early monocotyledon stock.

The gynoecium in the more primitive palms shows much similarity to that of primitive Ranunculales and Magnoliales amongst the dicotyledons. It is stipitate, follicular, conduplicate, with an open ventral suture, laminar or submarginal placentation and the locular canal remains open. Amongst monocotyledons the palms have primitive flowers, and this is combined with woodiness.

The distribution of the five lines of palms, and especially of those genera exhibiting primitive traits, shows 13 of the 15 groups occurring in South America and Africa (if fossil *Nypa* is included), with only *Pseudophoenix* and the caryotoids missing. These two regions also have a concentration of primitive genera. The eastern tropics show numerical superiority but this is largely due to the considerable proliferation there of the advanced arecoids and the climbing lepidocaryoids *Calamus* and *Daemonorops*. Of particular interest are two groups of the arecoid line, the Chamaedoroid and Geonomoid palms, found in America and in the Indian Ocean islands.

Modern reconstruction of the past positions of the continents shows that South America and Africa were joined as a single land mass, West Gondwana, until the late Jurassic, when they were separated by the opening of the Atlantic. The climate remained warm throughout the Mesozoic and early Tertiary. The physical setting might well have been conducive to palm evolution. The present evidence suggests that palms probably evolved very early in the history of the monocotyledons. Floral resemblances between monocotyledons, such as the Alismataceae, and dicotyledons, such as the Nymphaeaceae, are best regarded as convergent evolution by reduction to the herbaceous condition and aquatic habitat. The sheer antiquity of palms, with the advanced *Nypa* (one of the seven oldest known flowering plants), raises the possibility that monocotyledons and dicotyledons have a separate origin (comparable to that of birds and mammals) from a proto-angiospermous stock and are not evolved one from the other.

Economic uses. Coconuts and dates are central to the economy of many producing countries. An important by-product of the coconut palm (*Cocos nucifera*) is copra, and oil is also extracted from the oil palm (*Elaeis guineensis*) and species of *Orbigyna*. A major source of carbohydrate for many people living in the tropics is sago, which is processed from the pith of palms of the genus *Metroxylon* (sago palm) and some species of other genera (eg *Arenga* and *Caryota*). Palm wine (toddy) is another useful product of many palms including *Borassus* and *Caryota*. This is evaporated to produce palm sugar (jaggery) or distilled to form the base for the liquor known as arrack. However, the term arrack is most often applied to the alcoholic spirit obtained from the sap of the coconut palm.

Apart from their obvious importance as a source of food, the palms produce a variety of useful fibers. These include coir, which comes from the husk of the coconut, raffia fiber obtained by stripping the surface of young leaflets of the genus *Raphia*, and piassava fiber, from the leaf sheaths or fibrous stems of South American *Leopoldinia piassaba* and *Attalea funifera*. *Caryota urens* gives a black bristle fiber (kitul fiber) used for ropes and broom heads. For canework, the much-used rattan cane is invaluable; this comes mainly from *Calamus* species, which also provides malacca cane, a stout cane used for walking sticks and baskets.

Waxes are obtained from *Copernicia* (carnauba wax) and *Ceroxylon*. Vegetable ivory, from the ivory nut palm and others, was once an important commodity, used for buttons and a general substitute for real ivory. The betel nut comes from *Areca catechu* and is widely used in India, Malaysia and tropical Africa.

Many palms, with their tall slender trunks and dense crown of attractive leaves, are ideal ornamental subjects. Notable examples are the Cuban royal palm (*Roystonea regia*), the Chinese windmill palm (*Trachycarpus fortunei*) and the coquitos palm (*Jubaea spectabilis* (*J. chilensis*)).

T.C.W.

CYCLANTHALES

CYCLANTHACEAE
Panama Hat Plant
The Cyclanthaceae is a small family of perennial stemless herbs or climbers chiefly notable for the leaves from which Panama hats are made.

Distribution. The family is native to the West Indies and Tropical America.

Diagnostic features. The plants are either rhizomatous with no aerial stems, or somewhat woody climbers; a few species are partly epiphytic. A feature of this family is the watery or milky juice in all tissues. The leaves are either two-ranked or spirally arranged and distinctly palm-like, being very deeply bilobed, and each lobe being further subdivided. The petiole is sheathing at the base.

The flowers are unisexual with both male and female on the same plant, densely crowded on to axillary spadixes which are enveloped by two or more conspicuous

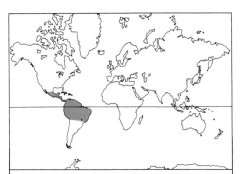

Number of genera: 11
Number of species: 180
Number of species: W Indies and tropical America.
Economic uses: the leaves are made into Panama hats and lesser products are mats, baskets, thatching and brooms.

(sometimes petaloid) non-persistent bracts. The arrangement of the flowers on the spadix is either spiral, the females single with about four male flowers around, or clusters of male and female flowers in superposed whorls. The male flowers have either a small, toothed, cup-shaped perianth or no perianth at all, and numerous stamens fused at the base with the filaments also adherent to the perianth when the latter is present. The female flowers have either no perianth or a perianth of four persistent, free or fused segments; sometimes those of several flowers become collectively fused, enlarged and hardened in the fruit. The female flower also possesses four short, or long and thread-like, staminodes. The ovary, of four fused carpels, is usually superior, and often embedded in the axis. It has one locule, containing numerous ovules attached either to one apical or to four parietal or apical placentas. The one to four spreading stigmas are either stalkless or mounted on a short style. The multiple, fleshy fruit has either separate or fused berries containing several seeds. The seed has a succulent testa and a minute embryo surrounded by copious endosperm.

Classification. The family may be split into two subfamilies on the basis of inflorescence and leaf characteristics.

CARLUDOVICOIDEAE. Male and female flowers in spirally arranged groups, spadix not screw-like, leaves cleft at the apex, fan-like or entire; *Carludovica, Schultesiophytum, Asplundia, Thoracocarpus, Evodianthus, Dicranopygium, Sphaeradenia, Stelestylis, Ludovia, Pseudoludovia*.

CYCLANTHOIDEAE. Male and female flowers in separate, alternate whorls, or sometimes part spirals, spadix screw-like, the leaves deeply cleft with a forked main rib; *Cyclanthus*.

The family is closely related to the Palmae, Pandanaceae and Araceae, and shows considerable evolutionary advances in the possession of much reduced unisexual flowers. It might be regarded as an advanced derivative

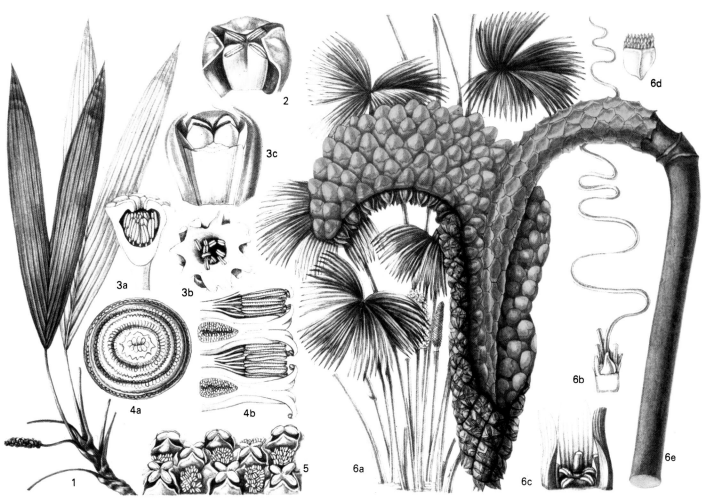

Cyclanthaceae. 1 *Asplundia vagans* habit ($\times \frac{2}{3}$). 2 *Stelestylis stylaris* female flower with one perianth segment removed ($\times 4\frac{1}{2}$). 3 *Evodianthus funifer* (a) half male flower in bud ($\times 4\frac{1}{2}$); (b) male flower ($\times 6$); (c) young fruit ($\times 4$). 4 *Cyclanthus bipartitus* (a) tip of spadix with alternating whorls of male and female flowers ($\times 1\frac{1}{2}$); (b) section of spadix showing male and female flowers ($\times 4$). 5 *Sphaeradenia chiriquensis* portion of spadix with male and female flowers ($\times 2$). 6 *Carludovica rotundifolia* (a) spadices and fan-like leaves ($\times \frac{1}{2}$); (b) female flower ($\times 2$); (c) young fruit ($\times 4\frac{1}{2}$); (d) male flower ($\times 2$); (e) ripe composite fruit cut open to show the stalk (pink) into which bases of the berries (orange) fit ($\times \frac{2}{3}$).

of the palm habit with the same degree of evolutionary specialization as the Araceae.

Economic uses. The family is economically important for *Carludovica palmata* (the Panama hat plant), from which young leaves are made into Panama hats. Ecuador alone exports over 1,000,000 of these hats per year. About six young leaves are required to make a single hat. Older coarser leaves are used for mat- and basket-making. The leave of *C. angustifolia* are used for thatching native huts in Peru and the leaves of *C. sarmentosa* are used to manufacture brooms in Guyana.

S.R.C.

PANDANALES

PANDANACEAE
Screw Pines

The Pandanaceae is a large family of tropical trees, shrubs and climbers.

Distribution. The family is distributed throughout the tropics and subtropics of the Old World and most members favor coastal or marshy areas.

Diagnostic features. The tall stems bear the annual scars of the leaf bases, are branched

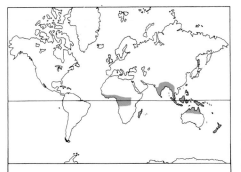

Number of genera: 3
Number of species: about 700
Distribution: Old World tropics and subtropics.
Economic uses: large edible starchy fruits, leaves used for thatching and basket-weaving, aerial roots for cordage, flowers used in perfumery and some ornamentals.

and are usually supported by aerial roots. The leaves are terminal in three ranks but as the stem is often twisted they appear to be spirally arranged. They are long and narrow, sometimes stiff and sword-like or in some cases almost grass-like.

The flowers are unisexual and arranged in a racemose spadix (except in *Sararanga*), subtended by a spathe which is sometimes brightly colored. Male and female are borne on separate plants and lack both calyx and corolla. In the male flower the numerous stamens are arranged in a raceme or umbel with free or fused filaments, and are sometimes represented as staminodes in the female inflorescence. The female flower consists of a superior ovary usually of many carpels in a ring, sometimes reduced to a row of carpels or a single carpel. There are one to many locules depending on the degree of fusion between the carpels; each locule has one to numerous anatropous ovules on basal or parietal placentas. The stigmas are sessile or almost so. The fruit is a berry or multilocular drupe, containing small seeds with fleshy endosperm and a minute embryo.

Classification. The trees and shrubs of the most important genus, *Pandanus* (about 600 species), bear cone-like fruits that resemble pineapples. Most species of *Freycinetia* (about 100 species) are climbing perennials with slender stems which bear roots that penetrate the supporting host. *Sararanga* (two species) differs from the other two

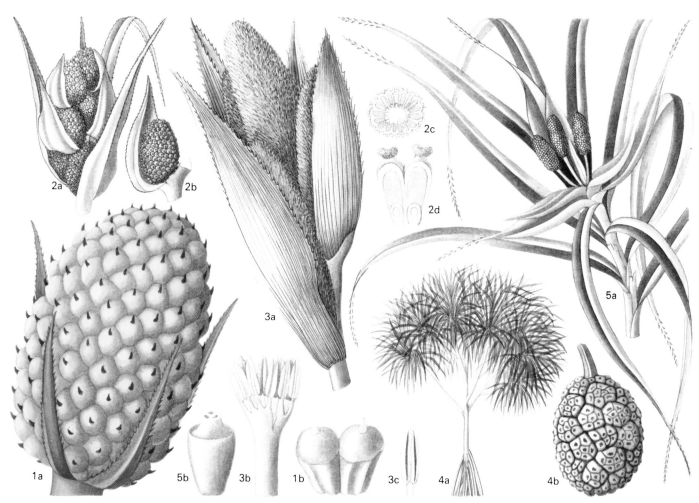

Pandanaceae. 1 *Pandanus minor* (a) cone-like fruit ($\times\frac{2}{3}$); (b) two segments of the fruit ($\times$1). 2 *P. pygmaeus* (a) female inflorescences ($\times\frac{2}{3}$); (b) female inflorescence and subtending bract ($\times\frac{2}{3}$); (c) cross section of female inflorescence ($\times$1); (d) female flowers showing sessile stigmas and with part of wall cut away to show basal ovules ($\times$4). 3 *P. houlletii* (a) male inflorescences and bracts ($\times\frac{2}{3}$); (b) male flower comprising a whorl of stamens with fused filaments ($\times$6); (c) dehiscing stamen ($\times$8). 4 *P. kirkii* (a) habit showing aerial roots at base of trunk ($\times\frac{1}{50}$); (b) fruit ($\times\frac{1}{5}$). 5 *Freycinetia angustifolia* (a) flowering shoot with sword-like leaves ($\times\frac{2}{3}$); (b) ovary and base of style ($\times$16).

genera in that it lacks the aerial roots, has a panicoid inflorescence and pediceled rather than sessile flowers. The fruit is a drupe.

The Pandanaceae is most closely related to the Cyclanthaceae, Palmae, Araceae and Lemnaceae though the relationships are distant.

Economic uses. Many species of the genus *Pandanus* (screw pines) are useful sources of food; *Pandanus leram* (Nicobar breadfruit) produces a large globular fruit which is usually boiled in water to form a mealy mass; *P. utilis* and *P. andamanensium* also have edible starchy fruits.

The leaves of the most common species, *P. odoratissimus*, are used for thatching and weaving, especially the thornless variety *laevis*. These leaves are dried, beaten to make them supple, soaked in water and then sun-bleached. Wide strips are used for thatching and matting and fine strips for hats and baskets. Fibers are made from the aerial roots and used for cordage and brushes. This same species is cultivated for its flowers which are used for the popular Indian perfume kewda attar. The fragrant white spathes of the male inflorescences are distilled in water and the vapor absorbed in sandalwood oil. In Malaya the fragrant leaves of *P. odorus*, which never flowers, are used in potpourris. Several species are ornamentals, notably *Freycinetia banksii*, a hothouse plant from New Zealand, which is commonly trained to grow around peat-covered pillars, and *Pandanus veitchii* which has glossy dark green leaves with a silvery white border.

M.C.D.

ARALES

LEMNACEAE

Duckweeds

The Lemnaceae is a family of small or minute aquatic herbs which may be free-swimming, floating or submerged. They include the well-known duckweed (*Lemna*), which often forms a green carpet over stagnant water, and *Wolffia*, the smallest known flowering plant.

Distribution. The family is found in fresh water all over the world.

Diagnostic features. Modification of the vegetative body has been carried so far that the usual distinction between leaf and stem is no longer maintained and representatives of

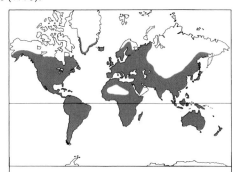

Number of genera: 6
Number of species: about 43
Distribution: cosmopolitan, in freshwater habitats.
Economic uses: food for fish and water fowl.

this family consist of undifferentiated fronds (thalluses) of various forms. Simple roots may be present or absent. Male and female flowers are on the same plant (rarely on separate plants) and are borne in pouches or sheaths. The inflorescence consists of one female and two male flowers, which are naked or surrounded by a spathe. The male flower has one or two stamens and anthers

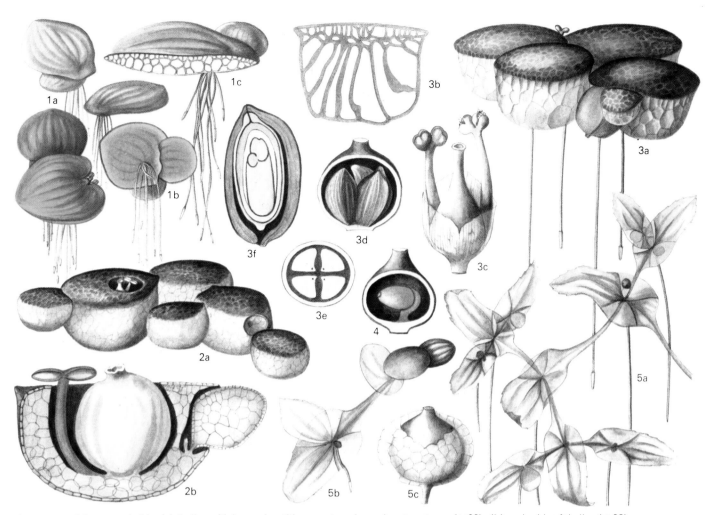

Lemnaceae. 1 *Lemna polyrhiza* (a) thallus with long adventitious roots and prominent root caps (×2⅔); (b) underside of thallus (×2⅔); (c) vertical section of thallus (×5⅔). 2 *Wolffia arrhiza* (a) floating thalli (×26); (b) section of thallus with budding pouch and male and female flowers in a single cavity (×52). 3 *Lemna gibba* (a) thalli (×12); (b) vertical section of thallus (×8); (c) inflorescence of two male flowers and one female flower enclosed in a spathe (×20); (d) half fruit (×20); (e) cross section of fruit (×20); (f) vertical section of seed (×40). 4 *L. minor* ovary with wall removed (×20). 5 *L. trisulca* (a) thalli with numerous side branches (×2⅓); (b) seedling (×6); (c) fruit (×26).

with one or two locules. The female flower has a short style and an ovary with one locule and one to seven ovules. The fruit is a utricle and the seeds are smooth or ribbed, with a straight embryo and either fleshy or no endosperm. Vegetative reproduction by buds or turions is known in the family.

Classification. Roots are present in *Spirodela* and *Lemna*, but absent in the other genera. *Spirodela*, with six cosmopolitan species, is distinguished from *Lemna* by dorsal and ventral scales on the fronds, several, sometimes many, roots and prominent nerves, usually seven to 15 on the broadly ovate thallus, the underside of which is often red-brown owing to the presence of brown pigment cells. *Lemna* (with 15 cosmopolitan species) has no thalloid scales and one root (sometimes no roots), only one to three nerves and no pigment cells. Roots are absent in the *Wolffia* group, and the genera are distinguished as follows. *Wolffia* and *Pseudowolffia* are floating plants and *Wolffiopsis* and *Wolffiella* are submerged. *Wolffia*, with 10 tropical and temperate species, has a floating globular and thick-ened thallus, whereas *Pseudowolffia*, with three species in North and central Africa, has

a thin flat floating thallus, the buds coming from a linear transverse slit in the thallus; in *Wolffia* this opening is circular. *Wolffiopsis* is represented by only one species, from tropical America and Africa, and is similar to *Wolffiella* which has eight species with a similar distribution, but *Wolffiopsis* has a symmetrical thallus and in *Wolffiella* the fronds are ligulate. *Wolffiella* is solitary or occurs in stellate colonies.

Wolffia arrhiza is the smallest known flowering plant; individuals are scarcely visible to the naked eye, and are generally seen as scum on the surface of water. About 12 flowering individuals could be accom-modated on a single frond of *Lemna minor*.

The Lemnaceae is closely related to the Araceae. The adult structure of *Lemna* is very similar to that of the seedlings of the monotypic aquatic genus *Pistia* (Araceae), and it seems highly likely that *Lemna* evolved from *Pistia* by paedomorphosis (ie a process in which sexual maturity is attained at the juvenile stage).

Economic uses. No direct uses for this family are known, but they are important as a source of food for waterfowl and fish and are serious weeds of still water.   S.A.H.

ARACEAE
The Aroids

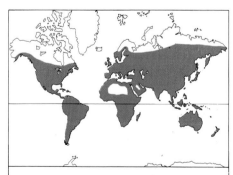

Number of genera: about 110
Number of species: about 2,000
Distribution: mainly tropics, with a few in temperate zones.
Economic uses: several species used locally and more widely for their edible swollen stems and a number are attractive ornamentals notably the arum lily.

The Araceae (the aroids) is a large family of mostly herbaceous plants, with great variety in vegetative habit. In the main they are

herbaceous with aerial stems or underground tubers or rhizomes, but there are a few woody members. The family includes a number of climbers and epiphytes as well as a floating water plant (*Pistia*).

Distribution. The family is pantropical, with a few species found in temperate zones. Some species are marsh plants.

Diagnostic features. Many members contain a watery or milky sap (latex) and raphides (calcium oxalate crystals). Many plants, eg those of the genus *Dieffenbachia*, are poisonous. The leaves are simple or compound, basal or produced on the aerial stems. The blades are often expanded with parallel, pinnate or palmate veins and are subtended by a petiole with a membranous sheathing base. The leaf of the fruit salad vine (*Monstera deliciosa*) develops large holes in the course of development.

The roots of all species are adventitious and most of the climbing and epiphytic forms develop two types, one of which is absorbent, growing downwards towards the soil, while the other, not influenced by gravity, grows away from the light and clasps firmly as it grows into crevices in the branches of the supporting tree. In some species (eg of *Philodendron*) the seed may be excreted by a bird on one of the upper branches of a tree where it may germinate, first producing clasping roots and later producing unbranched aerial roots which hang in the air as they grow downward towards the soil. Many aerial roots develop an outer water-absorbing tissue similar to the velamen of orchids. Some truly epiphytic species of *Anthurium* (eg *Anthurium gracile*), although producing both types of root, have no connection with the soil, and the absorbent roots obtain water and mineral salts from the humus which collects on the trunk of the tree on which they are growing.

The inflorescence is characteristic for the family, consisting of a large spathe (bract), often conspicuous and petaloid, subtending and sometimes enveloping a spadix of numerous small flowers which may be bisexual or unisexual. If the flowers are unisexual both types are usually borne on the same spadix with the male higher than the female flowers. The genus *Arisaema* is exceptional in having male and female spadixes borne on separate plants. The four to six small perianth segments, which may be fused to form a cup, are usually only present in bisexual flowers. The stamens vary in number from one to six and are often fused together as in *Colocasia*. Staminodes may be present in female flowers. The ovary is superior or embedded in the spadix, and comprises one to numerous carpels and one to numerous locules with one to numerous anatropous, amphitropous or orthotropous ovules on basal, apical, axile or parietal placentas. The style is variously shaped and sometimes absent, the stigma thus being sessile. The fruit is a berry, sometimes leathery, with one to many seeds, which are usually endospermic with a straight embryo, although a few species have no endosperm and a curved embryo.

The inflorescence of many aroids emits a nauseous, fetid odor which attracts carrion flies to effect pollination. *Arum* displays a highly evolved pollination mechanism. The spathe envelops the flowers and is lined with downward-projecting hairs past which the flies fall or crawl until they get to the bottom. The flies, which may be covered in pollen collected from the stamens of the male flowers of another *Arum* plant, crawl over the female flowers on the lower part of the spadix. As the lower hairs on the spathe wither, the flies crawl further up the spadix and become dusted with the pollen from the stamens of the male flowers which are now beginning to mature. Finally the upper hairs of the spathe wither, allowing the flies to escape and effect cross-pollination by being trapped in another inflorescence.

Classification. This very diverse family is difficult to classify and involves the use of internal as well as external features. Experts have variously grouped genera into a number of subfamilies or tribes. In one system emphasis is placed on the nature of the spathe and spadix, bisexual as opposed to unisexual flowers and the presence or absence of a perianth, while the other system groups genera according to the habit, the presence or absence of latex, leaf-form and details of floral structure. Genera lacking latex and with the spadix entirely covered with bisexual flowers include *Anthurium*, *Acorus* and *Monstera*, although the latter lacks a perianth. Laticiferous genera with the spadix entirely covered with unisexual flowers and possessing endospermic seeds include *Philodendron* and *Zantedeschia*. Genera such as *Arum*, *Amorphophallus*, *Arisaema*, *Alocasia*, *Xanthosoma* and most species of *Colocasia* all contain latex and possess unisexual flowers set on a spadix with a barren upper region.

The family is closely related to the Lemnaceae (duckweed family) and is considered to have been evolved either from liliaceous or palm-like ancestors.

Economic uses. Economically the family is of considerable importance, as the edible aroids of the genera *Colocasia*, *Xanthosoma*, *Alocasia*, *Amorphophallus* and *Cyrtosperma* are grown throughout the tropics and subtropics, where their starchy swollen tuberous corms are cultivated primarily as a subsistence food. However, the growing of *Colocasia* (taro, dasheen, eddo, cocoyam) and *Xanthosoma* (tanier, yautia) in some countries has reached a commercial scale. The taro or dasheen (*Colocasia esculenta*) is of Asian origin and consists of many varieties, some of which are adapted to upland and well-drained areas and others to lowland flooded conditions. The corms contain crystals of calcium oxalate which have to be destroyed by boiling or baking. The starch grains are small and easily digested, thus making it a suitable food for infants and invalids. Tanier (*Xanthosoma sagittifolium*, *X. atrovirens*, *X. violaceum*), of South American origin, is closely related to *Colocasia* but most varieties produce larger corms with coarse starch grains. The major food species of the other genera are *Alocasia indica* and *A. macrorrhiza*, *Amorphophallus campanulatus* and *Cyrtosperma chamissonis*, all of which are to be found mainly in Indonesia and the Pacific islands. The inflorescence of *Monstera* is sometimes used as food. Many genera contain species which are grown as ornamentals. perhaps the best-known being *Philodendron*, *Dracunculus* and the arum lily of florists – *Zantedeschia aethiopica*.

S.R.C.

Araceae. 1 *Philodendron verrucosum* epiphytic stem with clinging, adventitious roots (×$\frac{1}{9}$). 2 *Pistia statiotes* (a) habit showing floating rosette of leaves (×$\frac{2}{3}$) ; (b) inflorescence with subtending spathe (× 2) ; (c) vertical section of inflorescence with a single basal female flower with a curved style and above a whorl of male flowers each with pairs of fused stamens (× 4). 3 *Arum maculatum* (a) inflorescence comprising a large spathe enveloping the spadix (×$\frac{2}{3}$) ; (b) leaf (×$\frac{2}{3}$) ; (c) vertical section of inflorescence showing, from the base, female flowers, male flowers, rudimentary female flowers represented by hairs and the tip free of flowers (×$\frac{2}{3}$) ; (d) fruiting spike (×$\frac{2}{3}$) ; (e) ovary (× 4). 4 *Anthurium andraeanum* var *lindenii* spathe and spadix with bisexual flowers along its whole length (×$\frac{2}{3}$).

LILIIDAE

LILIALES

PONTEDERIACEAE
Water Hyacinth and Pickerel Weed
The Pontederiaceae is a small family of freshwater aquatics that includes the water hyacinth (*Eichhornia*), which is probably the world's most serious aquatic weed.

Distribution. The family is pantropical. *Pontederia* (five species), *Reussia* (two species), *Zosterella* (two species) and the monotypic *Hydrothrix* and *Eurystemon* are confined to the New World. *Heteranthera* (10 species) and *Eichhornia* (seven species) occur in both the New and Old World, and *Monochoria* (five species) and the monotypic *Scholleropsis* are Old World genera.

Diagnostic features. Both annual and perennial species are represented and these can be submerged, free-floating or emergent. The stems may be rhizomes, or stolons, or erect

Pontederiaceae. 1 *Pontederia cordata* var *lancifolia* (a) leaf and inflorescence with subtending spathe ($\times\frac{2}{3}$); (b) flower ($\times3$); (c) gynoecium ($\times4$); (d) cross section of ovary ($\times5$); (e) vertical section of ovary ($\times5$). 2 *Heteranthera limosa* (a) leafy shoot and flowers ($\times\frac{2}{3}$); (b) flower with perianth removed showing two stamens with smaller anthers than the other ($\times2$); (c) cross section of ovary ($\times3$). 3 *Eichhornia paniculata* (a) base of plant with sheathing leaf bases and swollen petioles ($\times\frac{2}{3}$); (b) inflorescence, each flower with conspicuous green and white nectar guides on the upper petal ($\times\frac{2}{3}$); (c) flower opened out ($\times\frac{1}{3}$); (d) gynoecium ($\times3$); (e) long stamen ($\times4$); (f) short stamen ($\times6$).

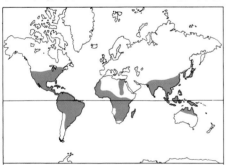

Number of genera: 9
Number of species: 34
Distribution: pantropical, in freshwater habitats.
Economic uses: aquatic ornamentals, edible leaves and weeds.

and unbranched. In many cases they are enveloped by sheathing leaf bases. In the free-floating species such as *Eichhornia crassipes*, buoyancy is provided by inflated petioles. The leaves are opposite or in whorls, with lanceolate to broadly ovate blades. In *Hydrothrix* they are reduced to hair-like pseudowhorls. In the perennial species fragmentation of stems and stolons is a common method of vegetative reproduction.

The inflorescence is a raceme or panicle subtended by a spathe-like sheath. The flowers are bisexual, regular or rarely irregular, blue, lilac, yellow or white and often showy. The perianth is usually composed of six segments. There are three or six stamens (rarely one). The ovary, of three fused carpels, is superior, comprising three locules with numerous ovules on axile placentas, or one locule with a single ovule. The style is long and the stigma entire or slightly lobed. The fruit is a capsule or nutlet. The seeds have a straight embryo and copious endosperm.

The floral morphology is exceptionally diverse for a small family. The genera *Eichhornia*, *Pontederia* and *Reussia* possess species with styles of three different lengths (tristylous) as well as species with styles all the same length (homostylous). In the tristylous species, flowers are of three distinct morphological types: with a long style and anthers at two levels below the stigma; with a medium style and one set of anthers above the stigma and one below; with a short style and anthers at two levels above the stigma. The pollen grains produced by the three levels of anthers differ in size. *Monochoria*, *Heteranthera* and *Scholleropsis* have members with dimorphic stamens, but their styles are of a uniform length. In *Hydrothrix* only one stamen is present. After flowering, species of *Eichhornia*, *Pontederia*, *Reussia* and *Monochoria* exhibit a downward curvature of the floral axis (hydrocarpy) and their fruits mature below the water surface.

Some members of the Pontederiaceae have interesting pollination systems. The aerial, showy flowers of the tristylous species are pollinated by insects and have conspicuous nectar guides on the perianth parts. There is a close association between North American populations of *Pontederia cordata* and a small solitary bee *Dufourea novae-angliae*. The flowering of the former coincides with the emergence of the bee and the bee appears to visit no other plant for nectar or pollen.

Classification. The Pontederiaceae, together with its most closely related family the Philydraceae, forms a peripheral subgroup within the Liliales.

Economic uses. Apart from *Eichhornia crassipes* and *Pontederia cordata* which are grown as aquatic ornamentals, the family is

Iridaceae. 1 *Crocus flavus* (a) habit ($\times\frac{2}{3}$); (b) capsule ($\times\frac{2}{3}$); (c) tip of trilobed style ($\times$4). 2 *Crocus* sp flower with perianth opened ($\times\frac{2}{3}$). 3 *Gladiolus papilio* (a) inflorescence (spike) ($\times\frac{2}{3}$); (b) cross section of trilocular ovary ($\times 2\frac{2}{3}$). 4 *G. melleri* (a) half flower ($\times\frac{2}{3}$); (b) tip of style ($\times$3). 5 *Iris laevigata* (a) apex of rhizome and leaf bases ($\times\frac{2}{3}$); (b) inflorescence with fully opened flower consisting of three reflexed "falls", three erect inner "standards" and three petaloid style branches behind the stamens ($\times\frac{2}{3}$); (c) standard ($\times$1); (d) stamen ($\times$1); (e) petaloid style branch ($\times$1). 6 *I. germanica* cross section of ovary ($\times 2\frac{2}{3}$). 7 *I. foetidissima* dehiscing capsule ($\times\frac{2}{3}$).

not utilized by Man to any great extent. However, members of the family are of considerable economic importance as aquatic weeds, the free-floating *Eichhornia crassipes* being the most widespread and serious. Other members of the family are weeds of rice fields. These include the emergent aquatics *Heteranthera limosa* and *H. reniformis* (United States of America), *Reussia rotundifolia* and *Pontederia cordata* (South America), *Eichhornia natans* (Africa) and *Monochoria vaginalis* (Asia). The leaves of *Monochoria* species are also utilized in Asia as a green vegetable.

S.C.H.B.

PHILYDRACEAE

The Philydraceae is a small family of perennial herbs native to Southeast Asia, New Guinea and Australia.

The plants possess erect aerial stems arising from an underground rhizome. The leaves are linear, and radical or clustered at the stem base. The flowers are solitary, bisexual and irregular, with a perianth of two whorls, each of two free segments. The single stamen has a bilocular anther inserted on a flattened filament. The ovary is superior and consists

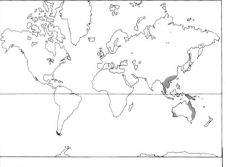

Number of genera: 4
Number of species: 6
Distribution: E and SE Asia, Malaysia, Australia.
Economic uses: none.

of three fused carpels forming a single locule with parietal placentation or three locules with axile placentation. There are numerous anatropous ovules in each locule. The style is simple. The fruit is a capsule containing numerous endospermic seeds with a straight embryo.

Three genera, *Philydrum*, *Philydrella* and *Orthothylax* are monotypic while the fourth, *Helmholtzia*, contains three species. The

Philydraceae is closely related to the Pontederiaceae and both families stand apart from the rest of the Liliales. The family has no known economic uses.
S.R.C.

IRIDACEAE
The Iris Family

The Iridaceae is a family of perennial herbs, including such horticulturally important genera as *Crocus*, *Freesia*, *Gladiolus* and *Iris*.

Distribution. The family has a worldwide distribution in both tropical and temperate regions, but South Africa, the eastern Mediterranean and Central and South America are especially rich in species.

Diagnostic features. Most of the Iridaceae are herbaceous and possess storage organs which are either corms (eg *Gladiolus*, *Iris*), rhizomes (eg many *Iris* species, *Sisyrinchium*) or more rarely bulbs (eg *Iris* of the Juno group). Some species are evergreen and usually possess a rhizome, which is sometimes very slender or compact and of little importance as a means of food storage. The leaves are usually narrow and linear, rather tough in texture and most commonly arranged in two ranks, often forming a flat "fan".

The structure of the inflorescence varies

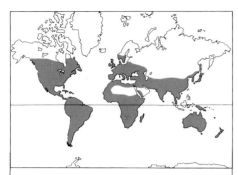

Number of genera: about 70
Number of species: about 1,800
Distribution: cosmopolitan.
Economic uses: numerous garden and indoor ornamentals (eg crocuses, freesias, gladioli and irises) a dye (saffron) and orris root.

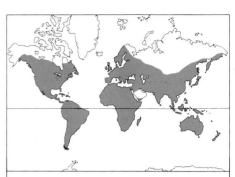

Number of genera: about 250
Number of species: about 3,500
Distribution: cosmopolitan.
Economic uses: many popular ornamentals (eg lilies, tulips and hyacinths), vegetables (eg onions, leeks, garlic and asparagus) and some medicinal uses.

considerably, but is usually terminal and cymose, the branches often reduced to one flower giving a spike or raceme (eg *Ixia*, *Gladiolus*). In some cases, for example in *Crocus*, the whole inflorescence may be reduced to a single flower which is practically sessile and therefore produced just above ground level.

The flowers show a remarkable degree of variability and some have become extremely modified from the basic shape. The whole family is characterized by having bisexual flowers which have six perianth segments, arranged either regularly (eg *Sisyrinchium*) or irregularly (eg *Gladiolus*) and either united in a perianth tube at the base (as in *Crocus*) or more or less free (eg *Moraea*). The perianth segments are in two whorls which may be more or less equal in size, giving a flower of completely regular shape, or arranged in two series of different appearance; the "bearded" irises are a good example of the latter, with the three outer segments deflexed or spreading horizontally and furnished with a patch of hairs (the "falls"), while the inner three segments are erect and glabrous (the "standards"). The stamens are three in number and arranged opposite the outer perianth segments. The anthers have two locules and nearly always dehisce extrorsely. The ovary is inferior (very rarely superior), comprising three fused carpels and three locules with axile placentas or more rarely one locule with three parietal placentas. The ovules are usually numerous, rarely one or few.

One of the most variable features is the style which in its simplest form is branched into three at the apex with terminal stigmatic surfaces (as in many *Crocus* species). However, in several genera (eg *Iris*, *Moraea*) the style has evolved into three flattened, often colorful, petal-like structures which are furnished with enlarged showy "crests" overtopping the stigmatic surface. In *Iris* these style branches curve outwards away from the axis of the flower and form, with three of the perianth segments, a protective

tunnel-like organ over each anther. Any pollinating insect is attracted by nectar at the base of the segments and by a colorful "signal patch" on the expanded blade of the segments and crawls along the tube, thus becoming dusted with pollen. Although most of the Iridaceae are certainly insect-pollinated, a few have adaptions to other methods such as bird-pollination (for example the scarlet flowers of *Rigidella*) or wind-pollination, as in *Dierama*, where the stems and pedicels are very long and slender. The fruit is a capsule and the seeds have a small embryo and copious endosperm.

Classification. The Iridaceae can be divided into 11 tribes, using such features as the type of rootstock and the degree of regularity or irregularity in the shape of the flower. The more important of these tribes range from the primitive, rhizomatous, regular-flowered SISYRINCHEAE (eg *Sisyrinchium*, *Libertia*) to the MARICEAE (eg *Cypella*), IRIDEAE (eg *Iris*), IXIEAE (eg *Ixia*, *Freesia*, *Lapeyrousia*), CROCEAE (eg *Crocus*, *Romulea*) and GLADIOLEAE (eg *Gladiolus*, *Tritonia*, *Acidanthera*) finally reaching the ANTHOLYZEAE (eg *Antholyza*, *Anomalesia*) which is considered to be the most advanced with extremely irregular flowers.

The family is related to the Liliaceae and Amaryllidaceae. The Liliaceae differs in normally having six stamens and a superior ovary.

Economic uses. The family is valued principally for its garden and indoor ornamentals and a great deal of work has gone into the production of cultivars and hybrids in such genera as *Gladiolus*, *Iris*, *Crocus*, *Freesia*, *Ixia*, *Sparaxis*, *Crocosmia* (*Montbretia*) and *Tigridia*. In the first two genera the hybridization has been carried on for well over a century and it is now virtually impossible to discover the origins of the hybrids.

Apart from their horticultural value, the Iridaceae have not been used to any extent for commercial purposes. Saffron, obtained from the scarlet style of *Crocus sativus*, was at one time used widely as a dye and flavoring agent in cooking; the plant was cultivated for this purpose throughout Europe and Asia. Orris root, from *Iris florentina*, is used in making perfumes and cosmetics.   B.F.M.

LILIACEAE
The Lily Family

The Liliaceae is one of the largest families of flowering plants and certainly one of the most important horticulturally, as it includes the lilies and numerous other outstandingly beautiful cultivated genera. Its chief economic representative is the onion.

Distribution. The family is cosmopolitan, although many of the smaller groups have a limited distribution in definite areas.

Diagnostic features. Most of the Liliaceae are herbs, and of these a large percentage have

swollen storage organs such as bulbs, corms, rhizomes or thick fleshy roots. However, some genera, for example *Aloe* and *Haworthia*, are evergreen succulents while a few, such as *Lapageria*, are evergreen climbers with woody stems. In Australia many of the genera have evolved in extreme xerophytic conditions and now bear little resemblance to any other members of the family. *Borya*, for example, produces tufts of needle-like leaves and dense heads of flowers not unlike those of an *Armeria*.

The leaf characters vary enormously within the family from basal and linear with parallel veins (eg *Ornithogalum*, *Endymion*, *Eremurus*, *Anthericum*) to cauline and broadly ellipsoid with net-veining (eg *Trillium*). In *Gloriosa*, tendrils are produced at the leaf tips while in *Asparagus* the leaves tips while in *Asparagus* the leaves are reduced to insignificant scales.

The flowers are usually regular and bisexual, and borne in a raceme, sometimes solitary (eg *Tulipa*) or more or less condensed into a cyme (eg *Hemerocallis*). The flowers of *Allium* are produced in umbel-like cymes which may be two- or three-flowered or may carry a very large number of flowers in a huge spherical head. There are usually six more or less equal perianth segments (rarely four or more than six) in two whorls

Liliaceae. 1 *Lapageria rosea* leafy shoot with solitary axillary flowers ($\times \frac{2}{3}$). 2 *Allium cyaneum* habit showing flower in umbel-like cymes ($\times \frac{2}{3}$). 3 *Calochortus uniflorus* habit showing basal bulb ($\times \frac{2}{3}$). 4 *Aloe jucunda* habit showing basal rosette of spined, fleshy leaves ($\times \frac{2}{3}$). 5 *Kniphofia triangularis* inflorescence ($\times \frac{2}{3}$). 6 *Lilium martagon* (a) inflorescence ($\times \frac{2}{3}$); (b) fruit—a capsule ($\times \frac{2}{3}$). 7 *L. canadense* half flower showing petaloid perianth segments, and superior ovary containing numerous ovules on axile placentas and crowned by a single style with a lobed stigma ($\times \frac{1}{2}$). 8 *Convallaria majalis* fruits—berries ($\times \frac{2}{3}$). 9 *Colchicum callicymbium* habit showing basal bulb, leaves beginning to emerge and flower with a six-lobed perianth, six yellow stamens and a trifid style ($\times \frac{2}{3}$).

of three, free (eg *Tulipa*) or united into a perianth tube (eg *Kniphofia*). The outer three segments are sometimes smaller than the inner and rather sepal-like, enclosing and protecting the three more showy inner segments during the bud stage (eg *Calochortus*). There are usually six stamens (rarely three or up to 12), always arranged opposite the perianth segments; the anthers have two locules usually with latrorse dehiscence. The ovary, of three fused carpels, is superior (rarely inferior or semi-inferior), usually with three locules and axile placentas, rarely with one locule and parietal placentas. The ovules are usually numerous (rarely solitary) and arranged in two rows in each locule. The styles are entire or divided, rarely free. The fruit is either a dry capsule or, less frequently, a fleshy berry. The seeds have a straight or curved embryo and abundant endosperm. Many of the Liliaceae are insect-pollinated, the attraction being in the form of honey secreted by the ovary or by exposed nectaries at the base of the perianth segments, these being well displayed in most species of *Fritillaria*.

Classification. Different authorities have recognized between 12 and 28 tribes within the family. It is thus difficult to recommend any particular system since it is obvious that a great deal of critical work is required in order to clarify the relationships within the family. Certain groups have, however, remained fairly uniform throughout the various treatments, for example the important horticultural groups TULIPEAE, containing *Lilium*, *Tulipa*, *Nomocharis*, *Erythronium*, and *Calochortus*, and SCILLEAE, containing *Scilla*, *Muscari*, *Chionodoxa*, *Eucomis*, *Ornithogalum* (chincherincheree), *Camassia* and *Puschkinia*.

The genus *Allium* and several related genera such as *Tulbaghia*, *Agapanthus*, *Brodiaea* and *Triteleia* are placed by some taxonomists in a separate family the Alliaceae, and by others in the Amaryllidaceae, but in this book are retained in the Liliaceae. The main differences between the various classifications of the family have centered round the inclusion or exclusion of *Allium* and its relatives, of *Yucca* and *Sansevieria* which are considered here to belong to the Agavaceae, and of *Ophiopogon* and *Liriope* which are liliaceous but have in the past been placed in the Haemodoraceae.

The Liliaceae is closely related to two other major families of petaloid monocotyledons, the Iridaceae and Amaryllidaceae. The Iridaceae, however, usually has flowers with three stamens and an inferior ovary, while the latter combines six stamens with an inferior ovary.

Economic uses. The main use of members of the Liliaceae is in horticultural display, for many of the genera are of extreme beauty. The most popular plants are probably the tulips. There has been a great deal of hybridization in the genus *Tulipa*, especially

in the last two centuries, and a vast range of large showy hybrids are now available, but some of the species have been known as garden plants since the middle of the 16th century. *Lilium* contains perhaps the most beautiful of species in the whole family while many other genera such as *Scilla*, *Muscari*, *Hyacinthus*, *Erythronium*, *Agapanthus*, *Colchicum*, *Kniphofia*, *Aloe*, *Hemerocallis*, *Hosta*, *Convallaria* and *Gloriosa* are widely known to gardeners.

Allium is the only important food plant genus with *Allium cepa* (onion, shallot), *A. porrum* (leek), *A. sativum* (garlic) and *A. schoenoprasum* (chives) being the best known. *Asparagus officinalis* is cultivated for its tender young shoots. Some of the Liliaceae have been used medicinally, such as *Aloe* (bitter aloes), *Urginea* (squill), *Veratrum* (hellebore powder) and *Colchicum*, the seed and corms of which yield the alkaloid colchicine. Apart from its medical uses colchicine is used in plant genetics to induce polyploidy. B.F.M.

AMARYLLIDACEAE
The Daffodil Family

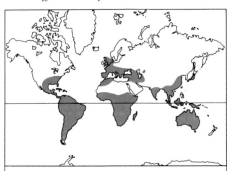

Number of genera: about 75
Number of species: about 1,100
Distribution: mainly warm temperate and subtropical.
Economic uses: many garden and indoor ornamentals, notably the daffodils and snowdrops.

The Amaryllidaceae is a large, horticulturally important family which includes the daffodils (*Narcissus*) and snowdrops (*Galanthus*) and many other popular greenhouse and house plant subjects, including the "amaryllis" (*Hippeastrum*).

Distribution. The family is mainly warm temperate, subtropical and tropical in distribution, although the genera *Narcissus* and *Galanthus* occur as far north as Britain.

Diagnostic features. Most members of the Amaryllidaceae possess a bulbous rootstock, although some have rhizomes or a bulb with a short rhizome attached to the base. They are mostly deciduous, but a few (eg *Clivia*) are evergreen. The leaves are more or less linear, growing from the base of the plant. The inflorescence consists of a scape carrying an umbel, although in many cases it is reduced to only a few flowers or to a

solitary flower (eg in many *Narcissus* species). In some genera (eg *Sternbergia*) the scape is much reduced and does not appear above ground level. The ovary is subterranean, at the base of a long perianth tube, until the fruiting stage when the scape elongates and pushes the developing capsule to the surface. This feature is often associated with autumnal species that flower at the beginning of a rainy season after drought.

The same habit has evolved independently in the Liliaceae (eg *Colchicum*) and Iridaceae (eg *Crocus*, where there are many autumn-flowering species). It has the advantage that plants can make full use of a short wet season, the flowers being produced early, often before the leaves, so the capsules and foliage have the rest of the growing period in which to mature before the onset of dry conditions once more. The subterranean ovary is protected below ground from any severe frosts that occur during the winter. Other Amaryllidaceae which exhibit this adaptation and which also occur in the cooler areas of the range of distribution are, for example, *Haylockia* in temperate South America and *Gethyllis* in South Africa. The majority of Amaryllidaceae, however, occur in warm regions and their flowers are carried on a completely aerial scape with a spathe or spathes subtending the inflorescence.

The flowers are bisexual and regular, and the showy perianths are made up in two whorls of three segments, either free from each other (eg *Galanthus*, *Leucojum*, *Amaryllis*, *Nerine*) or joined into a tube (eg *Crinum*, *Zephyranthes*, *Sternbergia*, *Cyrtanthus*, *Stenomesson*). In many genera there is a corona present, this being very obvious in *Narcissus*, where it appears as a distinct trumpet or cup, depending on the species. The origin of this corona varies from one genus to another; in *Narcissus* it is an appendage of the perianth segments, but in *Pancratium* it is made up of the expanded and fused filaments of the stamens. The stamens are six in number, arranged in two whorls of three, either more or less free, fused to the perianth tube, or joined together by their filaments into a staminal cup. The ovary of three fused carpels is inferior, containing three (or rarely one) locules with axile (rarely parietal) placentas. The ovules are anatropous and usually numerous in each locule. The style is slender, with a capitate or three-lobed stigma, and the fruit is either a loculicidally dehiscing capsule or a fleshy berry. The seeds have a small straight embryo and fleshy endosperm.

Classification. The family as defined in this book (ie excluding genera with a superior ovary such as *Allium*) can be divided into two broad groups, depending primarily on the absence or presence of a corona. The former state is thought to be more primitive and includes such genera as *Galanthus*, *Amaryllis*, *Crinum* and *Zephyranthes*. The more advanced genera, possessing a corona,

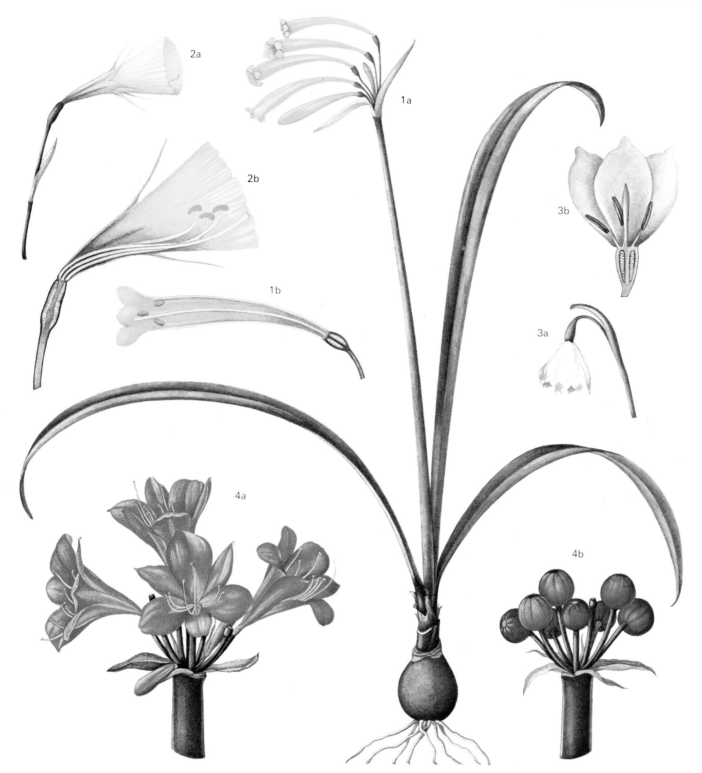

Amaryllidaceae. 1 *Cyrtanthus* sp (a) habit showing basal bulb, linear leaves, inflorescence borne on a leafless stalk (scape) and flowers with a tubular perianth ($\times\frac{2}{3}$); (b) half flower ($\times1\frac{1}{3}$). 2 *Narcissus bulbocodium* var *citrinus* (a) flower showing subtending spathe, and perianth with finely-toothed lobes and large tubular corona ($\times\frac{2}{3}$); (b) half flower ($\times1\frac{1}{3}$). 3 *Leucojum vernum* (a) flower with two whorls of free perianth segments ($\times\frac{2}{3}$); (b) half flower ($\times1\frac{1}{3}$). 4 *Clivia miniata* (a) inflorescence ($\times\frac{1}{2}$); (b) fruits—berries ($\times\frac{1}{2}$).

include *Narcissus, Pancratium* and *Hymenocallis.*

There is considerable disagreement as to which genera should be included in the Amaryllidaceae. The current tendency is to retain the genus *Allium* and its relatives (eg *Brodiaea, Agapanthus*) in the Liliaceae, but some authorities include them in the Amaryllidaceae, while others recognize a separate family, the Alliaceae. The problem with

Allium and its relatives is that they resemble members of the Amaryllidaceae in having an umbellate inflorescence, but have a superior ovary, as do the Liliaceae. If the taxonomist considers the form of inflorescence to be the most important feature of the plant, then they are classified in the former, but if he gives priority to the possession of a superior ovary then they must be in the Liliaceae. Others consider that the combination of

these characters justifies the formation of the Alliaceae. *Allium* and all its relatives are treated in this book as members of the Liliaceae.

Agave and *Vellozia* have also been considered as members of the Amaryllidaceae, but are here placed in the Agavaceae and Velloziaceae respectively. *Hypoxis, Curculigo* and five other genera (here included in Amaryllidaceae) have sometimes been made into a separate family, the Hypoxidaceae; and *Alstroemeria*, *Bomarea*, *Leontochir* and *Schickendantzia* have been made into the Alstroemeriaceae.

The Amaryllidaceae is closely related to the Liliaceae and Iridaceae.

Economic uses. The family is important horticulturally, but not economically important in any other way, although alkaloids exist in *Galanthus* and *Narcissus* and these may be of medical interest. The fleshy fruits of the South African *Gethyllis* are edible, but although considered a delicacy they are consumed only on a very small scale and are not cultivated for this purpose. The genus *Narcissus* includes the daffodils and is probably the most important of the family for garden purposes. Many thousands of daffodil varieties have been raised over a period of at least 400 years, resulting in a large and valuable industry. The Netherlands is especially important in this respect, exporting large quantities of daffodils all over the world. In addition to the many hybrids there are a considerable number of wild *Narcissus* species that are of value, especially in rock gardening.

Amaryllis belladonna and *Nerine bowdenii*, both from South Africa, are highly valued in gardens for their showy, late-autumn flowers. The hybrid *Crinum*, *C.* × *powellii*, is another hardy plant popular in temperate gardens, and the South American *Zephyranthes candida*, which has crocus-shaped flowers, is often planted in warm borders for a September display. *Sternbergia* is a small genus from the Mediterranean region, whose species all have yellow goblet-shaped flowers; *S. lutea*, an autumn-flowering plant, is especially popular. *Galanthus* and *Leucojum*, the snowdrops and snowflakes, are closely related genera, usually producing white flowers in early spring, although a few *Leucojum* species produce leafless inflorescences in the autumn. Most of the other genera are best treated as greenhouse subjects, the most important being *Hippeastrum* ("amaryllis"), the huge-flowered hybrids of which flower in winter, *Nerine*, *Stenomesson*, *Clivia*, *Cyrtanthus*, *Doryanthes*, *Haemanthus*, *Crinum*, *Pamianthe*, *Eucharis*, *Hymenocallis*, *Phaedranassa*, *Habranthus*, *Sprekelia* and *Vallota*.

B.F.M.

AGAVACEAE
Sisal Hemp, Pulque and Dragon Tree

The Agavaceae is a family of rhizomatous, woody, sometimes climbing plants. Many species produce valuable fibers, such as sisal hemp, and *Agave americana* is the source of the Mexican drink pulque.

Distribution. Members of the family are found throughout the tropics and subtropics, particularly in arid and semiarid locations.

Diagnostic features. The leaves are usually crowded at the base of the stem and are stiff,

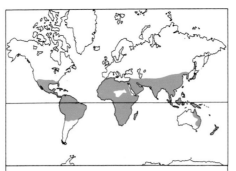

Number of genera: 20
Number of species: about 700
Distribution: tropics and subtropics mainly arid regions.
Economic uses: source of fibers (eg sisal hemp) alcoholic beverages (pulque and mezcal) and limited use as ornamentals.

often fleshy, narrow and sharp-pointed. They are entire or have prickles at the margin and may be as much as 10ft (3m) in length. Many species are succulents.

The flowers are borne in racemes or panicles and are regular or slightly irregular and usually bisexual; when unisexual, male and female flowers may be borne on separate plants or together with bisexual flowers on the same plant. The perianth is composed of two similar petal-like whorls, each in three parts, united into a long or short tube. There are six stamens inserted on the perianth tube or at the base of the segments. The filaments are thread-like or somewhat thickened towards the base, and the anthers have two locules which open by longitudinal slits. The ovary, of three fused carpels, is superior or inferior, and comprises three locules, with axile placentation and with solitary to numerous ovules in each locule. The style is single and slender. The fruit is a capsule or berry, containing one to numerous seeds with a small embryo surrounded by copious fleshy endosperm.

Classification. The most important genera are *Agave* (about 300 species), *Dracaena* (150 species), *Sanseverinia* (60 species), *Yucca* (40 species), *Furcraea* (20 species), *Cordyline* (15 species) and *Phormium* (two species).

At one time the members of this family were distributed in the Liliaceae and the Amaryllidaceae. They represent the xerophytic, fibrous-leaved members of both these families and thus form a rather heterogeneous group. They possess common features of morphology and inflorescence and grow in similar environments, but the individuals may be more closely related phylogenetically to members of the Liliaceae or the Amaryllidaceae than to each other.

Economic uses. The Agavaceae is a family of considerable economic importance. A number of species are the source of strong, durable fibers used for cordage, matting, fishing nets etc. Examples include *Agave sisalana* and *A. fourcroydes* (sisal hemp), *A.*

heteracantha (istle fiber), *Sanseverinia zeylanica* (bowstring hemp) and *Phormium tenax* (New Zealand flax). A red resin known as dragon's blood is obtained from *Dracaena cinnabari* and *D. draco* (the dragon tree). The fermented sap of *Agave americana* is the source of pulque, a national Mexican drink which either is consumed immediately, without aging, or is distilled to yield the spirit mezcal (mescal).

S.R.C.

XANTHORRHOEACEAE
Grass Trees

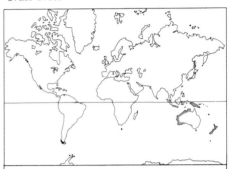

Number of genera: 8
Number of species: about 66
Distribution: Australia, New Caledonia, New Zealand.
Economic uses: *Xanthorrhoea* species yield a gum used for varnishes.

The Xanthorrhoeaceae is a family of stout woody rhizomatous perennials, often with tall, few-branched stems. Many are xerophytes.

Distribution. The family is found in Australia, New Caledonia, New Guinea and New Zealand.

Diagnostic features. The leaves are simple, linear, usually sheathing. The flowers are regular, often dry and papery, bisexual or unisexual (male or female then borne on separate plants), and usually borne in spikes, panicles or heads. The perianth is in two whorls of three segments. The stamens are in two whorls of three, the inner whorl often attached to base of the inner perianth segments and the outer whorl usually free. The anthers have two locules with introrse or latrorse dehiscence. The ovary, of three fused carpels, is superior, with either three locules and axile placentation or one locule and basal placentation; there are one to few ovules per locule. The styles are free or more or less connate. The fruit is a capsule or rarely a one-seeded nut; the seeds have a hard endosperm and a straight embryo.

Classification. The eight genera can be simply distinguished by their perianth characters. The perianth may be very small, as in *Chamaexeros* and *Acanthocarpus*, or with the outer parts glumaceous and the inner scarious, as in *Xanthorrhoea* and *Dasypogon*, or finally the perianth parts may be rigid and sometimes colored, as in *Kingia*, *Baxteria*, *Calectasia* and *Lomandra*.

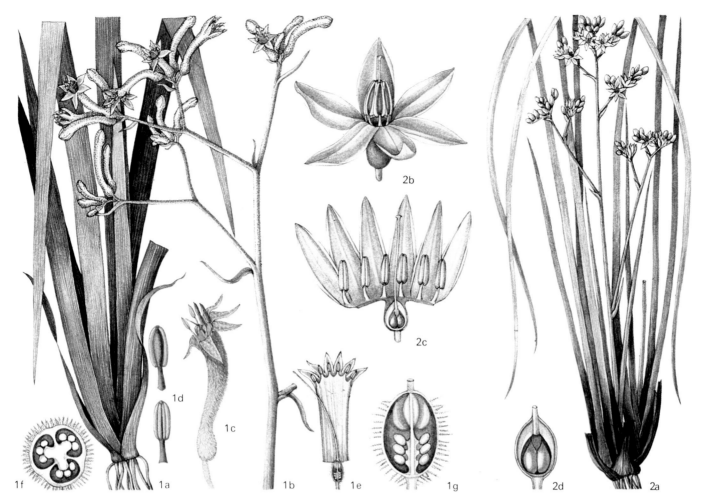

Haemodoraceae. 1 *Anigozanthos flavidus* (a) habit ($\times\frac{2}{3}$); (b) inflorescence ($\times\frac{2}{3}$); (c) flower showing curved green perianth tube and six stamens ($\times1$); (d) stamen front (lower) and back view (upper) ($\times3$); (e) flower dissected showing epipetalous stamens ($\times\frac{2}{3}$); (f) cross section of trilocular ovary with three axile placentas ($\times6$); (g) vertical section of ovary ($\times6$). 2 *Phlebocarya ciliata* (a) habit ($\times\frac{2}{3}$); (b) flower showing perianth in two whorls and six stamens ($\times6$); (c) flower dissected showing epipetalous stamens ($\times6$); (d) vertical section of ovary ($\times14$).

The family is closely related to the Liliaceae and Agavaceae, and has also been associated with the Juncaceae.

Economic uses. *Xanthorrhoea* species (grass trees) yield a gum used in making varnishes.
S.A.H.

VELLOZIACEAE

The Velloziaceae is a small family of fibrous shrubby plants.

Distribution. The family is native to arid regions of South America, tropical and subtropical Africa, and Madagascar.

Diagnostic features. The stems are woody and dichotomously branched, with narrow, drought-resistant leaves, usually clustered at the stem tips. When the leaves fall off, their thick, fibrous bases remain attached to the stem, making it appear thicker than it is. The base of the stem is covered with a dense mat of adventitious roots which can rapidly absorb any available water.

The flowers are bisexual, regular and solitary. They have a petaloid perianth composed of two series each of three segments, which may be free or united at the base. The stamens are either arranged in two whorls of three, or in six bundles in species where they are numerous. The gynoecium

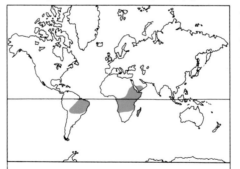

Number of genera: 4
Number of species: about 300
Distribution: arid regions of S America, tropical and subtropical Africa, and Madagascar.
Economic uses: none.

consists of three carpels fused into an inferior ovary with three locules and numerous ovules on axile placentas. The single style terminates either in a flattened head or in three distinct lobes. The fruit is a dry or hard capsule containing numerous seeds each with a small embryo surrounded by hard endosperm.

Classification. The four genera are *Vellozia* (100 species in South America and Africa

and one species in Arabia), *Barbacenia* (140 species in South Africa), *Xerophyta* (55 species in Africa, Madagascar and South America) and *Barbaceniopsis* (two species in South America). Features used to distinguish genera include the degree of fusion of the perianth and the numbers of stamens.

The family is related to the Haemodoraceae and the Taccaceae.

Economic uses. None are known. S.R.C.

HAEMODORACEAE

Kangaroo Paw

The Haemodoraceae is a family of tropical and warm temperate herbs, a few of which are cultivated as ornamentals.

Distribution. The family occurs in South Africa, Australasia (excluding New Zealand) and North and tropical America.

Diagnostic features. The plants are herbs with fibrous roots, tubers, rhizomes or stolons, and linear leaves arising from the ground and sheathing one another at the base. The leaves are hairy or glabrous, and have closely parallel or fan-like veins. The flowers are bisexual, regular or slightly irregular, and are borne in cymes, racemes or panicles, the whole often covered with a thick layer of woolly hair. These hairs may

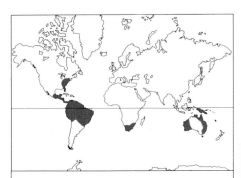

Number of genera: 17
Number of species: about 100
Distribution: Australasia (excluding New Zealand), S Africa, N and tropical America.
Economic uses: *Anigozanthos* species and a few others cultivated as ornamentals.

look like small feathers under a hand lens. The perianth is persistent, in one or two whorls each of three segments, and may form a straight or curved tube. When in two whorls the outer segments more or less cover the inner. There are three or six stamens with free filaments inserted on the inner perianth lobes, each anther having two locules which open by longitudinal slits. The ovary, of three fused carpels, is superior or inferior, with three locules, each locule containing one to many ovules on axile placentas. The style is usually filiform, with a capitate stigma. The fruit is a capsule, opening by three valves. The seeds have a small embryo and much endosperm.

Classification. The family can be divided into two tribes:

HAEMODOREAE. Perianth in two whorls, tube short or absent, stamens three or six. *Lanaria* (one species, South Africa), *Phlebocarya* (three species, Australia), *Schiekia* (one species, America), *Pyrrorhiza* (one species, Venezuela), *Wachendorfia* (25 species, South Africa), *Lachnanthes* (one species, North America), *Dilatris* (three species, South Africa), *Xiphidium* (one or two species, America), *Hagenbachia* (one species, Brazil), *Barberetta* (one species, South Africa), *Haemodorum* (20 species, Australia).

CONOSTYLEAE. Perianth in one whorl, tube often long and curved, stamens six, flowers always woolly. *Lophiola* (two species, North America), *Tribonanthes* (five species, Australia), *Conostylis* (22 species, Australia), *Blancoa* (one species, Australia), *Anigozanthos* (10 species, Australia), *Macropidia* (one species, Australia).

The family is related to the Liliaceae, in which some botanists place it.

Economic uses. Several species of *Anigozanthos* (kangaroo paw) are cultivated. They have racemes or spikes of tubular flowers clad in woolly hair, and are much prized in Australian gardens; they also make fine pot plants. *Anigozanthos manglesii* is the State emblem of Western Australia, with

orange to yellow, red and green six-lobed flowers. Other colorful species include *A. flavidus*, *A. rufus* and *A. pulcherrimus*. Other occasionally cultivated genera include *Conostylis*, *Macropidia*, *Blancoa* and *Lanaria*.

B.M.

TACCACEAE
East Indian and Hawaiian Arrowroot

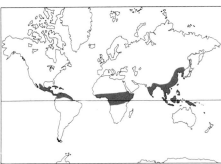

Number of genera: 2
Number of species: 31
Distribution: pantropical and China.
Economic uses: East Indian arrowroot.

The Taccaceae is a small family of perennial tropical herbs with tubers or creeping rhizomes, some of which are a source of food in the Pacific area.

Distribution. *Tacca* is pantropical; *Schizocapsa* is native to China.

Diagnostic features. The leaves are radical, large, broad, entire or deeply lobed, often with long stalks. The flowers are bisexual, regular, subtended by broad or elongated bracts, and borne in umbellate inflorescences. The bracts may collectively form a whorl or involucre below the flowers. The perianth is made up of two series, each of three segments, all fused together into a short, six-lobed, cup-shaped tube. The six stamens are attached by short filaments to the perianth tube. The ovary is inferior and consists of three fused carpels forming a single locule with three parietal placentas bearing numerous ovules. The style is short and terminates in three reflexed stigmas which are often petaloid. The fruit is usually a berry (rarely a capsule), containing numerous seeds, each with a minute embryo surrounded by copious endosperm.

Classification. The two genera, *Tacca* (30 species) and *Schizocapsa* (one species) can be distinguished on the nature of the leaves and fruit. In *Tacca* the leaves are either entire or much divided, and the fruit is a berry, while in *Schizocapsa* the leaves are entire and the fruit is a capsule.

The family is related to the Velloziaceae and Haemodoraceae, sharing with them such features as vegetative habit and bisexual flowers with a tubular perianth, six stamens and seeds with copious endosperm.

Economic uses. Economically the family is important for *Tacca pinnatifida*, whose

rhizomatous tubers yield a starch known as East Indian arrowroot. It is used in the Pacific islands and Africa for bread-making and as a starch in laundry work. The rhizomes of *T. hawaiiensis* (Hawaiian arrowroot) are used similarly. The leaves of some other species such as *T. fatsiifolia* and *T. palmata* are used medicinally to treat a variety of external and internal disorders.

S.R.C.

STEMONACEAE

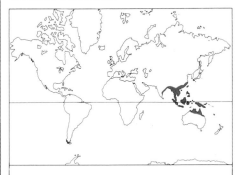

Number of genera: 3
Number of species: 30
Distribution: E Asia, Indomalaysia, N Australia, E N America.
Economic uses: *Stemona tuberosa* yields an insecticide.

The Stemonaceae is a small family of perennial erect or climbing herbs with rhizomes or tubers.

Distribution. The family is distributed throughout eastern Asia, Indomalaysia, and northern Australia, with some *Croomia* species in eastern North America.

Diagnostic features. The leaves are alternate, opposite or in whorls. The blade has a number of parallel main veins which are cross-linked by numerous transverse parallel veins. The flowers are borne solitary or in cymes or racemes in the axils of the leaves. They are regular and usually bisexual with a perianth of two series, each of two sepaloid or petaloid segments. There are four free stamens, and in *Stemona* the connective is extended well beyond the anther lobes. The ovary of two or three fused carpels is superior to semi-inferior and consists of a single locule containing few to many ovules on basal or apical placentas. It is surmounted by two or three sessile stigmas in *Croomia* and *Stichoneuron*, and a single sessile or subsessile stigma in *Stemona*. The fruit is an ovoid capsule, opening by two valves. It contains seeds which are often attached to the placenta by long stalks. The seed contains a small embryo surrounded by copious endosperm.

Classification. The three genera are *Stemona* (25 species), *Croomia* (three species) and *Stichoneuron* (two species). Some botanists place *Croomia* and *Stichoneuron* into a separate family (the Croomiaceae) because of several floral differences, including size of

Cyanastraceae. 1 *Cyanastrum cordifolium* (a) habit showing basal corm and heart-shaped leaves ($\times\frac{2}{3}$); (b) part of flower showing stamens with anthers free ($\times 2$); (c) stamen ($\times 4$). 2 *Cyanella lutea* (a) habit showing basal corm with fibrous covering and linear leaves ($\times\frac{2}{3}$); (b) flower showing six stamens: five smaller with anthers united, and one large and free ($\times 1\frac{1}{3}$); (c) large anther ($\times 2$); (d) small anther dehiscing by apical pores ($\times 2$); (e) gynoecium ($\times 2$); (f) cross section of ovary ($\times 3$); (g) fruit—a fleshy capsule ($\times 2\frac{2}{3}$). 3 *Conanthera campanulata* (a) leafy shoot and inflorescence ($\times\frac{2}{3}$); (b) part of flower with anthers arranged in a cone ($\times 2\frac{2}{3}$); (c) anther with extended connective ($\times 4$).

the periant segments and the nature of the placentation.

The Stemonaceae shows a number of vegetative and floral similarities with the Dioscoreaceae. It is probably most closely related to the Liliaceae.

Economic uses. The family is not economically important but the roots of *Stemona tuberosa* have been used for insecticidal purposes.   S.R.C.

CYANASTRACEAE

The Cyanastraceae (Tecophilaeaceae) is a family of perennial herbs with corms or tubers.

Distribution. Of the six genera three (*Conanthera*, *Zephyra*, and *Tecophilaea*) are native to Chile, one (*Odontostomum*) is native to California, and the remaining two (*Cyanastrum* and *Cyanella*) are native to central and southern Africa, respectively.

Diagnostic features. The plants perennate by means of a fibrous, tunicated corm or a thick, flattened, disk-shaped tuber. The leaves are generally either alternately arranged at the base of the flowering stem, or arise directly from the underground stem. They are variable in shape, but usually heart-

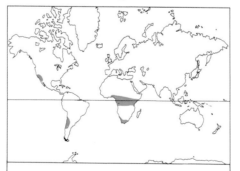

Number of genera: 6
Number of species: about 22
Distribution: Chile, California, central and southern Africa.
Economic uses: none.

shaped, disk-shaped, oval or long and narrow, and usually smooth and glabrous. The flowers are bisexual and regular, arranged in simple or branching racemes, and subtended by large or small, often membranous bracts. There are two perianth whorls, each of three segments. These are either free or fused together at the base into a short tube. The apices of the segments are either spreading or bent downwards. The

stamens are in two whorls of three, attached to the perianth segments. In some species, one of the whorls is sterile, in the form of staminodes. Instead of the more usual longitudinal dehiscence, the anthers of most species of this family liberate their pollen from a terminal pore on each locule. Another somewhat unusual feature is that the connective is often extended at both ends, the basal part being swollen or spurred. The ovary is semi-inferior and consists of three fused carpels which form three locules, with numerous ovules arranged in double rows on axile placentas in each locule. The ovary is surmounted by a thread-like and slender style, terminating in a three-lobed stigma. The fruit is a capsule containing numerous seeds, each with a large embryo, surrounded by fleshy endosperm.

Classification. The genera can initially be divided into two groups on the basis of details of the stamens. *Conanthera* (anthers converging into a cone), *Odontostomum* and *Cyanastrum* (anthers free) all have six equal stamens. *Cyanella*, *Zephyra*, and *Tecophilaea* have either dissimilar stamens or some stamens modified as staminodes.

This family shows a number of similarities

to the Liliaceae, particularly in relation to the floral structure (both families have regular flowers, the perianth in two whorls, the stamens usually six in number and the ovary with three locules and axile placentation). The tendency for reduction in some of the stamens and the semi-inferior ovary are indications of advancement and the Cyanastraceae might therefore be regarded as intermediate between the Liliaceae and the Iridaceae.

Economic uses. None are known.

S.R.C.

SMILACACEAE
Smilax and Sarsaparilla

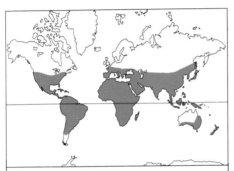

Number of genera: 4
Number of species: about 375
Distribution: mainly tropical and subtropical with a few temperate.
Economic uses: various *Smilax* species have medicinal use as tonics (sarsaparilla) and stimulants.

The Smilacaceae is a family of mainly climbing shrubs, the vast majority of which are in a single genus, *Smilax*.

Distribution. The family is mainly tropical and subtropical, but extends into temperate regions.

Diagnostic features. The prickly aerial stems arise from a rhizome and bear rather leathery, three-nerved leaves which, atypically for monocotyledons, display reticulate (net-like) venation between the main veins. The leaves are opposite or alternate, and the leaf sheaths may develop into tendrils, as in *Smilax*. These and the prickly hooks on the stem assist in the climbing habit. The flowers are regular, usually unisexual (bisexual in *Rhipogonum*) and arranged in axillary racemes, spikes or umbels. The male and female flowers are borne on separate plants. The perianth consists of two whorls each of three segments, free or rarely fused into a tube. There are usually two whorls each of three stamens (nine stamens in *Pseudosmilax* and three in *Heterosmilax*), with unilocular anthers. The female flower possesses staminodes. The ovary, of three fused carpels, is superior, consisting of three locules with one or two pendulous, orthotropous or semi-anatropous ovules per locule. The fruit is a berry containing one to three seeds with a small embryo and hard endosperm.

Classification. The four genera are *Smilax* (about 350 species), *Heterosmilax* (15 species), *Rhipogonum* (seven species) and *Pseudosmilax* (two species).

This family is closely related to the Liliaceae but differs in the leaf characters and in having male and female flowers on separate plants.

Economic uses. Various species of *Smilax* are sources of commercial sarsaparilla, used for treating rheumatism and other ailments. Other species have medicinal uses, the best known being *Smilax china* (China root) whose dried rhizome yields an extract with stimulant qualities. A New Zealand species of *Rhipogonum* (*R. scandens*) is sometimes used as a substitute for sarsaparilla. S.R.C.

DIOSCOREACEAE
Yams

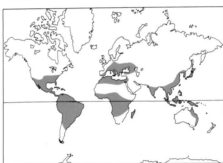

Number of genera: 6
Number of species: about 630
Distribution: pantropical with some temperate species.
Economic uses: staple food (yams) and diosgenin which has potential use in oral contraceptives.

The Dioscoreaceae is a family of mainly tropical climbers whose best-known members are the yams.

Distribution. The family is distributed throughout the tropics and some temperate regions.

Diagnostic features. All species, except for a few dwarf shrubs, are perennial herbaceous or shrubby climbers with well-developed tubers or rhizomes at their bases. The stems are unable to support their own weight for any great height and climb by twining on a support. The leaves are alternate and usually simply cordate, but are sometimes lobed as well.

The flowers are regular, small, inconspicuous and bisexual or unisexual (male and female then being borne on separate plants). They are usually axillary and borne in panicles, spikes or racemes, and have six perianth segments in two whorls, usually fused into a short bell-shaped tube at the base. There are two whorls of three stamens attached to the perianth lobes; one row is sometimes reduced to staminodes or absent. The ovary, of three fused carpels, is inferior, containing three locules, each with two (rarely numerous) ovules on axile placentas

(rarely a single locule with parietal placentation). There are three styles or a single style with three stigmas. The fruit is a capsule, a berry or a samara, and the seeds are usually winged, with endosperm and a small embryo.

Classification. Three genera (*Trichopus*, *Stenomeris* and *Avetra*) have bisexual flowers; *Dioscorea*, *Rajania* and *Tamus* have unisexual flowers. *Trichopus* (southern India) comprises a single dwarf shrub species whose fruit is a berry. *Stenomeris* (two species, western Malaysia) and *Avetra* (one species, Madagascar) are climbers with samara fruits, the former having numerous ovules per locule (all the other genera have two). *Dioscorea* (600 species, pantropical), *Rajania* (25 species, West Indies) and *Tamus* (five species, Canaries, Madeira, Europe and Mediterranean) are all climbers with capsule, samara and berry fruits respectively. The family is most closely related to the Liliaceae.

Economic uses. The only economically important genus is *Dioscorea*, the yams, the tubers of about 60 species being cultivated as a subsistence crop in three main centers, Southeast Asia, West Africa and Central and South America. Some species are the source of diosgenin, a steroidal sapogenin developed in recent years for its use in oral contraceptives.

C.J.H.

ORCHIDALES

BURMANNIACEAE

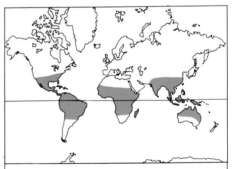

Number of genera: 5–16
Number of species: about 125
Distribution: pantropical.
Economic uses: none.

The Burmanniaceae is a small family of mainly tropical forest herbs, most of which are colorless saprophytes.

Distribution. The family is found throughout the tropics, especially in the tropical forests of Brazil, equatorial Africa and Southeast Asia.

Diagnostic fatures. Most species are small, annual or perennial herbs with slender, upright, unbranched stems produced from rhizomes or tubers. Leaves are often absent; when present, they are crowded near the base of the stem and usually long and narrow with the typically parallel veins of monocotyle-

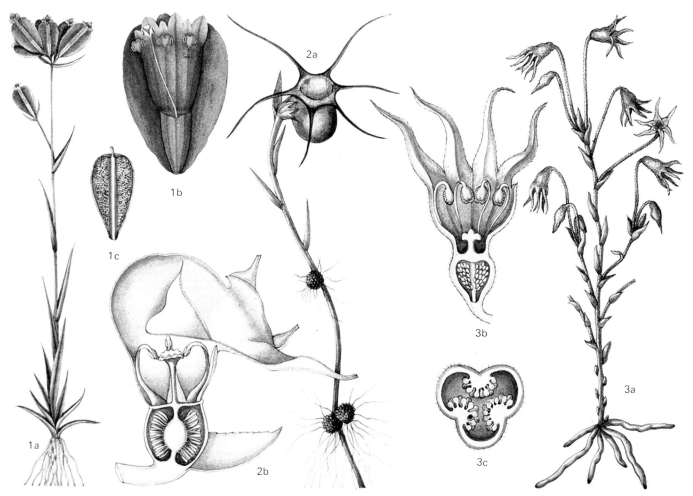

Burmanniaceae. 1 *Burmannia coelestis* (a) habit showing the slender, upright, unbranched stem crowned by an inflorescence of winged flowers (×1); (b) part of perianth opened out showing three sessile anthers and style with three stigmas (×4); (c) vertical section of ovary (×4). 2 *Afrothismia* sp nov (a) habit (×⅔); (b) half flower showing inferior ovary containing ovules on axile placentas (×8). 3 *Haplothismia exannulata* (a) habit (×⅔); (b) vertical section of flower; (c) cross section of unilocular ovary with ovules on three parietal placentas (×6).

donous plants. Those higher up the stem are very much smaller or scale-like and are arranged alternately. In many species the vegetative parts are colorless, in which case the plant feeds saprophytically on decaying materials in the soil and needs no chlorophyll for photosynthesis.

The flowers are usually carried at the tip of the upright stem as a raceme or cyme. Less often the flowers may be solitary. They are regular (rarely irregular), bisexual (rarely unisexual) and white, bright blue or rarely yellow. The perianth has six segments in two whorls which are fused at their bases into a three-winged tube. The outermost whorl encloses and protects the inner whorl in the bud. The innermost perianth segments carry three or six stamens without filaments. The ovary is inferior, of three fused carpels, forming either three locules with axile placentation or one locule with three parietal placentas. There are numerous minute ovules in each locule. The style has three stigmas.

The fruit is a single capsule dehiscing by three longitudinal slits. The perianth usually persists to give the capsule a three-winged appearance. The seeds have little or no endosperm and the embryo is very small.

Classification. The earliest classifications divided the family into three tribes: BURMANNIEAE with flowers possessing three stamens, and containing the important genus *Burmannia*; THISMIEAE with flowers with six stamens and an irregular perianth, and containing the genus *Thismia*; CORSIEAE with flowers with six stamens and a regular perianth. Some authorities have elevated all three tribes to family rank, while others have separated out only the last and given it family rank as the Corsiaceae, a family then containing two genera, *Corsia* (flowers bisexual) and *Arachnites* (flowers unisexual).The number of genera recognized by different taxonomists within these three tribes has varied widely. The Burmanniaceae is closely related to the Orchidaceae.

Economic uses. None are known.

B.N.B

ORCHIDACEAE
The Orchid Family

The Orchidaceae is a very large family distributed throughout the world. Prized for their spectacularly beautiful flowers, orchids are cultivated with sometimes fanatical devotion, and enormous numbers of new hybrids are produced, often commanding

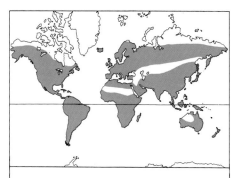

Number of genera: about 750
Number of species: about 18,000
Distribution: cosmopolitan.
Economic uses: basis of a huge floriculture industry and source of flavoring essence (vanillin).

high prices. Many species, however, are in danger of extinction through the destruction of natural habitats.

Distribution. The family is worldwide, with representatives in every country excepting a few isolated islands and Antarctica. Their ecological range is equally wide, with plants occurring in all but the most extreme environments such as the sea, the driest

deserts and the tops of the coldest mountains. Orchid species with surprisingly similar flowers can be found from the damp mountainsides of Norway and New Zealand to the dry savannahs of tropical Africa and South America, and from the coastal strands of the South Pacific to rocky ledges in the Himalayas.

Diagnostic features. Although the orchid family is very large, it shows less vegetative and major floral diversity than many much smaller families. Orchids have several characteristics, mostly connected with their flowers, which distinguish them from plants of other families.

Firstly, the seed from which a plant develops is very small, just a few cells forming a more or less undifferentiated embryo. The fruit (capsule) from a single fertilized flower spike may produce vast numbers of these seeds; figures of a million or more having been recorded from many species. In order to germinate, these minute seeds require the help of a fungus in a special symbiotic relationship; even so, it can take an inordinate time for a flowering-size orchid plant to appear. The ripening of the seed in an orchid capsule usually takes from two to 18 months; the germination period is similar, but it can take a further four years for the life-cycle to be complete. Under laboratory conditions this can be reduced to about three years, and if the ripening process is omitted by sowing green seeds or even excised embryos, it can be reduced by a further year.

For successful growth in the wild, and in cultivation, orchid plants must maintain their symbiosis with various species of fungi, the hyphae of which can be found in all their vegetative tissue, but mainly concentrated in the roots. About half of the world's total of species are terrestrial, with "normal" roots, but most of the remainder, all tropical or subtropical, are epiphytes, usually with long, tangled and dangling, dull gray or white, velamen-covered, aerial roots with a green, densely meristematic apex which absorbs moisture and the minimal amounts of nutrients required. These epiphytes generally have thick ligulate leaves with ligules, although many other types occur; all minimize the loss of water and encourage maximum photosynthetic activity. The extreme environmental conditions experienced by many epiphytes and lithophytes (plants growing on rocks and stones) have led to

actively photosynthesizing tissue being developed in such organs as the stems, roots and even the flowers of several species.

Many tropical and subtropical orchids, both terrestrial and epiphytic, possess special water and nutrient storage organs called pseudobulbs. These vary, depending on the species, from almost imperceptibly swollen stems to apple-like, very hard and shiny green organs from which the leaves arise. Sometimes a plant has only one pseudobulb, or they may form a closely packed cluster. With some tropical species, the pseudobulbs can be spaced out along a creeping or climbing rhizome. Pseudobulbs vary in size from mere pinheads in an Australian species to thick cylinders up to 10ft (3m) tall in an Asian species. Pseudobulbs are always on or above soil level, but in several groups of terrestrial orchids from the cooler, temperate regions there are similar organs developed on the roots in the soil. The swollen roots, called tubers, have given rise to the name "orchid"; the testiculate appearance of paired tubers led the Greeks to call them *orchis*, their word for testicle.

Although all of the world's orchids can be considered as either terrestrials or epiphytes there are some variations so extreme as to warrant a mention. The terrestrial habit is so very pronounced in a small group of Australian species that they spend their entire life-cycle underground, and apparently never surface even to flower. The nutrition of these plants is saprophytic, and there are many other examples of saprophytism in both terrestrial and epiphytic orchids. Some of the epiphytic saprophytes are so well adapted to the conditions of the humid tropics that they are better considered as very rapid growing climbers or scramblers. There are helophytic (bog) orchids but as yet no truly halophytic (salt-tolerant), aquatic or parasitic species have been recorded although some species are insectivorous-like, developing a bucket-type trap into which the pollinating insects are lured as part of the pollination mechanism.

The leaves of the Orchidaceae are alternate, often in two rows, rarely opposite, sometimes reduced to scales. They are simple, often fleshy, and sheathing at the base, the sheath usually enclosing the stem.

It is undoubtedly the flowers which most characterize orchids and serve to distinguish them absolutely from any other plants. They are nearly always bisexual and borne solitary or in spikes, racemes or panicles. Basically they conform to an irregular pattern with three sepals and three petals. The sepals are usually similar but the two laterals or the single dorsal may be elongated or bear a longitudinal crest. The petals, however, are usually dissimilar with the two laterals being quite distinct from the dorsal. It is this dorsal petal, termed the labellum or lip, which gives the orchid flower its characteristic appearance. The two lateral petals and the

sepals frequently are very similar morphologically, in which case they are termed the tepals, but whether or not the petals and sepals are distinguishable the labellum is always quite different. It can be two-, three- or four-lobed, or so divided as to resemble closely a lichen such as *Usnea*. It can be much smaller than the other perianth segments but is usually very much larger. Its surface can be ornamented in many ways with plates, hairs, calluses or keels and frequently it bears the most bizarre color combinations. Orchid flowers vary in color from white, yellow and green through enamel blues to deepest, dullest rusty maroons and purples: the petals and sepals may be of relatively uniform color, but the labellum generally has markedly distinct colors. It may be produced backwards to form a spur which can vary from the smallest sac to a long tube up to 12in (30cm) long; in some species the spur is bilobed.

Lying opposite the labellum in the floral whorl are the sexual organs. In orchids these are always united to form a single structure termed the column, which in its simplest, basic form is surmounted by the anthers with the receptive stigmatic surface just underneath them, usually separated by a flap of sterile tissue called the rostellum. There are one or two stamens with bilocular anthers and three stigmas, one of which is usually sterile and transformed into the rostellum. The many thousands of variations of columnar structure provide the basis for much of the technical classification of orchids. In evolutionary terms it is the columnar structure that has determined the particular pollinating agent of each species, and hence the great range of species found today.

The pollen is not an amorphous powder, as in most flowering plants, but is aggregated into two, four, six or eight waxy, horny or mealy pollen masses, called pollinia, and these are variously attached to the column apex, and usually are stalked. The simplest form of pollinating mechanism in orchids is the accidental removal, by a bee, of one or more or all of the pollinia which attach themselves to its head or thorax during its nectar search at the base of the flower or in the spur. Bees, wasps, flies, ants, beetles, hummingbirds, bats and frogs have all been observed as the pollinating agents of orchids; the underground species mentioned below probably adding mites or even snails or slugs to this list. The attachment of the pollinia to the insect is helped by a variety of additional mechanisms such as a quick-setting glue on the pollinial stalks or an explosive device that can project the pollinia up to 2ft (60cm) from the flower, and by the development of features, both visual and olfactory, that attract the insect to the right position on the right flower. A well-known mechanism is termed pseudocopulation. Although these mechanisms by and large involve specific orchid species and pollinat-

Orchidaceae. 1 *Bulbophyllum barbigerum* habit showing the swollen pseudobulbs at the base of the leaves (×⅔). 2 *Dendrobium pulchellum* habit (×⅔). 3 *Saphronitis coccinea* habit (×⅔). 4 *Oncidium tigrinum* (a) flowers borne in a wiry raceme (×⅔; (b) column (united sexual organs) (×⅓). 5 *Paphiopedilum concolor* (a) an evergreen orchid lacking pseudobulbs (×⅔); (b) column side view (×1); (c) column front view (×1). 6 *Coelogyne parishii* (a) aerial shoot with large pseudobulbs (×⅔); (b) column (×1⅓).

ing agent relationships, cross-fertilization can occur, and in orchids there are more naturally occurring hybrids than in all the other plant families put together. This "promiscuity" extends to hybrids between species in two different genera, and under the controlled conditions of the plant-breeding establishment up to 20 species and five genera can be combined into one plant. New man-made hybrids, many of them multigeneric, are entering the commercial world at the rate of about 150 each month.

Another characteristic feature of orchid flowers is the great range of scents produced, presumably as an integral part of the pollination mechanism. These vary from the smell of rotting carrion through sickly sweet vanilla-like odors to unquestionably very pleasing perfumes, often from quite mediocre inflorescences. Sometimes the unpollinated flowers, for example those of certain New Guinean species, live for nine months or even more, in contrast with the two or three hours' life of those of some tropical American species.

Orchid fruits, like orchid flowers, are also widely variable, ranging from single, long, narrow "pods" to clusters of many small grape-like capsules. The ovaries from which the fruits are derived are inferior and usually have one locule with three parietal placentas but occasionally there are three locules with axile placentation. There are numerous ovules in each locule. In every case the capsules open, when fully ripe, laterally by three or six longitudinal slits.

Classification. The classification of the orchid family is rather technical and largely based on characteristics of the column and, at the higher levels, the nature of the pollinia. It does not integrate closely with the life-forms and geographical or ecological range of species but, coincidentally, appears to correlate with the most commonly agreed evolutionary development of the group. The usually accepted classification divides the family into three subfamilies, six tribes, about 80 subtribes and about 750 genera. The smallest subfamily (the APOSTASIOIDEAE) contains one tribe which comprises one subtribe consisting of two genera, *Apostasia* and *Neuwiedia*, to give a total of about 20 species. The next subfamily, the CYPRIPEDIOIDEAE, has a single tribe comprising four subtribes and about 120 species of

lady's slipper orchids grouped into five genera, those most commonly encountered being *Cypripedium* and *Paphiopedilum*. Many botanists treat these two subfamilies as separate families, the Apostasiaceae and Cypripediaceae, respectively, because of the unusual structure of the flowers.

The third subfamily, the ORCHIDOIDEAE, contains over 99% of the family's species and consists of four tribes, the ORCHIDEAE, NEOTTIEAE, EPIDENDREAE and the VANDEAE. The genera in these tribes can vary from one to 1,200 species or more; many genera are rarely seen whereas others, from the smallest to the largest, are well-known to botanists, ecologists and growers and breeders.

The Orchideae contains mainly terrestrial orchids similar in general appearance to those found throughout Europe; commonly encountered genera are *Aceras, Anacamptis, Coeloglossum, Dactylorhiza, Disa, Gymnadenia, Habenaria, Himantoglossum, Ophrys, Orchis* and *Satyrium*.

Many of the Neottieae are saprophytic and most are terrestrial but some are better considered as epiphytes. Common genera are *Anoectochilus, Cephalanthera, Goodyera, Listera, Neottia* and *Spiranthes*.

The Epidendreae contains the majority of tropical epiphytic orchids but there are some terrestrial species. Genera commonly encountered include *Bletia, Brassia, Bulbophyllum, Cattleya, Coelogyne, Dendrobium, Epidendrum, Eria, Masdevallia, Pleïone, Polystachya, Sophronitis, Vanilla* and *Zygopetalum*.

The Vandeae are also predominantly epiphytic but include many genera which are basically terrestrial. Among the frequently encountered genera are *Angraecum, Catasetum, Cymbidium, Eulophia, Lycaste, Maxillaria, Miltonia, Odontoglossum, Oncidium, Phalaenopsis, Stanhopea* and *Vanda*.

The relationship of the Orchidaceae to other families is not at all clear. The Burmanniaceae, Liliaceae and Amaryllidaceae (especially the genus *Hypoxis* and its relatives) have been suggested, but probably the Orchidaceae has most in common with the Burmanniaceae, especially the segregate family, the Corsiaceae.

Economic uses. Excepting the flavoring essence vanillin obtained from *Vanilla planifolia* and the questionably nutritive "salep" from the tubers of certain species, the orchids have little direct economic importance other than as the basis for a vast floricultural industry. The legends surrounding the early discoveries, importations, sale, cultivation and breeding of choice orchids are among the classics of botanical and horticultural literature. The facts are no less remarkable; the privations suffered by the privately sponsored explorers, the vast losses of plants sustained on the long journeys back to Europe, the fabulous prices realized at auctions for fresh importations are well documented. Today, many orchid expe-

ditions are still being organized and there are many problems involved with successfully establishing exotic species in cultivation.

The orchid growing and breeding industry today is based in the United States of America, but it is also a major export earner in such countries as Singapore, Hawaii, Australia, Thailand, England, Holland and Western Germany. Orchid plants are cultivated in the controlled environment of greenhouses in the temperate regions of the world but in the subtropics and tropics they are grown out of doors in the same way as other plants. They are increasingly grown as room or "house" plants and in Germany, for example, special indoor greenhouses called "orchidaria" are used. Nearly all the most popular cultivated orchids (those of the genera *Aërides, Brassia, Cattleya, Coelogyne, Cymbidium, Dendrobium, Epidendrum, Laelia, Miltonia, Odontoglossum, Oncidium, Paphiopedilum, Phalaenopsis* and *Vanda* and their intergeneric hybrid derivatives) are epiphytes and require a special potting compost. This is ideally a mixture of osmunda fiber and sphagnum moss, but with difficulties in obtaining sufficient supplies of these materials natural and man-made substitutes are used today. These include fir bark, dried bracken, peat and shredded plastic waste. The terrestrial species, such as those of *Calanthe* and *Cypripedium*, require a loam rich mixture.

Orchid cultivation has progressed greatly since imported plants were first grown in Europe over 200 years ago. Recent research has shown that they were grown first of all in China nearly 1,000 years ago. A recent development has been the growth of societies devoted entirely to the growing and exhibiting of orchids. There are over 400 local orchid societies in the world.

In many ways the continued survival of certain orchid species is enhanced by their popularity in cultivation, but, on the other hand, the bizarre, attractive and unusual appearance of many plants leads to their destruction by continued collecting and flower picking. However, it is the ever-increasing destruction of suitable orchid habitats for urban development, and their alteration by drainage and other agricultural procedures, industrial pollution and military operations that is responsible for placing probably a quarter or even a third of the 18,000 species in danger of extinction.

Fortunately Man has realized the probable consequences of his actions and today throughout the world orchids are now among the best-protected plants. Legislation prohibiting their removal and sale or export, the establishment of nature reserves and the application of new technology, such as meristem propagation, to the raising of large numbers of threatened species are some of the ways in which orchids are being conserved.   P.F.H.

Orchidaceae (continued) 7 *Neottia nidus-avis* (the bird's nest orchid) a colorless, saprophytic plant ($\times \frac{2}{3}$). 8 *Anoectochilus roxburghii* leaf and flowering spike ($\times \frac{2}{3}$). 9. *Ophrys bertolonii* habit ($\times \frac{2}{3}$). 10 *Orchis purpurea* leaves and inflorescence ($\times \frac{2}{3}$). 11 *Corybas bicalcarata* habit ($\times \frac{2}{3}$). 12 *Cypripedium calceolus* flower section ($\times 1$). 13 *Apostasia nuda* (a) flower ($\times 4$); (b) detail of stamen ($\times 8$). 14 *Disa hamatopetala* spike ($\times \frac{2}{3}$). 15 *Cypripedium irapeanum* flower and leaves ($\times \frac{2}{3}$). 16 *Dactylorhiza fuchsii* flower (a) side view ($\times 2\frac{2}{3}$) and (b) front view ($\times 2$).

ILLUSTRATION CREDITS

Artwork panels: Victoria Goaman, Judith Dunkley, Christabel King.